# Endors

It is hoped for by many, but achieved by few: progressing from an inner city upbringing to farming in their own right. Peter Jennings' account of his farming life is an absorbing and readable story of his journey. He achieved his goals with determination, hard work, bolstered by his faith. A good read for anyone interested in the history of English farming from the fifies to the noughties.

**Richard Gould BSc**
Snr. Agricultural Advisor, ADAS

I first met Peter fifty years ago, when he won a place on the much sought after Advanced Farm Management Course at Wye, sponsored by the Worshipful Company of Farmers, which he modestly has not referred to in his book. Peter's career has been a triumph of determination and self-confidence, which blends with very significant religious belief. Clearly a rising star, he has shown that there can be a real career in farming. He has a keen sense, business acumen and fortunate good luck; who else would win a free Land Rover?! A great story with easy prose that flows.

**Peter Ward**
Ex NFU County Chairman; Member, Worshipful Co. Fmrs.

## Onwards and Upwards Publishers

4 The Old Smithy
London Road
Rockbeare
EX5 2EA
United Kingdom
www.onwardsandupwards.org

First edition, published in the United Kingdom by Onwards and Upwards Publishers Ltd. (2023).

ISBN:       978-1-78815-970-8
Typeface:   Sabon LT

**Author's note:** Some names of characters and places have been changed to protect the privacy of individuals. I trust my memory of the journey has been accurate, and thank all those who have helped me through both positive and negative events which have made me the man I am today.

# Buckets of Porridge

Farming through fifty years –
and surviving!

Peter Jennings

O&U
Onwards & Upwards

# About the Author

Peter Jennings was born 1940 in the East End of London, starting his first job on an Essex farm aged seventeen. Agricultural college and ten employers later, he has experienced farming over much of England from 'boy' to foreman, and from farm and estate manager to tenant. His regular column in the national farming press ranged from the serious to the faintly ridiculous, but always supporting the primary producer.

Peter's story covers all the ups and downs of farming and family life. He writes from the inside, having been 'in the thick of it', revealing what happens when the Countryfile cameras stop rolling.

From horses to sat-navs, from a wheelbarrow to over a thousand acres, ultimately, Peter is a farmer and nature-lover guided by the Almighty.

To contact the author, please write to:

Peter Jennings
c/o Onwards and Upwards Publishers
4 The Old Smithy
London Road
Rockbeare
EX5 2EA

Or send an email to:

peterjennings179@gmail.com

To my daughters
Nichola and Caroline
and the next generation...

# Contents

Buckets of Porridge

# Foreword by Michelle Ward

In his autobiographical novel, Peter Jennings sends us back in time to the middle of the last century, when farming was a constant battle between man and nature; when times were tough and work was demanding, but rewarding. Whether you are a retired farmer yourself, reminiscing about the good old days, or a couch potato dreaming of a more natural way of life, you will find something to enjoy in this book.

You will live through Peter's desire as a townie to escape the humdrum career lined up for him as an office worker; his struggles to gain enough qualifications and practical experience to earn him a place at agricultural college; the changing way of life in the countryside as horses and manual labour are replaced by ever bigger and better machinery; how to deal with unrealistic and unfair bosses; the practicalities of learning new routines when moving between different types of animal and arable farm; how to balance family life with the challenges of becoming your own boss; and not forgetting Peter's admiration for God's own countryside, with the descriptions of flora and fauna across the English and Welsh counties.

Whoever you are, and whatever your background, these stories will remain with you for the rest of your life. Enjoy!

### Michelle Ward BA (Hons) PGCE

Michelle is a CIEP-trained copyeditor/proofreader and founder of Brook Language Services. Formerly an MFL/SEN Teacher and RAF Reservist, she now specialises in copyediting and proofreading History (Local, Family, Social), particularly autobiographies. She loves nothing better than curling up by the woodburner with a good book and a glass of red wine after a dog walk around the fields near her home in the Welsh Marches.

www.brooklanguageservices.com

# Introduction

Most of us enjoy meeting new people, and before long we usually exchange a little about ourselves. It may be fleeting, but the initial question is often, "Where are you from?" Once this is established, the conversation may take many routes, either in sharing parallel experiences or simple astonishment.

So, to introduce myself, I am from London, but this book is about a journey – one that began when I moved to the countryside. Since then there have been many moves but not a vast distance travelled. The book also covers some other themes, such as: What was farming like after the Second World War? How can a city teenager survive in such an alien environment? What career path can you expect when your first day's working tools are a broom and wheelbarrow? There followed a succession of ups and downs, which seemed to me like walking through porridge.

I am sure many of you will relate to my experiences as you make your own journey through life; whether starting out, or from some way along the track. I have asked myself many questions as the road has rolled out; not seeing around bends, and occasionally finding them to be 'corners' sending me in another direction.

My road being farming, which naturally involves a lot of mud and sweat, has taught me self-reliance and a can-do outlook, but there is always much to learn, especially from those further along life's path. A major blessing has been the discovery and perfection of nature, which needs to be 'stood in' rather than observed from a train.

Perhaps your own journey has not crossed the countryside path but has nonetheless drawn you through different 'mud'. It may have led you to great pleasures and achievements on the way, but we can't be on the mountain top all the time. What do you make of the pitfalls and hardships? What lessons have you learned and what must be avoided, if possible? Of course, I cannot answer that for you, but I would like you to share *my* experiences. I want you to share my privilege of being involved with farming, from horsepower up to satellite precision, aided by the rich characters who worked and lived it with me. During that time, work attitudes, moral values and relationships have changed considerably, for better or for worse.

Enjoy!

# 1

# Goodbye, Home

"You are early. Take a seat and I'll call you when the committee is ready." The hotel receptionist was straight to the point; now, for us, an agonising wait. I turned to my parents:

"I knew we'd be early. I don't like waiting, it's like being at the dentist!"

In fact, it was my first interview for my first job. More accurately, I was being interviewed for entrance to further education. This would be both practical and theoretical: working by day with lectures in the evening – a basic introduction to agriculture. To me a crash course to working on a farm.

"Just think about why you want to work on a farm." Mum was always the first to speak; Dad was more the silent type.

I wanted to do farming but what could I say to the committee? Why would I want to leave London and work in the countryside? I was just seventeen and rather embarrassed that Mum and Dad had to accompany me; anyway, I supposed they wanted to know about the training course and what prospects it held for my career.

We had no relatives in farming, no interests in the countryside, no connection with animals or nature. My sister and I were not allowed pets "in case they died". I had circumvented this three years earlier by winning a goldfish at the fair on Wanstead Flats. I had brought it home in a polythene bag tied at the top and put it, still in the bag, in the bathroom basin full of water. Somehow it seemed better to leave it captive rather than have it swim in the handbasin, which would scare my sister, or perhaps she might let the water out and not handle 'Goldie' whilst refilling the basin. It also crossed my mind she might put soap in the water which the fish might not like. I reasoned this because I didn't like soap in my eyes and often washed without it, but I knew girls used soap and a lot of other noxious stuff.

I rushed to the pet shop for a glass bowl. But as I watched it swim round and round, I realised Goldie would become bored. I couldn't guarantee winning another fish, so I swapped a whole bag of marbles for one of Frank's goldfish, the smallest of the three he offered. All was well, and we were not too distressed when one died a year later...

This hardly qualified me for a job in fishing, let alone farming. What could I say to the interviewing panel to justify a place on their Farm Training Scheme?

My mind was drawn to a holiday on a farm when I was about nine and I'd loved it. Could that be the early catalyst? At our sole Parents' Evening I had told my French teacher, who doubled up as a 'careers adviser', that I only wanted a job in the fresh air rather than joining the majority of my classmates travelling on the Central Line to big offices in London. This he had called 'negative' so I had reacted quickly by adding a garage mechanic or the police as possible alternatives. My first choice was still working on a farm.

Our waiting continued, but my mind was back on that holiday. It was only two weeks but everything was new, strangely 'other', beguiling yet friendly. There was a regular pattern; unhurried but purposeful. The sun seemed to shine all day; hour followed hour, the job repetitive with a changing background. Hedges and views framed by trees, even an occasional church steeple. The banter the workers were sharing was part of the job; it was a joint contribution to the end of the task. This contrasted with the grey sky in town moving from dark to lighter and back again; the days driven by endless hours instead of purpose. Farm days there had been divided by timed breaks, refreshment whilst sitting in the field and then more work, getting the harvest in. On the farm time stood still; the job was central, purposeful, regulated by the elements. That fortnight I was outdoors in the weather with the rest of nature, part of the landscape.

The high spot was not only being in the harvest field with the men, but showing such interest that Joe, the farmer's son, asked if I would like to steer the tractor. This entailed a short lesson. First to mount the little grey 'Fergie' and reach for the clutch peddle, then to press the clutch and engage first gear. Great emphasis was placed on gently releasing the clutch peddle. I had observed every detail of Dad driving his Hillman Minx but never sat in the seat or touched the controls. Now this was for real. Not a car driver but a tractor driver and with the responsibility of a trailer-load of hay with a man on top. This was sufficient caution for me to obey every word of direction. The operation was to collect the sheaves being tossed up and stacked on the four-wheeled trailer by the men whilst the load moved at about half a mile per hour. My willing effort saved Joe jumping on and off the tractor and allowed him to move along the rows of standing sheaves.

I remember the harvest teas; Joe's mother and her sister coming out precisely at four o'clock with a big wicker basket each and a travel rug. This was laid double on account of the stubble and quickly smothered with plates of cake and sandwiches. I liked the scones and cream; it seemed cream came with everything, even cabbage at dinner time – I didn't like that. Eating was always welcome but it was an opportunity for a small town boy to ask questions. Joe obliged with fulsome detail.

"Why do you throw the sheaves up head first?" I asked.

"That's the valuable part, the 'ead. They can't fall out or get dragged out by branches down the lane. Ears ride in the middle, all straw points out. Will settles 'em in all across bed, and dripples[1] are wider at the top so weight presses 'em downward," Joe explained.

"So it doesn't need any string to hold them on?" I questioned. Some sort of bewilderment must have crossed my face.

"Not string, boy, that's round sheaf; not rope either cos weight tied they in," he confirmed.

I was wakened from the memory. The call came.

"Thank you." The secretary put the phone down. "The committee is ready to see you now."

Inside were two long tables pulled together in front of the windows. Seated behind were four men and two women. The chairman rose to indicate a small row of chairs facing him. Immediately his smile and gentle words emphasised the informal nature of the interview.

"We want to learn a few things about you... Peter, isn't it? And of course to answer any questions you may have," he continued to explain. "You know, the Town Boys' Training Scheme at White Court could be your great starting point, then after four or five months onto a job in farming. There is no more worthy occupation than producing food for the nation. My colleagues will ask you some questions; just answer them honestly, and I would ask Mr and Mrs Jennings to resist helping out at this stage."

The suits and waistcoats in turn asked about my reason for pursuing farming and what aspects particularly appealed. The nurse and housekeeper wanted to assess my ability to look after myself away from home. Suddenly, amid domestic detail, the urban office of suits and secretaries turned to the question of farming. My mind was in a space between two planets.

"What contact have you had with farming?" The cultured voice came from the green tweed suit next to the housekeeper.

My hesitation worried me as much as the panel's question. "We don't live near a farm, sir. But, but... I did work on a farm... once." The general stir of interest did nothing to settle my thoughts as I foolishly added, "I drove a tractor, sir." Quickly sensing that I might be digging a hole for myself, I blurted out, "I have grown wheat... in the garden."

I must point out that my parents were not keen gardeners of the small plot to the rear of our house in London E11, so it was decreed that my sister and I would be responsible for three yards on each side of the grass. I use the word 'grass' as being more accurate than 'lawn'. I observed later that the majority of farmers have an aversion to gardening, and I was hoping to become one of them. However, my sister and I could grow what we liked as long as it was tidy. I chose wheat.

---

[1]  large ladder-type ends of the flatbed trailer

"I mean, sir, a trial." I continued to dig another possible hole. "I wanted to see by how much the seed multiplied. I rubbed the grains out of twenty heads of wheat and planted each singly, in rows. When it grew I counted the heads and grains," I explained. I was struggling to remember the exact result so welcomed the smiles and mild mirth which followed. I must have acquitted myself reasonably well as we were soon back in the waiting room.

There was hardly time to reflect with my parents before we were ushered back in. The chairman rose as if to speak to a large gathering. It all seemed more formal with his chest puffed out, both thumbs hooked into his waistcoat pockets, fully displaying a gold watch chain as if it were holding him together. A formal clearing of the throat...

"Well, my boy, we think you will definitely benefit by coming on the Town Boys' Training Scheme and trust that with hard work and honest intent..." The other words floated over my head until his voice rose to a final demand. "What you need is buckets of porridge." And, as if pleased with himself, he repeated, *"Buckets of porridge!"*

He proffered his hand and it was over.

On the car journey home this parting comment both mystified and hurt me. Was I an eleven-stone weakling? I was a significant member of the school rugby team, playing hooker in the midst of the scrum. The scrummaging seemed to occupy most of the match as a schoolboy, on account of the London mud and the desire to collapse on the opposition, so showing who was boss. Surely I could hold my own, working on the land? Did he rather mean the work required stamina; real rations to fuel the day?

Some years later I came to understand that the life of a farmer often feels like walking through porridge, buckets of it! Whether it is the essential routine of caring for livestock even when one feels decidedly unwell, or the constant concern that the bank balance will not keep up with the remorseless drain of inputs before the harvest is sold. It does feel like struggling through sticky porridge. In better times, bright sun and birdsong make for a healthy breakfast and strength for the new day.

Wartime must have been difficult for my parents; not only for relationships and rationing, but day to day living. I was a premature baby. Mum had lost her first baby in 1938 and I was born in June 1940. When I was only fourteen days old, Dad drove Mum and the new baby down to Devon to stay with a distant cousin. This was the alternative to evacuation, which was the lot of school children. Families with pre-school children were advised to stay with relatives or friends away from London and other vulnerable cities. The journey to Devon was not easy as all road signs had been removed in case they aided invading Germans. Apparently, navigation was further hampered when stopping and asking locals the way. Dad, even in the excusable paranoia of the time, could hardly be mistaken for a German... but could he be a clever spy? In hindsight we were travelling to another danger area, Plymouth, which became a favourite target of the Luftwaffe. Our destination was a farm about ten miles west of the city.

We moved several times during the war, living back in Eltham with my grandparents until a close friend or relative could be persuaded to take us in. We 'yo-yoed' to Bradford, Leicester, Birkenhead; each time returning to Eltham or Catford – my grandparents' homes.

My parents must have suffered in many ways as a young couple starting a family at the beginning of the Second World War. Although not seriously injured, the separation and total uncertainties of life were an untold burden. After the war, Dad had returned home and started work as an insurance agent. He had been latterly in North Africa servicing aircraft and I had had a somewhat romantic notion of him in uniform and jolly evenings in the NAAFI. In fact, he returned home, demobbed when I was five and a half, and in army khaki. Disappointed, I was told it was better camouflage than Air Force blue in the desert! Later there were photos of crews sweating in desert heat, struggling to maintain aircraft with a 'Make Do and Mend' policy in the scarcities of war. Although he would never speak about it, I came to realise there was little glamour; it was horror and apprehension held together by camaraderie, knowing life was a lottery and brutally unpredictable.

We had put some Union Jacks on the front door and road gate, and written "Welcome Home" on some paper, but it didn't really seem a jolly occasion. My sister and I had never knowingly seen Dad, so the moment of meeting was somewhat muted; a few photos of him were a poor introduction. Dad was coming home, but what was he like? We had no moving pictures or even a voice to recognise. In later years I have often wondered how he felt at our reaction. This 'stranger' was part of our trio – Mum, Valerie and me. Here was Dad, but surely he had to tread carefully, as in any childhood anxiety we must surely have run to Mum. She had coped wonderfully through times of ration books and clothes coupons plus multiple home moves. She had run the household, been the decision-maker, shouldered all responsibility. Dad had moved from the theatre of war to civilian life, but hardly to the home he had left.

My mother came from a middle-class home in Eltham; her father was a marine engineer working for Queen's Engineering Works in Bedford and at the Admiralty in London. She worked in London as a secretary and shorthand typist. My father was born in Deptford where his father was a cooper and his mother a shop owner. Grandad was making barrels for the Navy, and Gran was selling confectionery in their corner shop. My father was an accomplished handyman from school age, apparently making an electric bell ring every time a customer trod on the doormat of the shop. His skills did not end there, as he was part of a five-piece dance band in the 1930s playing saxophone and clarinet.

As soon as it was safe, we moved back to my parents' house in East Ham which had been empty for most of the war. 'We' now included my sister Valerie, two years younger than me. All the houses were on one side of the road and a tall factory wall ran the length of the other. It always seem to smell funny but I was told it was a chemical factory.

# 2

# School Days

It was in East Ham that at just over five years old I first attended school. This was an experience I hardly seemed prepared for. The first day, forever etched in my memory, started badly. I was given a small slate about ten inches square, edged in a wooden frame, and half a piece of chalk. I don't remember what I was asked to do with it but I could do nothing. The slate was so shiny that no movement of chalk would make a mark. Others seemed to be doing something, but not me. The teacher walking around us all simply said, "Turn it over and draw your house." Behold, the other side was as impossible as the first! I can't recall any unfriendliness on behalf of the teacher but I was left with the unhappy conclusion that school was impossible. Even playtimes didn't restore any joy; I wanted to go inside the big brick air-raid shelter. I had been used to a small shelter in the garden with Mum and Grandma and thought it would be better with all the class together, but that was not allowed.

When I was six and a half years old we moved to Wanstead E11. Our house had larger rooms, and my sister and I had our own bedrooms. The area was greener, and in part of the High Street there was even grass and a bit of woodland just where our new school was situated. The junior school was old, built about 1790 as one of the early church schools, and it still had gas lighting. The boys' school had three classes: the first in a side room off the assembly hall; the second on the stage of the hall; and the third at the far end of the hall. Among the boys, most of whom were only mildly interested in learning, these classes were known as '1 in', '2 up', and '3 out'. It was impressed on me that 'out' would hopefully be to high school, hence needing to pass the eleven-plus exam. My parents emphasised the absolute necessity of passing this exam as my whole future would depend on the result. The eleven-plus became my first crisis in life; to fail would be a fate worse than death. I had happily moved from house to house, learned some social skills that appeared important to grown-ups and found a few boundaries in life. Now school was a fresh pressure.

My difficulty, in a class of over forty boys, was trying to understand what was written on the board. In arithmetic all one could see was the teacher's back and her hand vigorously chalking numbers. Then the moment of revelation as she turned to the class announcing, "If this number is divided by that, the answer should be written on top, here." I often wanted to ask why or how, but by that time she would be chalking more numbers, apparently at random.

I could put a hand in the air hoping for a personal explanation, but as soon as she came to my desk it was usually, "Start again down here and put the answer on the top line." Another waving hand and a bleat of "Miss!" would carry her away. No doubt I needed more understanding of the basics – but how? Dad was patient and taught me the importance of learning my tables, and even something of fractions and decimals. However, there was much more I would need to know to pass this looming eleven-plus exam.

In this new neighbourhood there was more than school to occupy me. I soon had two friends living in the next road and attending the same school. We were allowed to mooch around the scrub of trees and common land between roads, originally parts of Epping Forest before civilisation crept into it. This provided a source of staves and branches to swing on. A little further away from roads we would make makeshift dens, often cannibalised after a few days by other boys wanting to do the same. It was a welcome distraction from school.

Our new neighbour suggested to Mum and Dad they might like Valerie and me to join their twelve-year-old daughter at the Methodist Sunday school. Although they were not churchgoers themselves, there was some appeal in releasing us to Jill's care and having a quiet time on a Sunday morning. I have little memory of those mornings, except that when my Sunday school teacher sang, his Adam's apple wobbled up and down. I could not join in with the singing as I had never been taught to sing. It seemed an unnecessary skill to achieve and rather boring. What was interesting was a Cub and Boy Scout pack meeting in the church hall on Wednesday evenings. I joined as a Cub and soon learned knots and passed various proficiency badges like First Aid. After all the fun and some good games, we always ended the evening by getting into a circle. It seemed funny because Akela, the leader, would make us all be quiet because she was going to 'pray'. That meant talking in the air to God asking him to look after us and our families. I thought it odd because I could not see God and wondered how He would hear us anyway. On the other hand, these were all regular guys and didn't stand much nonsense, especially when we played British Bulldog. This game involves all the pack or patrol at one end of the hall trying to get to the other end without being caught by the 'bulldog'. He could tackle, trip, flail arms, use any means except biting, to apprehend one boy. It was probably more dangerous than trying to pass a real bulldog, but great fun.

Back at school I was constantly reminded of the impending exam; even the teacher was talking about it directly. I was being pushed to the edge of a cliff by parents and teacher, with no one to help me. My only hope was the God that Akela spoke to; if he cared for families then he would possibly help me, I reasoned. I dared not tell my parents so decided to lock myself in the toilet and speak to God every day, hoping He existed. All I could think of was repeating,

"God, you must help me because nobody else can." That seemed so short that after a moment I would add, "Please, please, God; you must be there... somewhere."

The exam day came and so did final advice from Dad:

"You must read the questions very carefully and understand what they want. And answer them all even if you don't know all the answers."

I understood that there had to be total silence; I could not ask any questions and nobody could go to the toilet. Indeed, God was my only hope.

The exam was over; there was nothing more to be done. There was some wait for the results although nothing was mentioned in the house. I rested in uneasy silence, consoling myself that I had done my best. Then, after some weeks, a long brown envelope with "Essex Education Department" printed on the top dropped on the mat. Dad handed it to me.

"I think this is yours." He half-smiled, not revealing any inner thought but probably as apprehensive as I was. I opened it carefully, in silence, which lasted a full minute.

Mum, who was often impatient, took it from me and read it in a moment. "You have got to sit it again!" she exclaimed.

In June, therefore, I sat the eleven-plus again with new papers, at another venue. To the great relief of my parents, and to my astonishment, I passed and was able to join two of my friends at high school; three out of a class of forty-four. God had answered my desperate prayer.

My parents had provided a comfortable and safe home with a freedom to grow up within my peer group. I was expected to keep on the right side of the law and not do anything to embarrass them. I took this to mean 'live amid possible "dangers" without inviting trouble'. I was allowed to explore the river Roding with friends, providing I didn't go in the water. This, I reasoned with friends Robin and Frank, meant no swimming or suspending a rope from side-to-side when we could use the bridge about three hundred yards away. This we obeyed, although mainly because we could find no rope long enough. The other side of the river had no houses but was a dump for mostly building and factory waste. It was therefore a constant source of wire and boards, even sundry wheels, to construct go-carts and dens. The other stipulation was never to touch the electricity pylon by the bridge or indeed any other pylon, on penalty of death. This we took literally, which was precisely the penalty they had in mind.

The river was a constant draw for three growing lads – Robin, Frank and me. There was always something to see or experiment with, theories to prove and treasures to find. It was rarely deep or warm enough to swim, so we did not go in the water but we did get wet occasionally. I particularly remember that the kind River Board had concreted a bend in the bank to prevent erosion, which made a reinforced plinth, ideal for experiments without getting wet feet, being a couple of feet above normal winter level. This enabled us to examine man-made detritus and occasional fish that hitherto had been beyond reach.

I particularly remember Robin had made a scoop out of an old paint can, handle still intact, and a hazel stick. This would scoop out anything worth investigation without risking getting wet. Our interest was intense as the can dredged the mud and caught something white. Robin was leaning over the river, peering down, when his face met the surface of the water. It was all in slow motion. He had not been attempting to swim or indeed paddle. It was just one of those things that happens when researching. Not only were his Wellingtons full of water but he had submerged in some thirty inches of river. The only course of action was to go over the bridge to the 'dumps' and light a fire. Having wrung out every item of clothing, we propped them around the fire whilst Robin sheltered in a roll of discarded mattress, rather like a core in an apple. The outcome was that his mother wanted to know why everything smelled of smoke. Personally I attribute this 'research' as the start of his career as a Doctor of Marine Biology.

After the summer holiday, the three of us were to start at the high school in Wanstead. Our new school required us to have a uniform, which was a black blazer and cap for boys and black beret for the girls. Black I thought entirely appropriate, as one gets 'grubby' so easily.

Mum disagreed. "Don't be so ridiculous; it will show every mark." (Being 'grubby' and 'ridiculous' in Mum's eyes were my constant failings.) "Anyway, you'll be studying now, not going down to the river," she said hopefully.

The list of uniform items included grey socks and a pullover, as well as black shoes and a plain black tie. The cost of this did not end there as every boy was expected to have a sports uniform. I would therefore need a pure-black rugby shirt and shorts and a contrasting white set, not to mention rugby socks and boots. The cost of all this was a considerable blow to the family budget, but not begrudged by my parents who balanced the cost with the benefit that education would bring.

Apparently the two sets of rugby kit were required on the basis that, gifted or not, every boy would play the game. Black was the proud and defining colour of the school's first team and to be aimed for by all. White was necessary in training when white played against black. In spite of all this sporting promise, inspiring some and to the dread of non-athletes, the first year of rugby was spent running up and down the tarmac playground. The idea was to perfect passing the ball slightly backwards. With this ability, the first team in Year 2 was able to beat most other schools.

The first day at school was a step change for me. The size of the building and use of rooms, together with rules that had to be observed, were bewildering. The new intake had been assigned to one of four classes: 'Alpha', 'A', 'Beta' and 'B'. (I had never been introduced to the Greek alphabet; perhaps that was the reason I was assigned to class B.) Having been drafted to the correct classroom, each class then filed into the assembly hall and stood in a straight line across its width. Years 2 to 6 were already assembled, nearly filling the entire hall. The headmaster in gown and mortar board was on the stage; teachers arrayed the length of the hall standing by their respective classes. There was already silence as it was the 'golden rule'.

"Good morning, school." The headmaster beamed, acting as informally and benignly as his attire allowed. "Today we especially welcome our new first years." At this everybody except us clapped. There followed various things that "we always observe", like walking on the right-hand side of the corridor, never running, and being in silence "because we want to think of others who might be studying," he intoned for our instruction.

The school was built as a huge open rectangle; in the middle, 'holy' grass never to be trodden on, with corridors all around. One side was taken up by the assembly hall. This we found out later was entirely duplicated on the first floor. The school was built on a slight hill which permitted the lower side to have three storeys, with woodwork and domestic science rooms below and various laboratories above. In the playground there were odd temporary wooden buildings of unknown purpose but which seemed well established, presumably built in wartime when money would have been scarce.

It was good to have individual desks of various designs, no doubt depending when they were purchased, arranged in lines one behind the other but all facing a blackboard covering the entire wall. There was no dodging one's head to see as the teacher wrote in sections, as necessary, and moved across its width. This enabled the slower ones among us a chance to dwell on, and hopefully assimilate, what was written at our own speed. My own progress moved from being initially in the bottom third of the class up to the top third by the time of GCE exams. This was not startling progress, but made sure school reports were measured in their criticism and tolerated by Mum and Dad. I showed a leaning towards science subjects rather than languages. French was my greatest nightmare, as the first lessons involved the teacher screwing her face into contortions and making exaggerated vowel sounds which sounded nothing like English. To my extreme embarrassment the class had to copy this behaviour. Soon we were making animal noises in unison. The later grammar lessons were another obstacle; strangely enough, each word in French had a gender. Science on the other hand was logical to my mind and involved the occasional experiment and even minor explosions.

The school regarded sport as important, probably more for character formation than for fitness. If fitness correlated with 'skinny', we were all fit except one boy (of considerable body mass) who managed to spend every exercise period in the library. We were encouraged to maintain high sporting prowess and had a reputation to maintain, with two former scholars who were Olympians.

I grew to enjoy rugby and athletics, particularly sprinting, representing the school at the former in the fifth and sixth forms. Scouting too had toughened me up and encouraged a competitive spirit in my desire to achieve badges. Part of the 'athlete badge' included high jump, which was not my strongest event. Resources were limited and the tests had to be held in the local park on a Sunday. The stands and crossbar were borrowed from a school. I managed the required height, which was only about four feet, but landed heavily, hurting my wrist. However accomplished my 'Western roll', it would have been a lot safer to land in a sandpit; the hard ground and short grass were a poor substitute.

There was little sympathy from Mum, who rightly called it "ridiculous". "Anyway, the hospital is shut on Sundays," she admonished me. "I will wrap this bandage tightly and it will probably be alright in the morning."

I couldn't sleep whatever position I tried, and it had swollen considerably by the next day. Mum marched me to the hospital for an X-ray, which showed a fractured wrist. I came out with my lower arm and part of my hand in plaster of Paris.

Fortunately, my academic prowess improved by the time of the GCE exams, and I passed in English, Maths, Biology, History and Geography; sufficient for pursuing farming. I stayed on at school for a further year doing 'A' levels, studying Zoology, Biology and Anatomy / Physiology / Hygiene. This allowed me to get older, aiming at entry to agricultural college and yet with sufficient time for practical experience on farms.

I was always grateful to Mum and Dad for never trying to dissuade me from a life of hard work and poor financial return. Never did they mention that the farming wage was lower than most manual labours, nor did they exhort the life of an academic as exciting. The latter, no doubt, because I had never exhibited great potential in that field. Their honest comment was, "If you chose what you do then you can't blame us for it." This seemed fair enough and they supported my ambition to do farming. It is worth pointing out that I never expected to have my own farm. Even if Mum, who gambled five shillings every week on the Littlewoods football pools, had won the top prize of £75,000, could she have purchased and equipped the size of holding I had in mind? Indeed, why should she selflessly fritter such winnings on a son who had yet to have any permanent employment?

# 3

# Real Work

I had secured my place in the Town Boys' Training Scheme at White Court, whether or not I had buckets of porridge. Within a week I had left high school and started the Training Scheme. Now followed a hectic time of assembling all the necessary clothing, checking the list sent to new entrants and making sure even small items were not missed. Working boots, ex-army, were recommended, and of course Wellington boots. Even socks (three pairs) were listed, as well as working jacket and trousers, again duplicated – anticipating wet weather, no doubt. In short, all the clothing that I had to my name plus much more. My wardrobe became bare except for a well-worn school uniform, minus the cap. The latter had been thrown out from the upper deck of a bus, my friend Roger shouting, "You won't want this anymore." I had told Mum I had lost it, which was essentially true and soon forgotten in the preparations for leaving home.

I cycled to the White Court hostel on the Braintree Road. My bicycle was my trusty steed that had liberated me from parental transport and now gave me wider freedom. It was strangely final, leaving home at about nine o'clock to cover the forty-odd miles. Mum and Dad drove down with two large cases and a travel bag, arriving early afternoon.

We had a quick introduction to the head of house, Mr Widdowson, and to the three ladies preparing the evening meal, then a tour of the otherwise empty premises. The head showed us my room on the first floor, which I would share with two boys currently at work somewhere. We left the cases, later to be stored under the vacant single bed. I was appointed a large single locker with hanging space which I was assured should contain all my belongings during my daily absence except for clothes necessarily left in the drying room downstairs.

There was time for a cup of tea and final questions asked of the friendly Mr Widdowson who, although running an ordered hostel, was seeking to make it homely; no doubt a comfort to parents seeing their offspring in a larger but 'adult' nest where boys were expected to become men. Mum and Dad departed with fond farewells and assurances of keeping in touch; after all, it was only for a few months and less than fifty miles from home.

Mr Widdowson wanted to introduce me to my farmer. Each boy worked on a separate holding and returned daily to the hostel for dinner and lectures in the evening. I had to take careful note of the route as I would be cycling to it at 6.30

am the next day. Fair Oaks Farm was five miles from the hostel and appeared very tidy, with a sweeping drive and crunching gravel. Somehow, I had expected at least some mud or sign of domestic animals. It transpired that the imposing house was part of the farm but in a very detached way; in short, a gentleman's residence with a foreman and staff kept at a suitable distance. We sat somewhat ill at ease and I was made to understand that my employment was more to assist me than enrich my 'benefactor'. However, I was assured of a fair passage for honest, even vigorous, endeavour at times, if I was prepared to learn. This brief encounter over, I would be expected to be punctual at 6.50 am the next day, when I would be introduced to the foreman.

On the way home, Mr Widdowson filled in the timetable, which I did my best to take in whilst assiduously watching the return navigation. Dinner would be at 6.45 pm – everybody having washed and changed from work clothes. This was an unwritten rule enforced by the fact that non-compliance resulted in no dinner. Needless to say, teenage boys working on farms and in danger of starvation arranged their priorities accordingly. My two room-mates were sitting on their beds having calculated the time necessary to wash sufficiently, even shower, and dress by 6.45 pm. I was obviously clean enough but it was suggested a shower at least every third day was necessary to pass anywhere close to Mrs Widdowson, who had an uncanny knack of knowing the date of your last shower.

The food was plain but wholesome, and generally met with approval, which was more than could be said for the packed lunch we each received at breakfast. My sojourn at the Town Boys' Training Scheme coincided with the invention of sliced bread. The packed lunches consisted of eight slices of bread, with tomato inserted between two slices, cheese between two others, and jam or marmalade between the remaining four – all being reinserted in the plastic bag they had arrived in from the baker. I quickly learned these were best cut in half and consumed two savoury at bait-time (the men's breakfast break at 9.00 am), four at 1 pm (lunch) and the remaining two at 5 pm if having to work an hour overtime or unsure if one could survive until dinner at 6.45 pm. In any event, I developed an aversion to jam sandwiches, especially when compressed, bent and often tepid on hot days. In addition to sandwiches, we were each allowed a bottle of diluted orange squash to last the day. This likewise did not travel well; weak due to over-dilution and similarly warmed, it was no competition to cold water from the cowshed tap.

The next day I was keen to meet all the deadlines. I had not slept well but was excited to consume some cereal and toast, collect a packed lunch and pedal off to the farm. I arrived in good time. I met three men, who were obviously expecting the new boy, in the open cartshed – the first of many wooden buildings in front of the brick-built barn and seemingly two large cowsheds.

"I am Charlie; Mark is at the house," the first man said.

He was in a waistcoat that had seen better days and wore a well-used red-and-white handkerchief tied around his neck.

"I am Peter." We shook hands as Bill appeared.

"Bill, this is Peter," Charlie introduced me. We shook hands.

"He looks alright, Charlie. Do you think he will last?" Bill jested.

This, I learned, was referring to the last boy who gave up after three weeks, due to unpunctuality, lack of energy and aversion to grease and mud. He obviously had not read the not-so-small print below the heading 'Farm Work'. I obviously needed to do better. Bill was younger than Charlie and a little taller, dressed in an open-necked shirt and bulging pullover with a thick leather belt seemingly to keep everything together. The good thing was, we all shared similar head-gear, namely a cloth cap. Mine was conspicuously new but no doubt would weather in time.

The foreman, Mark, arrived from the house where he had received the orders for the day. It was not the custom for this farmer to engage directly with the men unless absolutely necessary.

"So, you are our new young man, Peter, the boss tells me." Mark's face was all wrinkles so I wasn't sure whether it was a smile or a frown, but his eyes were piercingly bright as if looking into the distance. "Yer look as if you mean business." Mark eyed me up and down. "Got the right boots! A tad shiny!" he observed.

Turning to the men, he said we were to prepare for harvest, making sure we were ready to go in a week, if the weather held. Mark led Charlie and Bill towards two large sheds; they would be repairing any broken weatherboarding above the stone walls and generally making the barn bird-proof. I was to accompany Les who had just joined us. He was second cowman and joined the general farm workers whenever there was no pressing need within the dairy herd. Les explained the cows were "out at the moment", which I later understood to mean sleeping in the fields during summer rather than in the strawyards, their winter quarters. This was a much easier time, not having to carry feed and bedding to them. I was later to discover that the cows did not need as much cosseting as the pastures. Heavy hooves, 120 x 4, soon churned up grass and wet Essex clay to a mud bath. This would result in much later grass production in the spring.

The tithe barn was used to store sacks of grain and needed to be clean of debris and excessive dust. I was told to sweep the concrete floor from the walls towards the centre whilst Les disappeared for a wheelbarrow and shovel. I poked the broom at the bottom of the wall and corners with small strokes, not appearing to find anything to sweep. It occurred to me that I had never had to use a broom, at least not in anger. Mum swept the front doorstep and fifteen feet of pathway daily but I never saw her move any debris. I had looked on it as a ritual to good housekeeping, and a chance to pass the time of day and share any gossip with one or two neighbours who mysteriously appeared at a similar time.

Les was not impressed.

"Let me show you," he demanded.

He took the yard broom and made a series of sweeps from the wall toward the centre whilst progressing one step forward with each arc of the broom. This resulted in a tangible row of 'dust' appearing. He turned round and pushed this row a further two or three feet towards the centre of the floor.

"You were prodding, lifting the broom and prodding in the same place like goading a chicken," Les continued with his commentary. "One stroke, one step forward, next stroke, move, cover the ground."

I took the broom and tried to copy, imperfectly, but eventually noticing the volume of dust and debris growing. After about an hour there was a central row down the length of the building and I was exhausted. My hands ached from gripping the handle and I had a serious red patch in the middle of my right hand, which I'd used to push the broomstick, that was throbbing. I shovelled the rubbish into the barrow. Les led me out around the tithe barn to the grassy area behind the cowshed. There was a small tip which he said would be added to the dung-spreading sometime later. I would never have thought there was an art to sweeping but at least I had learned something. Fortunately, Les announced it was breakfast time.

When working around the yard, the men had breakfast together in the stable adjoining the cartshed. Working in fields they would find a sheltered spot, sitting on whatever was present, using an overcoat as a ground sheet. Protocol separated the cowmen who cycled home for a cooked breakfast; they had been working since 5.30 am and were considered a different 'department', again with a distinct pecking order: head cowman, second or under cowman, and dairy boy. Les, it seemed, was something of a bridge between dairy and arable, having to work with us at busy periods when needed.

The stable had half a dozen bales around the walls, which acted as a backrest at meal breaks. There were assorted pegs as coat hangers and I had been allocated one of these two hours previously with the instruction, "Always hang yer bait bag up." This, I learned later, was to be out of reach of rats, stray dogs and anything that might break a Thermos flask; the latter not being relevant to my squash bottle. It was rather dark even with the stable door kept open, but my eyes were drawn to a large horse collar high on the back wall.

"Are there any horses now?" I wondered aloud.

There was silence and Mark walked out as if to check something. Charlie leaned closer.

"Yer don't talk about 'orses; it's not done, Peter." He hesitated, choosing his words and pointing to the collar. "It was his 'orse; he was head carter."

"I am sorry," I muttered, grasping the situation and dismissing any thought of further questions. Mark returned, having kicked a bucket or tin can in the cartshed.

I self-consciously studied which of my sandwiches was suitable for breakfast, whilst the others chatted about the weekend's football. Normality was restored. We were sitting in a stable – more accurately a collection of four stables. Perhaps they had had two horses in each box? There were no horses on the farm now. It had never occurred to me, the depth of feeling and emotion caused by advances in farming practice. In a few decades the move from horse power to tractor power had been dramatic. The ethos of 'progress' had impinged on society generally and had been largely welcomed. However, it had ignored the affinity of relationships: horse and horseman toiling together in a common task. This working through weather, good and bad, together with the joint daily routine of feed and harnessing, cemented a bond hardly less than that of blood.

# 4

# Really Farming

As I cycled the five miles to Fair Oaks Farm it seemed the natural life. I had never travelled this route but cycling was my personal transport. School was far behind me; even the hostel I had only spent a night in was just a necessary lodging. The farm job was mine; I had become an adult. Although I didn't know it then, it would take buckets of porridge to become a man. I reasoned farming and porridge went together: natural, plain, sustaining food. But was there a more subtle intent behind those words?

My second day was spent working with Charlie on fixing gates. This was further preparing for harvest, hopefully a seamless operation: corn to be combined, transported, stored. It entailed gateways being cleared of overgrown brambles, gates that would open and close with a minimum of effort, and ditches and culverts cut back, making them obvious to tractor drivers. No excuse for letting a trailer wheel slide into an unseen hazard. I was shown how to hold and use a feg-hook[2]. Charlie used a billhook[3] to chop out a hazel stick for me. This I was to use as a wand, lifting or pushing undergrowth with my left hand to expose the area to strike, with the feg-hook held in the right hand. He demonstrated, with consummate ease, clearing a square yard with a few swipes. I was very conscious of my badly blistered right palm from yesterday's sweeping. I tried to copy him but with little effect. Using considerable force there seemed nothing to hit at. The hook met the target grass and brushed over the top, leaving the tufts to bounce back more or less scathed.

"Yer only worried it. Cut with the front 'arf of the hook," Charlie advised. "Yer need a pad for that; don't pull the dead skin off." He viewed my hand with some concern.

"Yer 'ave to toughen yer hands. Have you an 'anky?"

I offered a fairly clean handkerchief which he folded into a pad and then foraged in his sack for a glove.

"Try this but grip hard," Charlie instructed.

I tried a couple of swings at the tufts but hardly made any difference in my unskilled way, and it would require hours of back-breaking practice to reach his

---

[2]  a feg is a thick layer of dead grass left as fodder
[3]  a heavy blade curved at the tip, with the top edge fashioned for use as a hand-axe

standard. Charlie produced a carborundum[4] from his sack of tools and, with the skill of a butcher using a steel, sharpened the hook. In the absence of water he spat on the blade and rubbed the part of the stone shaped like a 'relay baton' in vigorous strokes across the top side of the blade, concentrating on the top half. The underside of the blade, that nearest the ground, was left with only a few 'cleaning' wipes of the carborundum to take off any little burrs, making the top face as sharp as one would sharpen a wood chisel on a stone.

Gate posts were checked for plumb[5] and, if necessary, heaving the post upright using the open end of the gate and ramming stones on the inside of the post. All this was new and certainly entailed muscles I did not know I possessed... until night-time. I was learning jobs and hopefully would acquire skills that would make me a useful farmhand. Could this be what needing 'buckets of porridge' meant?

Towards the end of the week the weather was brighter and I helped Les to prepare the baler. The field of already-harvested barley straw would soon be ready for baling. I became Les's shadow as he used a grease-gun on the nipples all over the machine. He soon handed me a smaller 'push-on gun' and told me to clean any nipples first with my finger and then to give them two squirts from the gun.

"Wherever there's a moving part, it needs grease," he instructed.

"I don't know what moves," I countered.

He came from underneath the front end and showed me the 'knotters'. They bristled with greased nipples.

"Yer may not 'ave seen them, but they all move an' all need two squirts." This was kindly advice without any impatience.

I was in my element; this was farming and I wanted to know everything.

"How do they work?" I asked

Les was keen to show me what a baler does. He pulled my arm to a box on the side and lifted the lid.

"This is the string box." He reached for a large paper bag nearby, shaking out two large balls of string a foot tall and almost the same across. Les dropped each next to the existing balls inside the box. "You'll have to do this tidy or we'll have broken bales," Les instructed. He pulled the loose end of string from the outside of the half-used ball and tied it to the inside string of the new ball. "Can you do a reef knot?"

"I was a Boy Scout," I enthused.

"Well, do the same for the other knotter," Les said.

"Outside of old to inside string of the new one," I muttered reminding myself of the sequence.

---

[4]  an abrasive stone
[5]  upright

"Good bor[6]! Pull it tight so 'e don't undo," he said as he looked over my shoulder.

I followed the line of string passing through the two holes in the end of the string box and under the machine to the drawbar.

"That's this frame joining the tractor" – Les smacked the main frame – "and these are the needles." He pointed to two cast-iron prongs pointing upwards, the string threading though 'eyes' and disappearing into the bale chamber. "You'll see much better in the field tomorrow."

The next morning the forecast was sunny and the order was to prepare for baling after lunch. Les drove the baler to the field of straw with me set to be shadowing him again. The idea was to make me useful to Mr Broadhurst, which would entail training as one would an apprentice. Every minute I was picking up how a farm worked and the reason behind each task. I propped myself next to Les and the mudguard, holding it tightly. Behind was the baler towing a sledge. We passed three or four fields of grass (later to be known as pasture) and then two fields of unharvested wheat, before turning into a field of barley stubble.

The first task was to start the diesel engine on the baler and "run things over". The engine running the baler was mounted on top of the bale chamber; more instruction was necessary as it had to be started manually.

"I know. I've turned the starting handle for my father." I was keen to show at least a little knowledge.

"Not so fast," Les cautioned. "This is a diesel and she can give you a kick. That little lever" – he pointed to it on top of the rocker box – "takes the pressure off. Yer turn it over sharply and pull that in."

I knew that petrol engines had spark plugs to ignite the fuel mixture and diesels had higher compression to ignite the 'explosion' in the cylinder, but I didn't know it could be decompressed to make starting easier. Les explained how the lever opened a little hole or 'port' to allow the fuel mixture to escape easily as the starting handle got the flywheel moving. At Les's shout, I had to snap the lever shut and the engine should start. We had a trial run without success. Les went over the procedure again.

"Now!" he bellowed as he let go of the crank handle.

I pushed the lever home and it fired up. The mechanism was eased into life and everything turned. It seemed alive: the large ram moving noisily up and down the empty chamber; the packer arm moving the invisible straw from the pick-up into the bale chamber to be compressed by the heavy ram. It was meticulously timed.

"Stay where you are and see what happens." With this he forked some straw from the swath[7] onto the pick-up. This was pushed by the revolving tines into

---

[6] boy
[7] row of straw

the packer chamber and swept at right angles through the side of the bale chamber just as the ram was at its shortest cycle of rotation. With each push of the ram, the bale grew about two inches in length.

"Watch the knotters," Les shouted.

He pulled up a metal arm, which I later found to be the bale length device, and immediately 'needles', threaded with string, came up through the bale; in a flash the knotters rotated 360 degrees, making a knot and cutting the string. I was spellbound. The bale was pushed along to the rear as the 'string', or baler twine, was laid for the next 'mouthful' of straw, which all happened at bewildering speed.

Les stopped and came to my side.

"See what happened?" He smiled.

"Sort of. It was really fast," I replied.

"Yer'll never see what happens." He smiled again. "It's still dawny. We'll have bait and then see what it's like."

"What's 'dawny'?" I enquired.

"Sort of dampish." Les hesitated. "Like washing is ready for ironing but you could wear the shirt without ironing." Another pause. "Only, with straw and hay, if it's made dawny it will go mouldy."

We collected our lunch bags from the tractor and sat down, backs against the rear wheel. An hour later Les walked into the swaths left by the combine, turning them upside down and burying his face in the straw. I followed as a shadow, taking in the whole procedure.

"Is it OK?" I asked.

He handed me the armful which I dutifully tested in the same way.

"Seems better than before lunch," I commented, trying not to sound knowledgeable.

"You're learning. We'll give it a try," Les suggested.

This was real farm work and a great summer's day; nature was gently buzzing and I was going to be paid for it. The rows of straw went round the field as the combine had cut and threshed the barley. It appeared as a giant maze with row upon row leading to the centre. Les got me to stand on the front edge of the sledge to catch the tied bales of straw and stack them on the back part of the metal slats. I was told to catch the bale as it came off the bale chute, turn around with it and place it across the metal slats behind. It sounded simple enough.

Les moved off and a moment later the sledge chain attached to the rear of the tractor took up the slack. This had precisely the same effect as snatching a tea tray from under me at the speed of lightening. It was akin to a complete novice standing on roller skates not expecting them to move. Although I didn't fall to the ground, I was three steps nearer to the rear of the sledge, but still with eyes on the advancing bale. I grasped the strings of the first bale and tried Les's pirouette. The bale was reasonably square when number two came pushing at my heels. Les stopped and came down to me.

"Swing that bale tight and tidy with the first, across the width of the sledge." He motioned that the next two should go on top but longways, then the next pair in the same direction as the first two, etc.

It was the 'etc' that was bothering me as I attempted to lift and place bale numbers seven and eight.

"Stack them four high; two across, two on top the other way and same again on top of them. Like kids' bricks. I'll go steady so yer get the hang of it," Les instructed again.

We stopped again and Les pushed and poked the stack into some symmetry.

"Now what yer do is push them off." Les pointed to my only handhold on this flatbed. He lifted the steel crowbar out of its snug tube and planted it in the gap in the slatted floor. "Hold it firm and without me stopping, the sledge will pull from under 'em," he instructed.

Within half an hour we had finished the headland with several stacks dotted around. I was now told to try and offload stacks in a line as we baled the main part of the field. This was to ease and speed bale collection when they were carted to make a 'straw stack', either in the open or in the 'Dutch barn'[8] in the yard. By the end of the afternoon, I had made a reasonable job of 'lines'. It had entailed setting off four bales from the start of a row and offloading a set of eight next time, coming back on the return trip. The 'odd' four could be stacked against the nearest eight, minimising rain damage. It taught me that manual workers, particularly farm workers, could with a little thought make it easier for themselves and more efficient for their employer.

I soon settled into the working week, which included 7 am to 12.30 pm on Saturdays. Whilst at school I had had a job at weekends cutting lawns and doing some garden-tidying, providing useful pocket money. Now I had a proper job and real wages.

Wages on the farm were dispensed weekly at strictly 12.30 pm on Saturdays. I was introduced to the procedure at breakfast by Mark, the foreman, and it was certainly no casual occasion.

"We goes up in order; you stand with Charlie," Mark instructed.

I thought no more of it that first payday until about noon, when there was a gradual slowing down and a coming together from various tasks. We were returning hand tools and tidying wet weather gear around our pegs. I had to make sure I was taking my squash bottle and wrappers with me in my ex-army 'bait' bag; others were clearing the odd cigarette packets and litter. Finally, some were kicking off mud from their boots and running them under the tap in an effort more determined than on any other day.

---

[8]  a roof on legs

We all followed Mark across the yard. Being foreman, he led the patrol to the side of the farmhouse.

Charlie pulled me behind him and whispered, "Say, 'Thank you, sir.'" He hesitated, possibly wondering if I needed that prompt. "He likes that."

We filed in order of seniority to the sash window that had just risen. A hand passed a brown packet out and, with the slightest nod, Mark responded, "Thank you, sir."

We duly followed. I brought up the rear.

Mr Broadhurst added, "Don't spend it all at once," and pulled the window down.

We returned to the cartshed, calling out, "See you Monday," mounted our various bikes and went off.

Peddling back to the hostel I was surprised at the deference, the 'them' and 'us', that I had not expected. I was definitely one of 'us'. Of course, we had always addressed school staff as "sir" or "miss", particularly in deference and respect to the headmaster who unilaterally decided what punishment needed administering. But on the farm there had been an ease of working with nature, a common ally that set the rules. Now on payday there seemed a distinction; some people more worthy than others. I had spent that week in a countryside which allowed everything, man and beast, to co-exist in a natural harmony. During breaks we had sat amid vegetation, earth and insect in a compliant peace, dependant on each other, large and small equally necessary.

Weekends were more urban; I was back at the hostel and with the Town Boys. Half of them were going home for the weekend; others seeking shops, football and Wimpey bars. I would be staying and exploring life away from home and school. I got changed and cycled into Braintree with no fixed purpose. I had money but only a little. The pay packet contained about £5.2s.0d. of which £3.9s.0d. had to be paid out for the hostel board and lodging. I wandered into ex-army and camping stores looking at outdoor clothing and cheap offers on fishermen's socks. I didn't buy anything, and sauntered onto an open grassy area which had more appeal. I had time to explore side alleys and a riverside, even finding a church.

Sunday dawned and the place seemed empty. I decided to cycle to town and the Methodist church. When I had been a Boy Scout, we had met in the church hall at home. I didn't remember the service but I did the friendliness. As I was about to leave, a lady approached asking if I was new to town. I mentioned White Court and things seemed to fall into place.

"Oh, you are learning farming. Where do you come from?" she asked.

"London," I simply answered, as if she might not have heard of any district, my subconscious saying, *I am used to the city and I have never been here before.*

"What is your name?"

"Peter."

"I'm Mrs Willis. My son Alan is at home; he'd like to meet you. Come and have some lunch."

I was rather taken aback at the offer.

"You aren't doing anything else, are you?" Mrs Willis enquired.

"No..." I hesitated. Then, not wishing to sound ungrateful, I added a quick "Thank you!"

I walked my bike with Mrs Willis the two or three streets to her townhouse, similar to those I knew at home. Home it certainly was; wonderful aromas wafted from the kitchen as I compared notes with Alan and Mr Willis. There was an immediate ease that did not come from common interests but a desire to welcome a stranger in need of something familiar. There is nothing like a Sunday roast to introduce companionship. Indeed, this was the start of many Sundays which for me joined hostel and home; I had an exciting job and now a homely retreat.

I thanked Mrs Willis profusely at about 3 pm and wandered around town pushing my bike. There was not much to interest me, window shopping was not my scene, but I wanted to find my way around. I left feeling there was an old-fashioned quaintness, and shops for essentials but little else. I had been spoilt by London and the multitude of things to do, especially with friends.

The hostel was quiet; four boys watching football, nobody in the quiet room. I was a rugby boy; that had been compulsory – no school football team. Rugby suited me nicely; it was tough, physical, but matey with no hard feelings after the final whistle. The quiet room, strangely named, had a few books and board games, so not a useful library. Perhaps it was intended as a retreat but it was of no interest to me at the moment – I preferred the outdoors. I wandered across the grass to the chain-link perimeter fence and followed it around, reaching a scrubby pasture the other side. There was a break in the fence which I had rather hoped to find. It would be easier to justify, if accosted, than climbing over and being accused of trespass. Over the other side there were three Nissen huts that looked interesting. The door of the first was hanging on one hinge, inviting me in. There were the remnants of use: two broken stools and a fitted table surface between two cupboards. A relic of wartime, but the roof was still sound. As I ambled about, I thought of modern uses; surely somebody could keep chickens and let them run out on the grass? I could suggest it to Mr Widdowson but guessed he knew all about the huts. Anyway, they probably didn't belong to him. On further reflection, I wanted to work on farms not smallholdings. I ruminated on my farming future in time for the light tea that would be the last bite until breakfast.

The start of my second week promised fine weather and a continuation of harvest. We met in the stable at 7 am as before, a routine I was becoming used to. No work had been done on Sunday but there was a buzz that the harvesting would proceed unhindered. Mark, Charlie and Bill would be starting a straw-rick, and Les and I prepared for a day baling straw. As usual we expected to have breakfast together before being scattered to various fields. We settled for 9 am 'bait' in our usual positions within the stable.

"What were you doing yesterday, bor?" Charlie enquired with a grin before I could answer. "Find some poppsie in town?"

"No!" I was indignant. "I went to church, if you must know."

"Sorry to ask, I must say. Nothing wrong with looking the girls over." Charlie was taken aback.

I had not been used to any talk at home about girlfriends. At school the girls had been just mates; 'girlfriends' would mostly be sourced from the 'girls only' establishments. It must have been unusual that the subject of girlfriends was never mentioned at home, probably because my parents didn't want to encourage any distraction from study. Anyway, I felt the subject was private.

"Leave the bor alone." Mark was studiously peeling an apple. "It's his business."

I felt sorry about my reaction which had created a bit of tension on such a nice morning.

"I was invited to lunch by Mrs Willis, which was very kind," I added to redeem the situation.

Talk was dropped. Les touched my elbow.

"Cum'n, we best see what the straw's like."

We were able to start about mid-morning, all greased and fuelled up, the straw beginning to crackle in the warming sun. I was soon in the swing of stacking the sledge and planting the crowbar to push them off. At 1 pm Les stopped everything and we sat on a bale, both thankful the noise and dust had stopped as well. He started his sandwiches and I peered into my plastic bag to select a couple of cheese sandwiches, leaving two jams for 5 pm and the expected overtime. We only had half an hour for lunch as it was harvest time and the work had to proceed apace. The morning's effort of grabbing heavy bales by the strings had made my fingers very sore. Les tore a rag that was in the tractor box and bandaged my two fingers, index and middle, together on each hand. He showed me how to let those 'cushioned' fingers take most of the weight, the others supporting them, whilst lifting and positioning the bale onto the sledge.

By mid-week the weather had changed and the remaining fields of straw could not be baled. We were all consigned to carting and stacking bales. I was introduced to teamwork and labour-saving techniques learned from years of experience. We rode out on two empty trailers, leaving one at the gateway and taking the other to the furthest line of bales. Mark stood on the trailer to stack the bales. Charlie and Bill, each with a bale fork, would both spear the same bale, one each end, and hoist it over their heads onto the trailer. Because the forks were slightly curved, the weighty straw would slip off as it landed on the trailer. My job was to lift the top bale off the field stack and drop it at their feet.

I also had to drive the tractor carefully to the next stack. Mark received all the bales in the middle of the trailer and, with the least movement, was only a couple of paces from each corner of the trailer. I soon discovered minimum effort was important in getting through the day. This teamwork was productive and the second trailer retrieved from the gateway and loaded likewise. Except that I was introduced to loading with Charlie, Bill taking my easier job. Charlie showed me how to pierce the bale and lift it in unison over our heads, then dropping it at Mark's feet.

I had seen it done and the theory was fine. The first bale landed in the right place but with my fork still stuck in it. There were grins all round as if they had expected this.

"Nar, bor, yer meant to hold on t' fork!" Mark pulled out the fork and speared the stubble beside me.

Charlie added, "Don't stick it in too 'ard, only 'arf way."

This improved the job but I was showered with straw and chaff as each bale passed overhead. Tomorrow I would be sure to bring my cloth cap as mentioned in my must-have list. During a brief breather, Mark pointed out how the bottom layer of bales were all stood on their rough sides to stop any slippage on the shiny wooden floor. The following bales were stacked with strings uppermost, presenting the rough stalk ends to bind with bales well pressed together, so hindering lateral movement.

The two trailers were carefully stacked and, being six layers high, did not need roping, thus saving time. Eight layers would be roped, with regard to overhanging trees or public roads. Arriving at the stackyard, there was an elevator like a wooden escalator, with metal spikes about every eight feet, driven by a small petrol engine. Mark, who had stayed atop the load, moved a few bales to make a platform for himself on about the fourth layer. I was to clamber up to Mark and serve him with bales from the ends of the trailer so he could ease the bales onto the moving conveyor. Charlie and Bill climbed onto the stack to receive the bales and place them in their final place for the winter. After twelve layers Mark and Bill drew the next in, leaving a foot of ledge all around, and similarly with the next layer, like a staircase. This gave it the appearance of a 'house' of straw. Finally they stood bales on end, lying up the 'stairs', making a sloping roof which was tied on with string to the bales underneath.

Charlie took me to collect a great wooden ladder which was on wall brackets in the old tithe barn.

"It's heavy, mind." Charlie told me to stand by the other bracket only about five feet up the wall. "We'll ease him off and let it slide down to ground."

Charlie was my height, five foot nine, and must have been in his late fifties. We both grunted as we lifted it off and slid it down.

"Cor, that was heavier than it looks," I commented looking down. "Why don't you just leave it on the ground?"

"Cos tractor drivers like you would back a trailer over it!" was his quick retort.

We stood about five feet from each end and carried it by putting an arm through the rungs and clasping that wrist with our free hand. This was deemed the safest way rather that shouldering the long ladder.

"It's a twenty-four-runger thatching ladder," Charlie puffed from behind.

At the stack Les joined us, and whilst Charlie stood on the bottom rung, we walked it up to vertical, easing it onto the roof.

"Don't make 'em like that today," Les smiled as he passed on his way to the cows. Charlie had disappeared and returned with a bundle of steel rods, passing them to Bill who pushed them through the end bales as a precaution against winter winds.

# 5

# Time to Move

After harvest and the end of bale carting, work turned to ploughing and preparing for sowing the winter wheat. I was learning all the time and relishing it. Every turn of the weather meant a different task. I found that Mr Broadhurst often drove around the farm, spending time talking to Mark who in turn organised our jobs. It seemed that the men all knew what to expect or at least had an opinion on what should be done. This was the topic at most breaktimes. There was a deep commitment to the farm and a concern for the job in hand. It was 'their' farm, the workers', and pride in the quality of their work was a window of skill to other farmers and villagers. As summer turned to autumn, the corn fields and stubbles turned as brown as fine seedbeds, framed by trees and hedgerows in autumn plumage, matching the season.

Mark and Bill did the majority of the cultivation. No doubt Mark had carried on from ploughing with horses to the use of iron ones. Bill would have started with tractors as the motive force and seemed knowledgeable about mechanics. Charlie did the hand work, so necessary to the welfare of fields being drained, gateways and culverts serviced. I lacked the experience of cultivation and sowing of the winter crops, but gained valuable knowledge working with Charlie on the fundamentals of the countryside.

We were sent ditching, which started with walking the main ditches from boundary fence going upstream.

"Yer always start at the low point and work upstream." I was grateful for Charlie's openness, always prepared to instruct me. He walked a couple of paces ahead, spade over shoulder and long-handled slasher[9] in the other hand. "We're looking for land drains," he called over his shoulder.

We walked on the grass, which he referred to as the "brew", between the track and the ditch, and which was obscuring the drainage pipes with a season's grass and wild growth. He seemed to have a sixth sense as to where a land drain may be.

Dropping the spade and poking through the vegetation with the slasher, he exposed my first land drain. It was a red clay pipe at a right angle to the ditch, about thirty inches below the surface of the field.

---

[9] like a straight scythe

"That's it but it ain't running; need rain yet," Charlie announced.

"That's how water gets into the ditch?" I surmised.

He cut away the grasses and briars back to the banks, exposing about a yard around the pipe. We walked on to find the next drain.

"You can do this one but don't hit the pipe," Charlie instructed.

I tried a few swipes of the slasher with little effect. He took it from me and patiently demonstrated the finer points.

"Don't swing it – start about a foot away and make a smart pull. Then yer haven't broke anything and can see the wood for the trees."

I tried again.

"Keep the hook like yer shaving the bank and keep combing it." A further demonstration, and at least I knew the theory.

Occasionally we had to scoop out some mud and debris to make sure water would fall into the ditch rather than block the flow. A proper 'ditching' would follow later depending on other more pressing jobs.

The teamwork continued until lunch. Charlie surveyed the area for the best spot, taking in the wind direction, and chose a dry, slightly elevated area. We settled for a couple of tree stumps twenty yards away. There we ate in silence until Charlie suddenly questioned me.

"Do you always go to church?"

Before I could answer he continued, "I mean... I didn't mean no offence, you know, about 'girls'."

My mind rushed back to Charlie's tease.

"None taken," I said.

"What I mean," Charlie persisted, "is it important for you to go to church?"

"Well, yes, it is," I replied.

"Do you believe in all that?" he asked.

I hesitated. It was like a secret that I had never told anyone, not even my parents. Of course, they knew I went to church when I could, but we never talked about religion. Dad, on the only occasion he ever referred to the church, said, "If you had seen what I have, you wouldn't believe in God." And that was that.

It had seemed so final. How could I, a mere boy, argue, even discuss, what had affected him so deeply? How could I own up to praying and God answering my prayers? It moved me to think about it, but I had never told anybody that God had answered my prayers. I couldn't tell Mum or Dad, so how could I tell anyone else? Time had gone by, some seven years, but I was still certain that the truth was God had answered my cries for help.

Charlie seemed genuine and he was becoming a mate.

"Well, Charlie, keep this to yourself." I took a deep breath. "I wasn't very good at school," I confessed.

"Nor was I," he butted in, but I continued; there was no way back.

"There was no way I could pass the eleven-plus exam. No way! I knew it was so important but it was impossible. My parents couldn't help, my teacher couldn't help. The only chance was the Boy Scouts; I mean, they finished every evening by talking to God." In case he thought I was really stupid, I added, "God wasn't actually there but He seems to hear us, even though He's sort of invisible. Well, I asked and asked to pass the exam."

"Did you? I mean did you pass?" Charlie asked.

"Yes and no," I muttered.

"What do yer mean, yes and no?"

I had to tell the whole story. "The letter said I had to sit the exam again and I passed in the June."

"Where does God come in?" Charlie asked.

"If I had passed the first time I may have thought I'd managed it myself. But I didn't pass, or fail, and I had never heard of anyone having to sit the exam a second time, nor had my teacher."

Charlie looked puzzled but I continued.

"You see, God did answer my prayer, and He did it that way to show me." I was on a roll now. "If I had simply passed first time, I could have thought, 'Well, that's good; maybe I wasn't so bad after all.' But because there was no result and I had to sit the exam again, it proved it was God's answer."

The secret was out. I felt both exhausted and relieved.

"So that's why I go to church," I finished.

Charlie said nothing but seemed satisfied.

The summer had passed with the harvest and autumn planting well underway. I was surprised that time seemed to pass so quickly. I had time to reflect during meal breaks on the farm as the men often dozed off, especially after lunch. I suppose over the years they had cultivated complete relaxation before the next bout of manual work. I just looked at a fresh scene wherever we had been working and drank it in. There was time to think that had never occurred in town. Perhaps it was the number of people and their frenetic activities that caused the sense of rush, whilst nature proceeded at a leisurely pace hardly noticed in the routine of the home-commute-office merry-go-round. In the country, nature predominates and human activities have to fit in with her. Her timing is gentle but remorseless; working the land has to be exacting and in sympathy with the conditions. Nature is a wholesome mix of events that morph into a compound which cannot be undone by human hands. This God-given wonder is ever evolving and challenges the farmers and growers to obey the rules that have been passed down through generations of experience. I soon learned that we countrymen and women are tenants on earth and should leave the land in better order than we found it.

After two months Mr Widdowson had promoted me to 'head boy' at White Court, which was something of a double-edged sword. I became the conduit between pupil and authority, and turned out to be a mediator role, softening the blows of officialdom by explaining some reasoning for edicts passed down from on high. In the reverse direction I suggested small adjustments that would aid the smooth running of the establishment. One such example was to allow the drink of the day, tea or coffee of course, to be taken in our rooms rather than in the formal dining room. The position of head boy was not too onerous and may just have benefitted my future employability.

One or two of the evening lecturers encouraged us to look to our futures. "Where would you like to be?" The Town Boys' Training Scheme was available to us on a somewhat open-ended timescale depending on what progress individuals made towards their goal. Some obviously lacked aptitude and would never make a farm worker. It has to be said, some were averse to any manual labour and were soon culled. Others stayed until they had reached a reasonable competence and had an idea of what they wanted from the industry. I was focused and knew I had to gain as much varied experience as possible. After this introduction to arable farming, I thought a dairy farm should be my next step.

As the autumn and all its changing glory slipped by, the thought of leaving grew. I was very happy at Fair Oaks Farm and had become attached to the men; moving would be a wrench. My colleagues knew they would probably have a new boy, but urged me to stay on and join the dairy enterprise there. Indeed, Mr Broadhurst must have heard about my leanings towards dairy experience and urged me to be under his head cowman. My training officer urged me to leave as he wanted the vacancy at my farm for a new entrant. Anyway, he said, a farm that was solely dairy would be focused and in a different area, adding to my experience.

A dairy farm near Colchester had a vacancy and an interview was arranged with the farmer. My training officer drove me one Saturday afternoon to a completely different set-up. The chain-smoking farmer had his relief milker working but promised he would teach me all aspects of dairy farming. After a few cursory questions and a visit to the cowshed, the interview was over and I was told I would hear from him within a fortnight.

My last day after over four months at White Court and Fair Oaks was a mixture of apprehension and anticipation. I was really sorry to leave the security and friendship I had enjoyed, but at seventeen years old I was about to experience my second farm employment. There were goodbyes all round and calls to "come and see us sometime". On my final payday, Mr Broadhurst came out of the house and shook my hand. He thanked me and wished me well. I responded with thanks for the great introduction to farming he had given me. With a few waves I set off cycling back to the hostel.

# 6

# Dairy Farming

My training officer had found Goblets Farm for me and even digs in the village, thus saving me searching the local paper and trudging round lodgings asking if they could accommodate a farm worker. The early rising and dirty, indeed *smelly*, occupation would have deterred most landladies from welcoming a young stranger into their home. Not only was I spared doors slamming in my face, but the experienced training officer must have extolled the virtues of a clean young man that he knew well and needed to move from a hostel where he had proven his worthiness. When my mother learned of the move to independent living, she pictured a family home where the mother of teenagers would exchange one about to leave home for a fee-paying replacement.

I had packed all my clothes and worldly goods – far too much for my cycle panniers, and I was grateful for my parents' help in transporting them by car to Colchester. I left in good time to cycle ahead and hopefully arrive together at the new address. This was achieved and so I was on hand when Miss Lark opened the front door to them.

"Miss Lark, my parents." I was ridiculously formal. Mum stood there as if I were a stranger. Plainly the frail old lady who purported to be my new housekeeper, even surrogate 'mother', was in need of a carer herself. After various pleasantries and a very weak cup of tea, Mum and Dad left somewhat apprehensively. I had a few concerns but was focused on the prospects of a new job.

Miss Lark showed me to my room which, it was probably fortunate, Mum had not been given the opportunity of seeing. The house itself was a modest semi, probably a hundred and fifty years old and originally a farm worker's cottage. My room was small with a single bed, a dresser and single wardrobe slightly impeding the door from fully opening. I refrained from testing the springs of the bed whilst Miss Lark was with me. She had a number of rules that I needed to heed:

"Now, I expect you'll want to be early to bed; I lock the front door at 9.30 pm."

I listened without comment.

"I expect you will be back for breakfast about nine o'clock which will suit me nicely. I cook in the evening for about six-thirty," she continued.

"I don't know what times I will have to work, but I'm sure I can fit in with you." I felt agreement was called for. "By the way, where is the bathroom?"

"Oh yes, we only have one, but there is a lock on the door," she wanted me to note.

She moved across the landing to open a small bathroom. I followed and had to enquire why the bath was on the landing.

"Oh, I don't have a bath." She seemed oblivious to the large white enamel tub with two taps right in front of me. "That's not a bath. I mean, you can't have a bath," Miss Lark ended flatly.

I was sure a cowman's job was not too dissimilar to a coal miner's in terms of such a necessity.

"I'm sure you can have a perfectly good wash in the bathroom." She made it sound final.

I had the next day off before starting my new employment on the Monday. The bed was satisfactory and I was sure I would sleep well, especially after a day's work. I made a point of lingering around the bath before going down for breakfast, hoping Miss Lark would not hear me on the landing. Incredibly, the lovely new bath was not for use. Taps it had, but no pipes leading water to or away from it. I wondered if it was about to be installed – but why there? Except I could see no other room for it. Over the weeks of passing this pristine vessel, I conjured up scenarios as to why it was there at all. Was it waiting for a plumber? Was the plan to build a plasterboard wall around it? There was no room for a bath except there, with perhaps a simple curtain on all sides. The thought of Miss Lark stepping through, skinny-leg first, dispelled any such notion.

Breakfast was adequate in quality but lacking in quantity. I resolved to address this the following morning as it would be more urgent after two to three hours' hard work. In fact, the first week I started work in the mornings at the same time as Joe, the only other worker, who welcomed me as if we needed no introduction and had been acquainted for years. He was a little taller and more muscular than me and had been working for Henry Baker since leaving school.

"I'm supposed to show you the ropes," he smiled as if it were a joke.

"Where is Mr Baker?" I enquired, which caused a broader grin.

"Milking, and he doesn't like that! And by the way, he's Henry, he doesn't do 'Mr' with us. By the way, I'm Joe."

"I'm Peter," I immediately returned. "Why doesn't he like milking his cows?" I questioned innocently.

"Cos he doesn't like farming. Anyway, I think it's the Old Girl's farm." Joe was giving me background before I had even had picked up a shovel.

"What do you mean, 'Old Girl's'?" I asked.

"That's his mother; sometimes she is an old battleaxe."

Another huge grin from Joe as I followed him to the food store at the end of a row of stables. There was a stack of small buckets that children might play with.

"Have you fed calves before?" he asked.

"No." I was keen to learn but was certainly starting from scratch.

Joe used an old tin to put half a measure of dried milk powder into each of two buckets. He then went to the Ascot on the wall, letting about two mugs-worth of hot water into each bucket and whisking briskly.

"Why don't they have real milk?" I thought it a reasonable question on a dairy farm.

"Cos they have had colostrum and this is to follow on... and it's cheaper," Joe added.

I was instructed to watch from over the stable door as Joe, carrying two buckets in one hand, slipped in and leaned back to close the door and stop any escapee. He then held the buckets by the rim rather than the handle and deftly lowered them to calf level. The two calves emptied their respective bucket in seconds.

I let him out of the 'box' (they had been stables, but were now 'calf boxes').

"There is only one calf in the next box, so you can feed it," Joe offered.

I slipped in, with Joe right behind, but the calf sniffed at the bucket with some indifference. Joe came to the rescue, putting his finger in the calf's mouth to suck and lowering his hand into the milk. With a couple of sucks the calf must have remembered last night's 'lesson' and was away.

"Yer won't 'ave to show it a finger tonight!' Joe smiled.

I was cautioned:

"Never let the buggers get out. As yer open the door a few inches, stick yer knee in first," Joe insisted.

The next day, much as I tried to heed this advice, we had a rodeo. Fortunately, Joe was nearby and headed to close the gate to the road. At least they were contained and it was only two calves. I dashed forwards, hoping to frighten them into the empty cowshed. With low cunning they immediately separated, one into the cowshed and the other across the yard. Joe yelled, "Slide the door!" referring to the main entrance the cows used twice a day. Calf number two was now ambling around the large dung clamp[10], which might be regarded as more her territory than ours as I didn't fancy doing a rugby tackle there.

Joe joined me at the cowshed.

"Let's get this one first."

We quietly closed the end door, standing inside. Joe motioned quiet stealth as we took account of our options. The calf obviously understood the signal and

---

[10] heap of manure waiting to be spread on fields before ploughing

walked away from us to a side door thinking it might be an exit. Joe knew it to be the dairy, housing the milk churn cooler and a blind end.

We rushed and cornered the calf into the ten-foot-square dairy without damage to any party or equipment.

"Hug the neck for dear life and I'll grab the hind quarters," Joe ordered.

We unceremoniously carried the calf to its box and shut it in. In the confines of the box, Joe slid a halter over the calf and tied it to the doorpost. Leaving the door open we quietly and patiently circled the other calf, moving only as the calf allowed. All was now calm, and slowly she headed for her friend, seemingly glued to the open box. Not only did she join the other one, but she walked right into the strawed box as if it were home. Needless to say it was a steep learning curve for me and I took the greatest care to never allow a repetition. However, the quiet ending left me with a nagging feeling that they had 'blooded' the new keeper and were pretty smug about it.

Joe took me though the daily tasks: feeding the calves twice a day, littering the boxes with straw, if necessary, and feeding hay in nets to the older calves. He also introduced me to some of the cowshed routine once Henry had finished milking and had returned to the farmhouse. At the time of year that I started, the cows were still walking back to a field to graze rather than living in a Dutch barn with an enclosed yard. Joe said we had to clean up after Henry, ready for him to mess it up again in the afternoon. I was getting the message that Henry was a reluctant farmer doing the minimum on the two-hundred-acre holding, stressed between obeying his mother and enjoying his hobbies of painting and photography.

The cowshed accommodated thirty-two cows for milking; sixteen on each side, chained, facing a stone manger and in pairs, separated by a wall coming some five feet out from the manger at right angles. Henry took me under his wing and showed what happened at milking time, whilst Joe did the calf feeding and other jobs that I had not yet imagined let alone experienced. My attention was firmly on milking, with the farmer as my tutor. It was only my second afternoon and I was to follow Henry without getting in the way. As all things were new to me, I was particularly alert to detail, asking as many questions as possible.

We walked to the field where the cows were grazing and I was surprised they were all near the gate.

"Just stand to the side and bring up the rear. I'll start tying them up."

With that, Henry set off back to the cowshed.

The cows made a steady procession following him, taking little or no notice of me. I walked behind the last one taking some care to avoid a lifted tail and the summary deposit of a cowpat. They seemed to know precisely where to go, even to the extent of reading their name over their standing. I noticed Henry slipping their chains over their necks, reaching for the other end underneath and poking the 'T' piece through the link.

"Tie some up that side; they're quiet enough." He added, "Let 'em know you're coming."

I had noticed he spoke as he approached in between each pair, mentioning a name or just, "Move over, girl." I obeyed, with some trepidation, but soon grew in confidence.

The next job was rolling two empty churns out from the dairy to the centre of the milking shed under the apex of the roof. This precision was to keep them well away from the cows' swishing tails and something much worse if nature took its course! Henry took me back to the dairy and assembled the churn funnel. This entailed placing a circular cotton pad over the bottom sieve and dropping a similar one on top. Milk from each cow would be tipped from the milking-machine bucket through this filter and into the central churn. Next, I was shown the milking-machine motor and a demonstration of the cooling process. We each carried a bucket of warm water and a dishcloth back to the cows. Henry took his position between the first two cows and washed their udders, much as a mother treats her imperfect son's attempt at cleanliness. I must say that a cow, apart from the occasional lick, makes no attempt to keep that region clean.

I watched as Henry started the vacuum pump motor and carried the milking-bucket unit with a cluster of four cups dangling from the lid into the first cow's box. He called out to me:

"First plug into the air line... and don't forget to turn it on," he demonstrated.

He bent down and, holding the cluster, lifted up each cup in turn and put it onto the teats. There was an immediate sucking noise and milk started to course its way to the bucket. He turned his attention to the neighbouring cow.

"If you don't turn the vacuum on first, you can't fit the cluster."

Sound advice for me to remember. Henry beckoned me to join him between the next pair.

"Put one hand on her flank to let her know yer there, and wash her bag and each teat."

I tentatively copied what he had done.

"Don't be afraid. They're a lot tougher than us. And they know if you're not in charge," Henry added.

I certainly was not in charge; I had never stood so close to a cow before in my life. Having completed the brief cleaning, I was urged to put the cluster on... which promptly fell off. Henry did the job, holding each cup for a millisecond for the vacuum suction to take hold. Another little trick for me to remember. When the churn was full, the filter was swopped to the empty one standing nearby.

"Always put the lid on straight away." He slapped the lid, which had hung on the churn handle, firmly on top making sure there was no chance of 'foreign bodies' entering it. Using the firm lid, he tilted the churn and rolled it a yard away, motioning me to try it. "Tilt it against your knees... and feel the point of balance."

Henry quickly had second thoughts and took me to the dairy.

"Practise rolling the empty churn back to the shed."

I soon rolled it with ease.

"Now get the full one on the point of balance, and if you have to stop, let it just fall back to being upright," he instructed.

I struggled whilst Henry removed the first machine and moved to the cow's neighbour. He joined me in the dairy and, hanging the churn lid on the handle, lifted the cooler into the fresh milk. This consisted of a domed lid with a copper pipe 'whisk' below it placed into the full churn. A hosepipe sent water through the hollow whisk, rotating it in the milk, and then running as waste over the outside of the churn and onto the floor. It was simple and soon cooled the milk from blood heat to 2-3°C.

Milking completed and all churns and buckets safely removed, I was left to untie the cows, carefully placing the end ring of the neck tie onto its hook in each standing to avoid grovelling for it in the morning. The cows knew the way back to their field with no other options, i.e. open gates, leaving me to shut the last field gate.

That was not the end of the day's work. The next job was to clean out any dung from the channels behind the cows' standings and barrow it to the dung clamp across the yard. This was followed by buckets of water being sloshed across the central area where the churns had stood and any remaining debris swept into the dung channels running the length of the shed. A thorough sweeping was done and then the feed barrow was rolled out. I had to put a scoop of rolled cereals in each standing "for them to come into", this being the secret of knowing their own place. In the morning this 'aperitif', common to all, would be supplemented by additional cereal commensurate with yield. My introduction to the process of milking and the detail of routine had dispelled some of the doubts about my new employer and his scruffy holding, especially in comparison with Fair Oaks Farm. I had just received a crash course in milking.

The next morning I had to start at 6.30 am and this time with Joe as my teacher. I dressed and crept out of Miss Lark's house, fearing wakening her. It was dark and cold, but only a mile away from the farm. There was nobody about, but I opened the cowshed and put on some lights, leaving my cycle in a small space by the milking-machine motor. I threw a few buckets of water down the middle of the shed. Joe was ten minutes late and I was thinking of Plan B should he be ill. Dare I risk waking Henry who didn't "do early mornings"?

Joe answered my query as he breezed in without a care.

"I'll get things lined up if you come in behind the old girls," he said.

I walked down the track and opened the gate, confident now they knew the way. I noticed a few slow in rising and circled the field to make sure there were none that, like Henry, didn't do mornings. Joe was tying up the early arrivals and I finished off. We started the milking, with Joe keeping an eye on my progress.

"Did yer say you'd never milked before?" Joe asked.

"Never been close to a cow before," I replied.

"Henry must 'ave shown you something yesterday. Can yer roll the churns OK?" Joe asked.

"Did yesterday," I replied with little confidence.

"Good. Just don't grab the lid off, that's all," he warned.

It was pleasing that we got on so well.

"Don't do Susan; she's a bit frisky. Leave 'er to me."

I watched as Joe gave a running commentary, for Susan's benefit as much as mine.

"OK, girl, it's yer old mate."

He ran his hand over her back and down her flank, bent down and pushed his head firmly in front of her leg, giving a quick wipe with the damp udder cloth. He returned with the machine and same chat as before. The cluster was accepted as if this cowman were an old friend.

"That's why yer wear a cloth cap." There was a note of pride in his voice.

I stood amazed; the friskiness had turned to acceptance.

"If you stick yer head in you can feel the kick coming so yer press a little harder, but yer only got a second before it reaches 'er leg," Joe explained.

"I reckon you are having me on. Pull the other one," I retorted.

"No, serious. Don't try to run away; if yer feel it, push harder."

"What does that do?" I was still not convinced.

"Think about it. She don't like standing on three legs and puts her foot down solid."

A moment's reflection and I believed him; after all, I had just witnessed the result. If only a little irritation or a more significant reaction, the signal to Susan was that she wasn't fully in charge, Joe was, and anyway he did provide the rolled oats.

Later Joe taught me to hand-milk.

"Yer should always draw a couple of squirts before putting the machine on." He showed me the three-finger action on an old girl with big teats and a compliant nature. "Starting with the top finger next to the thumb, then the next, then the next. Like a rhythm."

It wasn't easy, but I thought of the milk being at the top and chased down by the sequence: one, two, three.

Milking finished and cows returned to the field, Joe showed me the rest of the dairy routine. In the dairy he took out a pint measure, like a can with a long handle curved over at the top. He used this to dip into overfull churns, clasping the rolled top and pouring the contents into underfilled churns, looking carefully for the indentation inside near the top, being the ten-gallon mark. He got me to do it, making sure the mark was covered with no doubt possible once it arrived at the dairy.

"If you are by yourself this is what yer have to do," he continued.

Joe opened the door at the roadside where there were three steps up to the concrete churn stand. He rolled the first churn to the bottom step, getting me to observe the best lifting technique: standing, feet slightly apart and nearly touching the churn. "Keep yer back straight." With that, he hoisted the churn upright onto the first step, then the next and the next. Standing on top, he rolled the churn to the far end of the stand. I tried the next churn and soon there were five ready for the dairyman to collect.

"Now we must stick the labels on or Alfie will do his nut. It must be done before we lift 'em here, cos the labels and pen are downstairs in the dairy cupboard." Joe obviously had experienced this cause of delay. "Yer put me off!" he teased, but I noted the advice.

Now Joe pointed to the rubber stamp 'A & H Baker'.

"Yer the scholar. Write the date and '10 gals'," he instructed.

I did this five times and a final "6 gals" as he directed. We returned to the stand and pushed the luggage-type labels, not requiring string, over the nib on the neck of each churn. The next job was to slosh three buckets of water over the centre concrete of the cowshed. Another little tip to ease cleaning up later.

We had an hour for breakfast and so I cycled back to Miss Lark's. The small table was laid just for me; presumably Miss Lark had already breakfasted.

"There are cornflakes and milk," she pointed out, and then asked, "Do you like egg and bacon?"

That was not a difficult question as my stomach insisted it was well past time. My cereal bowl was beautifully decorated and made of fine china, although was better suited as a sugar bowl. I took the liberty of a second helping of rather-less-than-crisp flakes but had exhausted the contents of the tea-party-like milk jug.

"Miss Lark, may I have some more milk, please?"

Her face appeared around the kitchen door. "Isn't there enough in the jug?" she enquired.

We looked at each other for a moment, both understanding the situation but silently coming to different conclusions; she to "that should have been ample" and me to "it was only enough to whiten a cup of tea". However, the small jug was replenished. The egg and bacon arrived, but not the tomato, mushrooms and fried bread. Miss Lark had returned to the kitchen before I started on the single egg married to a single rasher of bacon.

"Please could I just have a slice of bread to go with my egg?" My request sounded rather feeble as if the answer might be no. However, a slice of bread arrived on a fresh plate as if it were another course.

Miss Lark caught me as I was struggling into my bib-and-brace overalls left in the back porch. "I've been thinking that you need rather large portions and I had not recognised that when I set the rent. I'll speak to you this evening." With that she retreated into the kitchen.

I returned to the farm. Joe, who didn't seem to go home for meals, had started cleaning out the cowshed. This was another wheelbarrow trek to the dung clamp across the uneven hardcore and ballast surface with sometimes a very 'sloppy' load. The rest of the morning we shared the calf-feeding, strawing down with bales from the Dutch barn, and filling hay-nets. Joe broke off to start the old standard Fordson tractor and collect ten hay bales from the other end of the barn where the hay was rather weathered. The principle was that the best hay was for the calves and the somewhat poorer hay for the cows. Joe demonstrated the difference by pulling out a tuft from the middle of a bale and burying his nose in it. He got me to do the same. I detected a difference but didn't expect to sneeze.

"There!" The cheery grin that was always Joe. "I didn't tell you to eat it!"

We took the bales to the cows, who were expecting us and had gathered around the two hayracks. I had chased the cows away to allow the tractor and trailer to stand between the racks. Joe cut the strings whilst I lobbed the cut-bread-like slices of hay into the racks. The cows on the other free sides soon pulled at the hay.

"Poor buggers haven't got enough grass," Joe explained. "This time of year they need more, but Henry says 'ten bales' so ten it is."

I was quickly getting the picture of a rather poor dairy farm. Mr Broadhurst's farm at Fair Oaks had seemed much more together and well run.

# 7

# Sole Cowman

It was at the end of my first week that Henry asked me to meet his mother, Mrs Baker, after breakfast at 10 am on the Saturday. Normally the working week ended at 12 noon but dairy farms differed in practice. At Goblets Farm the custom was to leave when all the dairy work was completed. The afternoon milking began at 3 pm after the cows had been tied up ready to start. Basically, the weekend milkings were flexible, providing all the jobs were finished and preparation for the next milking was not skimped.

I returned to Goblets Farm after breakfast that Saturday morning in a reasonably clean and tidy state knowing I would be meeting the owner of the farm.

"Mum, you haven't met Peter," Henry introduced me, "and Mrs Baker."

Henry indicated that I should sit opposite them across the dining-room table. It was a big room and obviously not used daily. The impressive dresser had some silver plates on the top shelf and a silver bull. I briefly wondered how long ago that had been presented; no doubt a reminder of more opulent days.

Mrs Baker asked if I had settled in and whether I was happy with my accommodation. I had no choice but to answer with a brief "yes, thank you".

Henry saved any potentially embarrassing questions by getting straight to business.

"Mum, I've told you Peter has been picking up the job very quickly and has applied himself. I wanted to discuss his placement here and what terms we can offer him."

"Henry has told me you have started very well and we hope you can become cowman for us."

Beams all around.

Mrs Baker continued, "Of course, that's a big responsibility for a young man."

Henry added, "We envisage you being responsible for all the milkings but with Joe or myself always available to help you."

"I'm sure I would need that backup," I said, showing keenness.

"You realise, of course," he said, quickly glancing at his mother, "that it would mean more money for you and different hours. You would start at 6.30 am as you have been and finish about 5.30-6 pm weekdays and rather earlier at the weekend. But you would have a half day off." He delivered the "half day" as if it were a bonus. "The previous cowman had Wednesdays off. That means milking Wednesday mornings and getting off at breakfast time, like at weekends. But you will have much more money in your wages." According to Joe, "more money" was not part of A & H Baker's DNA.

There was a moment before my reaction. I wanted to stay calm but be sure I understood what they were really offering and what was expected of me.

"What do mean, much more money in my wages?" I asked.

Henry glanced at his mother, who might well have been responsible for wages and who took up the interview.

"At the moment you get £4.18s. a week for forty-eight hours, and I think as cowman you will doing about fifty-one hours."

It seemed modest, just three hours extra... until the penny dropped.

"But Sunday is overtime – and Saturday afternoon," I stammered.

"Oh yes, of course!" Mrs Baker didn't seem too embarrassed. "I'll work that out."

Henry was eyeing the packet of Players cigarettes on the table but resisted the temptation.

"Is that OK, Peter?" he asked.

I agreed and thanked them, thinking this would be the experience I had hoped for.

"Well," Henry concluded, "you can start on Monday."

The bombshell hit me. "Monday? But I've only been here a week," I said.

"We'll support you and, as I mentioned, you have done well." Both owners of the farm smiled and the matter appeared settled.

I was bewildered, and enjoyed stepping into the fresh air of the farmyard. What had I taken on? How would I manage in practice? I couldn't ask Joe all the time; he might be anywhere on the farm. I couldn't ask Henry because he wasn't available until at least 10.30 am. I had the weekend off but had to find Joe before Monday. He was preparing to plough a field at Upper Goblets next to Mrs Baker's farmhouse, both holdings being managed as a single unit. I feigned helping him, attaching the tractor to the plough, rather than risk Mrs Baker thinking there was some collusion.

I related as much as I could to Joe, who gently smiled throughout.

"I'm not surprised. They have two or three ads a year for cowmen, but they only last a few months." Joe was dismissive.

"Did the last one get the sack?" I asked.

"No, couldn't stand it. He had a family and needed more money." Joe was casual but pulled himself up straight. "Yer mustn't worry. They like you," he added.

"It's not a question of liking; I need help," I asserted.

"Look, mate! There's you and me on this farm and we help each other," Joe concluded.

With that I let him get on, saying I would see him on Monday.

I phoned my parents, telling them I had settled in and everything was OK, mentioning that I was now milking. I omitted to use the word 'cowman', thinking it would hardly sound credible after only seven days' employment. However, I had negotiated a weekend off per month and said I would go home as often as possible. I returned to my digs, let myself in and flopped onto the settee. I needed to take in the new situation but was startled by Miss Lark appearing from the kitchen.

"Oh, I didn't think you were in." I sounded guilty but recovered with, "I will be going out soon. Are there any public baths in Colchester and a laundrette?"

She gave me directions and casually asked if I remembered that she didn't cook an evening meal for me at the weekend.

"Yes, but I will be back for the evening in my room," I replied. I could well manage with my own company and, packing dirty washing into a bag, I left for town.

The police station answered all my enquires regarding cleanliness of baths and the proximity of a local park. "Slipper Baths" was chiselled over the doorway; I would have taken the building for the Town Hall. Entering, I enquired if I could have a bath as my digs didn't have one. I felt the need to differentiate from 'swimming pool'.

I was handed a large towel and piece of soap and told I had half an hour. The individual cubical was of Victorian proportions with bath to match, all scrupulously clean and with copious hot water. The luxury of a bath was never more appreciated. I resolved to make this a fixture for Wednesday mornings. Exiting into a weak November sun, I found a laundrette and then the park.

The cool breeze had deterred me from staying in the park all day, but I headed for the roofed seating area at the confluence of four paths. Carefully choosing which of the four ways was most sheltered, I sat down to contemplate. Being the only one in the shelter helped concentration. I felt elated at the opportunity of learning dairying but apprehensive at the challenge, never having expected to parachute in at the deep end. I needed buckets of porridge. Porridge would have to be everything for me; copious nutrition and steadying, in the sense of being grounded. I would also need its 'stickability'. I wondered how I would cope with only one weekend off a month, and that after having milked on the Saturday morning. The issues would resolve in time.

*Issues.* The word suddenly came into focus. "Issues! Issues!" I spoke the words aloud. When did I last have serious 'issues'? At the time of the eleven-plus exam. Immediately I asked for God's help; only He could pull me through. The task couldn't be easy. There had been several cowmen, no doubt skilled, but for various reasons (or could it be for the same reason?) they had moved on. I prayed immediately, knowing God hears whatever and wherever our situation. My experience some seven years earlier had proven this point.

Greatly relieved, I walked back into town and found a cinema. The film was some wartime romance, and I considered doing greater planning for my limited spare time in future. It was dark when I came out and I wondered what to do. The film had been a distraction without being memorable. A café seemed appropriate and it would be warm. After scrambled egg, beans and a doorstep of fried bread, not to mention a mug of steaming tea, I was fit to retrieve my bike from the baths and cycle home.

On the Sunday, I decided to get better acquainted with the town. I came across three churches but did not feel moved to walk into any of them. I had been welcomed by Mrs Willis at the Methodist church, which was like the one my Boy Scouts troop had attended; the imposing Church of England somehow seemed too formal, and anyway, I was conscious that I would not be a regular attender due to work. I returned early and read.

Monday morning I got to the farm in good time, put on the cowshed lights and started the routine. All went without a particular problem except being a little delayed due to me not turning the water heater on at the same time as the lights. Joe appeared about half past eight to make sure I was managing OK. He reminded me to feed the calves first after breakfast and then get the feed barrow ready for the afternoon. He was ploughing for the rest of the day.

I had just finished the calves when Henry appeared.

"Thought I would leave you to get on this morning to sort yourself out. Everything OK?" he enquired.

"Fine, I think." I smiled briefly.

"Tomorrow I think the cows will need to start the kale; there's really no grass now and the milk yield is dropping. Give them three or four bales of hay extra this evening and I will get Joe to take you to Upper Goblets in the morning to cut a load of kale. He'll show you the ropes." With that bulletin, Henry returned to the house.

Joe came to the cowshed the next morning before breakfast, offering to feed the calves, saying we needed to go cutting the kale together. When I returned he was carrying a bucket of hot water from the dairy to the old Fordson.

"What's that for?" I asked.

"Give the old girl a drink." Joe's smile was etched on his face, part of his whole being.

"Which old girl? Not Mrs Baker?" I quipped.

"I'll pour it in her radiator. Yep, every drop." She was not Joe's greatest friend.

He wasn't pulling my leg. He had to drain the radiator this time of year so that it would not freeze.

"Don't you have anti-freeze?" I was incredulous.

"Henry hasn't heard of it… cos it costs money. And before you ask why the water's hot, it's to thaw any damp that may have frozen a little," he explained.

Joe was practical, doing his best in struggling with the difficulties imposed upon him, but with a softness as if he and the old tractor had to struggle together.

He shut the drain tap and poured the bucketful of water in as carefully as possible to avoid a second journey across the yard. He swung the starting handle a couple of times. It started on petrol and, when warmed up, turned onto paraffin. We hooked up a small four-wheeled trailer and puffed up the road to Upper Goblets. The kale was short and sparse in the gateway. Joe showed me how to cut the stalks about three inches from the soil with the swing of a slasher. We worked each side of the trailer trying to keep the heads falling in one direction. This was hard where the plants were sparse. Before moving on, the cut plants were loaded heads outward. It seemed to take ages to get a load eighteen inches high all around the flatbed. Joe said we needed half as much again, if not double.

We were cold and wet through, my trousers trying to fill my Wellington boots.

"Joe, how much more?" I asked.

"Really need double this or we will be here back again tomorrow. Trouble is the crop is too poor, the field needs more fertiliser," he added. In those days the fertiliser came in one hundredweight paper bags; later the bags were made of plastic.

A combination of the wet conditions and the handle slipping in my hand was producing a blister similar to my experience on day one at Fair Oaks. By about noon we made for the gateway and the track past the Upper Goblets farmhouse.

There was a shout and a waving duster at a bedroom window.

"What do you call that?" Mrs Baker yelled.

"We are starting the cows on kale, Mrs Baker," Joe called up politely.

"It's a bird's nest; you can't fool me." She was loud enough for the whole neighbourhood to hear.

I wanted to explain we were wet through and I for one hoped never to see kale again. Fortunately, Joe had more tact.

"We have to stack it all around the edge to grab the stalks for unloading," he explained.

"Go back and put more on." The window slammed shut and we turned around.

After another half an hour of cutting we drove to the new pasture that the cows were going into after milking and I threw and kicked the kale off whilst Joe drove slowly across the field. There was hardly any more grass in this field than the one they were leaving but the kale would supplement their diet. I sneaked off home in the lunch hour to change into my other set of work clothes.

I was experiencing the realities of hard labour, lack of protective clothing and the start of winter in the field. Plainly my memory of teatime in the harvest field was a minor part of the farming experience. Like all jobs, some days are more satisfying or pleasurable than others, and I had to accept that today was hard work; physically hard and dispiriting, as a harsher relationship was being revealed between employer and employee. Gone was the world of Fair Oaks Farm, working together to achieve the best result. Status and order had been observed, each offering their own skill to the team, including Mr Broadhurst and his money. Now I was experiencing 'them' and 'us' with little contribution from management. The other downside was the distancing of countryside. The wide landscapes of fields and trees had morphed into smaller enclosures and trees that overshadowed rather than enhanced. The picture was one of mud and messiness, barbed wire and broken stakes. Dowdiness had replaced brightness. I had come to a halfway house between town and country.

I settled into a winter routine of milking and feeding; and a week punctuated by a half-day holiday. I had taken to listening to the weather forecast and cutting enough kale with Joe on better days to hopefully carry over to the wet days. Wednesdays were bath mornings and for minor shopping. The afternoons were for exploring the villages within ten miles in fine weather or the cinema and coffee bar when inclement. Shopping was a new experience, as Mum had previously supplied my clothes and decided when something was worn out. Now I had to make my own decisions and weigh up what constituted a reasonable purchase. There was little doubt that I needed underpants and working socks; equally, I had limited disposable income. I soon came across an outfitters who sold suits, shirts and possibly pants although there were none in the window.

I told a smart salesman what I wanted.

"Underpants, if you have them," I asked, hoping I had not come to the wrong shop.

"What sort, sir?"

"Well, underpants." I was somewhat taken aback.

"Brief or long?" he enquired further.

"Ordinary." It was the only reply I could think of.

"What sort do you wear now, sir?"

I didn't know if he expected me to show him; there were others in the shop who were not undressing.

"Brief or full leg?" He indicated on himself.

"No leg at all," I replied.

He obviously thought it would be simpler to get two or three examples from the drawers behind him.

I pointed to the sort that I was wearing.

"Waist size?" he enquired.

"I'm afraid I don't know."

"If you undo your coat, sir, I will just check."

He slipped a tape measure around my waist.

"Medium. How many pairs?" Shopping seemed an endless series of questions.

I said, "Two," I suppose. Then I ventured, "I want, could do with, some work socks."

He seemed relieved when I pointed to some on display sticking out of a pair of Wellingtons.

"Ah, fishermen's socks," he exclaimed, somewhat relieved he had got there in one.

Fortunately, he didn't ask me the size, just assuming seven to eleven.

I visited the Wimpy coffee bar, which was rather dead at midday on a Wednesday, and ambled back with my purchases. Fortunately, Miss Lark would feed me, it being a weekday.

The next morning I was pleased to try on my new fishermen's socks over my usual ankle socks as a double layer against the cold. Joe noticed them immediately when he looked into the shed just I was measuring the milk in the churns.

"Cor, going fishing?" he pulled my leg.

"Thought I deserved a little comfort on this concrete," I retorted. "By the way, this morning a cow was riding another as I fetched them in. That means she is ready for the bull, doesn't it?" I asked.

"Very likely. Well done." Joe continued, "Henry deals with all that. He phones the artificial insemination service (AI). Call at the house now; somebody will answer."

"Let's both nip to the field and check up first." I was rather less confident and Joe agreed to come with me. We watched them for only a few minutes.

"Yep, yer right. I think that's Mavis. When you milk this afternoon, don't let her out."

Back at the house I told Mrs Baker Junior that a cow was bulling and, "Could we have the AI?"

I was a few minutes late for breakfast and told Miss Lark it was on account of Mavis needing the AI man. She didn't share my excitement but simply stared, putting the plate in front of me and leaving without a word. Perhaps she didn't understand the process of it being necessary for a cow to have a calf before you can get milk. On reflection, as I consumed the egg, bacon, sausage and fried bread under my enhanced regime, I thought it better not to enlighten her further.

Miss Lark was a person of few words and, strangely for a lifelong resident of a village, hardly mentioned anything concerning local life or farming. She seemed content with a few ladies visiting for tea during the week and reading books in the evenings. Revealing even this much of her diary was probably her way to ensure that I would not use the lounge and would be as unobtrusive as possible. During working hours I would be on the farm, but on Wednesday afternoons and some weekends there was a danger that I might appear, if only to traverse from the front door via the lounge to my room. I had no cause to say Miss Lark was class-conscious, but had the impression that the farm or my person was not the topic of polite conversation. It may have been like the bath on the landing – a necessity but not connected. Perhaps it was a case of "we don't talk about a lodger but how else do we maintain standards?"

A week later Miss Lark had something to tell me at breakfast.

"I find that your boots and socks smell, and it affects my chest."

I looked up in surprise as I always left them in the porch outside the back door. "Really, I'm careful to wash them every time I leave the cowshed," I said defensively.

"I must ask you to leave them in the coal shed." She had obviously made her mind up.

"I'll have to come and go in slippers," I observed.

"That's as may be; it is only a few steps." This seemed to seal the matter.

The AI man called at the farm just before afternoon milking. All the cows were in and tied up; I was washing down the central concrete working area as he strode in already dressed in rubber apron and arm-length plastic gloves.

"Just in time," he announced. "Mr Baker told me to expect Peter."

"That's right," I confirmed, resisting extending my hand to one who had every appearance of a scrubbed-up surgeon. "It's Mavis, here." I pointed to the cow and stood back.

"I'm Charles," he mumbled, two feet of long tube held in his mouth. Left hand on Mavis's back and the other foraging around inside, he quickly opened up the way for the tube. Then, left-handing the tube, guided along his inserted right, the ejaculation was completed. Mavis, apparently contented, concentrated on the hay in her manger.

"All done," Charles announced.

"I have never seen that done before." Somewhat amazed, I added, "It didn't bother her."

"Less troubling than a real bull," he smiled. "Now, can I have that bucket of water?

Charles tipped it over the front of his apron and boots in two practised moves.

"I must get on but good to meet you, Peter. Stick at it." And so he left.

The routine milking proceeded and all was back to normal. I mulled over the insemination and its no-fuss speed, also the fact that the 'straw' of semen could come from any bull of choice. That meant it could be from a bull of top quality selected for his genetic qualities for milk or beef production. As I was cleaning up, having shut the cows back in their night-time field, Henry came into the cowshed.

"All went OK?" He obviously meant the AI.

"Yes, fine. Do you use the same bull each time?" I asked.

"Mostly, but we change after a year or two, or if we are not keeping a cow for an extra lactation. In that case I would use a beef-breed bull, then her calf would be more valuable and she would go as a barrener[11]." I was beginning to understand the decisions needed in management.

"I wanted to mention Christmas," Henry started, having changed the subject abruptly. "It's usual for the cowman to work over Christmas, but I could give you New Year's Day off."

I had not thought about Christmas and not being at home with parents. It would be strange and, of course, a disappointment for them. Henry might have observed these thoughts on my face.

"Of course, if there was a problem or emergency, Joe or I could help you deal with it." He obviously meant this as some consolation without giving way on the usual practice.

After dinner I stayed in the lounge with a book, hoping to find an opportunity to discuss Christmas arrangements with Miss Lark. This was going to be sensitive, indeed unknown, territory for both of us. I resolved to follow Henry's approach with boldness.

"Miss Lark, about Christmas, it is normal for cowmen to milk over Christmas Day and have time off over New Year." I didn't wait for her reaction. "I hope this is alright with you?"

"I certainly had not expected you would be here at Christmas," she asserted boldly.

"If it is difficult, may I just sleep here and do my own limited catering?" I thought it necessary to add, "In practice I would not be here all day."

"I'll think about it." She took up her book again.

I was uneasy and feigned reading.

My next half day I cycled to the station before bath-time and asked for the train times between Colchester and London, in order to visit my parents. Rather than consult the small print on timetables, the booking office confirmed I could travel to Romford with my bike in the guard's van. I would not be allowed to travel personally in the guard's van but would need to step back smartly onto the platform and into the nearest passenger carriage. Travelling back from home on a Sunday evening, I would need to get back to Miss Lark's by 9.30 pm before she bolted the door.

Mulling over the details as I soaked for my twenty-five minutes, it seemed a good working plan. I could rush to catch the 9.20 am from Colchester on the

---

[11] 'barrener' means 'don't breed from this animal again'

Saturday, providing the cows cooperated and there was no malfunction of machinery. It was important to take my cycle back with me to see friends and be flexible whilst at home; also not to risk it being stolen from the station yard. Next weekend I would go home as a pre-Christmas treat and prepare Mum and Dad for the next occasion – New Year.

I had prepared for the exit with Joe's help. We cut as much kale as time permitted to feed the cows for two days. I had even made out churn labels to save the odd minute or two on the day. I cut every possible corner. I had taken my weekend bag to work, including shoes and two Mars bars. I thought this would give flexibility, allowing me to change at the station or even in the train toilet depending on necessity. I left my Wellingtons in the dairy in favour of shoes but kept my other working clothes. Leaving the farm at precisely 9 am, I peddled as fast as possible, arriving at the station with four minutes to spare. The calculation was now whether to risk changing in the station toilet; could I do it in four minutes? Possibly. But supposing the train was two minutes early? I had already lost fifteen seconds in decision-making.

I waited, discretion being the better part of valour. The train was half a minute late by my watch, but I was relieved to get the cycle into the guard's van and then to find somewhere to lean it rather than let it fall. A relatively quick exit and the whistle blew. The train was moving, albeit slowly; I might just get to that first carriage door. I sprinted for it, apprehended by a loud shout and a burly porter.

"NO! IT'S MOVING!" he shouted.

I was aware of that but there was just a chance... There was *no* chance – I was in the warm embrace of a uniform of someone twice my weight.

"That is unlawful and extremely dangerous, sir," he intoned.

"But my bike! It's in the guard's van." I was still staring at the unconcerned train gaining speed.

"Come with me, sir."

I was led to the stationmaster's office.

"Burt, can you phone through and get this gentleman's cycle put off the 9.20?"

I gave the colour and make of my bike to the stationmaster and waited as directed.

In ten minutes the call came that it had been put off at the next station, assuming I would be travelling to collect it. I quickly confirmed that I would. After waiting over an hour, I leaped on the next train and walked through a couple of carriages to about the middle, hoping that would be the likely stopping place nearest to a waiting room. I was conscious my previous detailed plan had not been successful, but surely I could not fail twice. We slowed into the station, I saw my cycle and was ready. A dash to the rear and the guard was there! He accepted the bike, asking where I was going. "Romford, but don't let the train start till I've got a seat," I called, hoping he would make it possible. I didn't wait for a reply but grabbed the first carriage door I could find.

I cycled home but resolved to leave my bike in Colchester on future occasions. It was good to be home. Everything was of course familiar but I had grown up. I was independent and earning my living. Subtly I had morphed from adolescence to an independent thinking adult and accepted as such by my parents. We talked freely about my digs and their various shortcomings and similarly the job. Joe was introduced as a great ally although I knew little of his home life. He lived with his mother about half a mile out of the village, but never mentioned his father or whether he had brothers or sisters. They lived in a cottage, his mother being a full-time housemaid in a farmhouse. However, my parents were pleased Joe had been such a friend and helper, like a big brother.

The idea of Christmas moving to New Year appeared to be no problem. Similarly Miss Lark's landing bath had been circumvented by having use of excellent facilities on Wednesday mornings. They seemed to do 'funny' things in the country, but so be it. The gap between town and countryside was to grow ever wider but with the same sort of placid acceptance.

Whilst at home I made time to visit an old school friend, Roger Stacey. We had met, quite literally, in Year 2 at high school during a fire drill. Classes were evacuated two at a time, each in a sort of dual file, to assemble in the upper playground. Classes 2A and 2B were walking side by side through the heavy swing doors to the playground. The meeting took place shoulder to shoulder with each other and the doors. As I pushed forward, Roger hesitated; as I hesitated, he pushed outward. This swinging forced us tighter at the shoulder and firmer to the doors on our opposite shoulders. The evacuating traffic was held up as we could not free ourselves either by going forward or by reversing. The ensuing dance came to the attention of a teacher who barged at the point of junction, forcing us to face our respective doors and thereby be 'thinner' and able to pass. The headmaster, having been informed that we caused a serious interruption to the drill, had in mind to cane us, but "as it did not appear a planned nonsense" we had to accept a severe reprimand.

Our friendship blossomed from that day. Roger stayed on to complete 'A' levels whilst I left school a year earlier. I filled Roger in with my new strange life whilst he was aiming at a more conventional career in medicine. I did point out that his father's dairy firm, retailing milk, relied on my hard work.

The working over Christmas Day and Boxing Day had gone without a hitch, aided by feeding extra hay in place of cutting kale on those days. My presence in the digs was satisfactory on the basis Miss Lark and I had agreed, but with hardly a festive air. I began to feel her idea of a little income from a lodger was not suiting either party. After a pleasant but short New Year, two days at home, Miss Lark voiced her dissatisfaction.

"I really think I can't go on looking after you," she announced. "Farming is much more disagreeable than I thought."

I had not looked on the relationship as 'mother and son' nor had I felt at home. Indeed, everything was skimped, from food to furnishings; nothing was generous. I had spent my time tiptoeing around not to upset the elderly lady's sensibilities.

"I really must ask you to find other accommodation," Miss Lark said.

"I'm sorry I don't suit you." I was hurt at the ultimatum. Was it really my fault?

"I don't mean you must leave immediately." Miss Lark was somewhat conciliatory.

"I will look straight away but I have my job to consider," I offered.

"Very well, but do try or I will have to give you formal notice."

There was no deadline set but I knew I must make haste to move.

# 8

# Living on the Farm

I asked Joe whether he knew of any lodgings locally, but it was an emphatic "No!" I wondered if he assumed I was looking to his mother for help. He simply advised I should inform Henry so he would be aware of my situation; he might actively help if he thought he would lose his cowman. I visited the library on Wednesday and scanned the local paper with little optimism. I took three phone numbers and mentioned my plight to the librarian. She suggested I inserted an advert in the local paper myself or put a card in the newsagent's window. I called the three numbers that evening but two baulked at the idea of a farm worker and the other was too far out of town.

Henry came into the cowshed on Friday saying his mother would put me up if I could not find a suitable place. I thanked him and redoubled my efforts. The next week I visited another newsagent's and the local pub. There were only two adverts in the second shop window, both again being too far to even inspect. The pub did not have rooms, which I was pleased about as I had realised their hours of business would not have been conducive to my sleep. I was forced to ask if I could view Mrs Baker's accommodation.

Henry arranged for me to meet his mother that Saturday morning. I had breakfast, quickly washed and changed into fresh clothes, and arrived at Mrs Baker's at 10.30 am. I decided on the back door on the basis that I was expected and because I had learned the 'country code' that the front door was for formal occasions only.

"Come in, Peter," Mrs Baker responded to my confident knock. "I hear you are looking for accommodation."

"Yes, I hope you can help," I replied, hoping I sounded enthusiastic rather than resigned.

"Follow me and I will show you a spare room." Mrs Baker was brief and to the point.

I followed her through to the large kitchen, where everything seemed to happen, into a darker hall and then upstairs. There were at least four rooms set around a substantial landing lit by a single skylight. She waltzed into a large bedroom with leaded light windows.

"You have a nice view of the fields from here," she announced.

"Yes." I could see the half-harvested kale immediately below.

"You have all the usual furniture." She was leading the sales pitch.

I had glimpsed the double bed and iron headboard in crossing to the window. I refrained from testing the quality of the mattress and springs, and instead checked the wardrobe she was demonstrating.

"There is plenty of room for hangers, and on these shelves for other things up the side." She turned before I could respond. "And a dressing table over there," she finished.

The room was vast after Miss Lark's accommodation, with brown lino dominating the scene and a single light bulb and fringed lampshade overseeing it all. I had noticed an old armchair that she had not included in the inventory, possible because the stuffing was seeking to escape. Mrs Baker led me to a bathroom across the landing.

"This would be yours; I have another one," she continued.

This too was ample and had all I would need.

"You will not need to fill the bath; I suggest using hot water and then adding a little cold, as the boiler is not very large." I understood she meant that hot water was limited.

Returning to the kitchen it was warmer, even cosy.

"We eat here." She waved her hand over the large oak table and offered me a coffee. "Now, do you think this will suit you?" It was the first chance I had of offering any opinion.

"Yes, nicely, I am sure." I was even more sure that it was 'Hobson's choice'.

"Whatever you are paying Miss Lark will be deducted from your wages… if you are happy with that?"

"Yes, thank you – and can I sit here in the evenings?" I was thinking of the cold bedroom and ancient chair.

"Yes, I think we can be informal. Use this as you wish. We will eat here, and I have a television, you see." She waved her hand again over to a TV on top of what looked like a large chest of drawers.

She continued in a more relaxed way over the coffee, explaining that boots and outer clothes were to be kept in the lobby where there were several hooks and her 'farm' coats.

I was pleased with the mug of coffee, and the kitchen Rayburn promised an improvement on Miss Lark's hospitality. I could now break the good news that she would have her little cottage free of farmyard smells from the following weekend.

Leaving Miss Lark would be a relief for her, with the benefit of allowing her to please herself and entertain her friends. I understood it must have been a burden for her, catering for a lodger and not having the total freedom that one needs in old age. She would now have only herself to please, even to stay in bed if she so desired. The financial advantage of a little extra money was outweighed by the lifting of the psychological blanket of caring by one who would soon need a carer herself.

I was moving into a farmhouse. The practicalities were easier, with not even a small commute to work, and the common business interest of embracing 'farming' as not only a job but a vocation. In short, I was more personally involved, although not privy to management decisions. There also turned out to be a few downsides as I settled into the farmhouse. Winter was advancing and my large bedroom was cold. The farmhouse windows were not double-glazed and the leaded lights were not sound in the frame. I tried sticky paper over the worst gaps. Mrs Baker occasionally cut the paper or forced the windows open to let in the fresh autumn air. The yards of cold lino were another heating problem, particularly to bare feet. I soon found it necessary to walk on tiptoe to switch off the light, at least on a percentage basis, as less flesh was touching the lino. The alternative, I reasoned later, was to wear 'bedroom' socks rather than 'bed' socks. I soon hung my 'work' socks on the iron headboard and wore clean ones as 'slippers'. It was also handy to leave 'working' jeans on the floor halfway between bed and windows so that curtains could be drawn without getting cold feet. Often the frost was on the inside of the glass, necessitating asking for an extra blanket.

The bathing situation was marginally better than in Miss Lark's bathroom, which lacked the item that bore its name, but now the water temperature encouraged haste rather than relaxation. I still had the fallback of the slipper baths on my half day off. My diet improved with Mrs Baker knowing the needs of farm workers, not only satisfying appetites but also offering good home cooking of quality. In short, my new digs were reasonably satisfactory and should improve in spring and summer.

On the farm I enjoyed the job and the routine, spending much of the day on my own as Joe was more involved with land work. The cows were getting used to me as we 'talked' and largely 'walked' together. The odd rubbing of ears or neck and words of condolence as I tied them up for milking made for good relationships. On the land I pressed Henry for some more nitrogen fertiliser for the pastures and he fortunately agreed. In a few weeks we saw the response in the grass coming quicker and lasting further into summer. Alfie, my milk collection man, would share a word and pass on a bit of gossip given the chance. I asked him for an extra churn as the milk increased.

"A lot want an extra one this time of year," he chided me.

"I think we will soon want two; some are due to calve soon," I warned.

"I'll do what I can, as I have one farmer who is installing a bulk tank. He will soon have his milk collected by the tanker."

An extra churn arrived the next day and a further one the following week. It was obviously difficult for the dairy to manage in the changeover to bulk transport.

## Making Hay

Henry pointed out that some pastures should be shut up for hay. This meant carefully rotating the herd around fewer fields, leaving the 'hay' fields to grow in bulk and mature. Not much attention had been paid historically to getting most of the herd calving in the spring when nature produces the most grass. The insemination of cows had often been missed and calving was spread throughout the year. The succession of cowmen had not helped and Henry had not been observing this aspect of management. I dried off a few cows that were giving very little milk and put them on poorer pasture along with three dry ones, so saving the better grass for the milkers. This enabled three fields to be shut up for haymaking.

Henry had to make the decision as to when the grass crop had bulked up sufficiently and the weather was promising enough for the grass to be cut. I learned much of this later in my career but the principle is to calculate when a dry week is likely and to mow the grass in expectation of 'haymaking' weather, ideally sun and breeze together. The grass is then tedded[12] and turned[13]. The vital detail is not to bale until the hay is fully 'made'. This is a fine art requiring an accurate forecast and experience, not to mention luck.

Joe mowed the first field, the heaviest crop. The time clock was then ticking. The gamble would be to cut just one field or risk cutting two fields within the weather slot forecast. The crop was left for a day before moving it. The second day I took sandwiches and had lunch sitting in the field. Joe had started turning it about ten o'clock; dry on top but wet underneath. It was standing up a little from the flat state of the previous day. There was the delicious smell of new hay, a gentle fragrance in the warming sun.

"I love that smell, Joe." I sniffed an exaggerated inhalation.

"Better than the usual smells around here," Joe commented. Then he added, "I wasn't so happy yesterday; I drove backwards as much as forwards." He was referring to the old 'finger' mower jamming as it hit a tough spot or a stone, stopping the reciprocating knife. "I had to rivet lost sections three or four times; the fields need harrowing and rolling in the spring." Joe knew the treatment but Henry probably didn't see the need.

"Pity we can't bottle this." I took another draught.

"Don't know about that; I'd like to see him make silage."

Joe was thinking of the modern trend of making silage for cows. It was like pickling the grass rather than drying, and was much quicker and a less weather-dependent process.

"I bet they will teach you all about that when you get to college," Joe suggested.

---

[12] fluffed up
[13] toasted one side and turned over

"I hope I know about it before then," I replied. "I've got to do three years' work before I can get in."

"Three years?" Joe repeated.

"Well, I can understand it. It's because I'm not a farmer's son," I explained.

"What's that matter?" Joe persisted. "Yer soon learned milking here."

"It's not just book work; I have to experience all farm jobs," I insisted.

"I suppose so," Joe pondered. "But how long in college?"

"Two years; five with the practical work," I replied.

I just wanted to rest and savour the hay field before milking... It was these joys that had originally drawn me out of London.

I was called to help in the field as much as the milking routine permitted. Once the hay had been made, Henry phoned his brother-in-law to bale it. The hay was dry and fragrant and the weather set fair. I arrived in time to find Andrew, Henry's brother-in-law, setting up the baler.

"Peter, bury your head in this." My boss handed me a great wad of hay. The dry, soft hay could have been slept on. I sniffed it and felt the dry softness on my cheeks.

"Marvellous, surely ideal," I exclaimed, "for a hay mattress!"

"I don't think you would get it much better than that," Andrew confirmed the verdict.

He finished baling the field. I helped Joe load the flatbed trailer and Henry stacked them. It was harvesting work in early July, reminding me of the pleasures of that farm holiday in Devon that held greater interest than the beach.

They unloaded the bales into the Dutch barn and continued carting whilst I saw to the milking. We continued through to 8 pm, leaving the last load for unloading the next day. After all the effort it was satisfying that the hay was sweet and soft, ideal for calves. The next field would be cut the next day whilst the weather held. We were all in good spirits with the satisfaction of a crop well harvested.

As the rest of the haymaking came to an end, I was considering my own position. I had settled in and learned a lot by being thrown in at the deep end, but the prospect of another winter was daunting. I was not thinking of a career in dairying and doubted I could learn much more on this farm. I was also mindful of harsh conditions with old or inadequate equipment, a combination of poor crops, except the hay, and lack of forward thinking. I needed to consider other branches of farming. It was time to scour the *Farmers Guardian* and ask God for guidance.

# 9

# Arable Farming

There were very few 'situations vacant' that fitted my requirements; I was single-minded in getting experienced and securing a place at the agricultural college. There were adverts for harvest workers but I needed permanent work on a progressive holding. As time went on, I remembered my old school friend who had a relation in farming; although I knew nothing of the details, I would phone Roger. His father, good to his word, contacted his cousin, Jim. After a lengthy renewal of the relationship, he asked if it was possible that he had a vacancy "for Roger's friend". I have often wondered what powers of persuasion were need for such a shot in the dark. There was no vacancy advertised, no knowledge of the candidate, no previous history of needing more than his two permanent workers. Jim's response was, "Send him down and I will see him." A visit was arranged for my next weekend off, when I would accompany Roger and his parents to the farm.

It was now June and a sunny day to see an arable farm in north Essex. On arrival, Roger's parents joined Margaret, Jim's wife, whilst Roger and I were sent out to find the farmer. We found Jim welding in a large workshop. He wiped his hands on an old pair of trousers hanging above the bench, the cloth deputising as a rag or 'oven-glove' as need dictated. We shook hands.

"Young Roger, you've grown a bit; you are not in shorts anymore," Jim welcomed him.

"I know, it's been a long time. This is Peter." Roger introduced me and we moved into the daylight.

"Well, Peter, you've started farming, I hear!" I had no idea how much Roger's father had said about me, but at least I wasn't introduced as a cowman.

"Yes, I am really keen to learn about arable farming, Mr Stacey," I said.

"Call me Jim. We don't stand on ceremony."

This was refreshing as my only previous experience had been with a gentleman farmer, and latterly a more or less absent gentleman. Jim had every appearance of a working farmer. He was lithe, about six feet tall with dark hair greying at the front and a trimmed moustache.

We looked into the buildings and passed a few machines before standing in a small meadow at the back of the yard overlooking most of the fields rolling north. There were no dwellings or animals to be seen. The countryside was far from flat, and fields in various shades of green or golden corn spread into the distance. Hedges were small with gaps along their length, strewn as if the artist were suggesting boundaries. There was no need for gates or fences without animals to corral.

"I'll show you a field or two. Jump in the van."

Jim drove out of the yard along tracks with the central grass wiping under the engine. We stopped at the junction of two tracks.

"These are the only fields of spring barley; it's mostly winter wheat otherwise." Jim waved his hand out of the window.

We got out and stood in the sun. Roger was hardly interested.

I stepped into the full heads now turning towards yellow and swung my hand through them. "Quite thick," I muttered, more as an observation than knowledgeable.

We passed wheat just coming to ear, and stopped at the next green field.

"What's this?" Roger enquired.

I was grateful for his question as I didn't want to show my ignorance.

"It's peas." Jim smiled. "Don't you recognise peas?"

"How do you pick all these?" I was again pleased Roger was enquiring.

"They are dried peas for canning," Jim informed us.

"What's the process?" I couldn't resist knowing more.

"They dry off and we sort of make hay with them, then combine them," Jim replied.

There was much more I wanted to ask, but we had arrived another field.

"These will be sugar beet." Jim saved our questioning.

We returned to the yard and Roger wandered around the buildings whilst I sat in the van with Jim. He asked what I had done since leaving school. I ran through the Town Boys' Training and Fair Oaks Farm and onto the job at Goblets Farm. He then asked what I wanted to do in the future. So I emphasised getting into agricultural college.

"Did you do any sport at school?" Jim enquired.

"I played rugby in the first team," I announced proudly before adding, "and for the Air Training Corps."

"Did you play for 61 Eastern Group?" Jim surprised me.

"Yes," I replied.

"I like a bit of flying myself." Jim hesitated. "I have a little Auster."

It was as if he were casually referring to a pet.

The talk turned back to farming.

"I think we could teach you a thing or two, if you are prepared to work," Jim said.

"I will work," I asserted.

"If you can come before harvest I'll give you a chance," Jim promised.

"Thank you very much." I did not hesitate.

We moved into the house, Jim standing in his work clothes and asking Margaret if she could add one more to the family.

The journey home was all joy. Roger and his parents were pleased to have found me a farm, and my relief was palpable at securing a new job which promised everything I desired. It seemed that I would be accepted on the basis that I wanted to learn and that hard work would be rewarded. As a bonus the accommodation was in the farmhouse with what appeared to be a normal family. Time would tell.

I broke the news as soon as I returned to Mrs Baker. "I had to get arable experience to get into college and out of the blue my friend's relative has a farm in Essex." I had rehearsed the conversation and it seemed logical enough. "I must leave by the end of July," I told Mrs Baker.

"Very well; you must tell Henry in the morning." She seemed resigned to the idea, perhaps softened by many previous departing cowmen. Henry wished me well and fixed a date of the last Sunday in July. Joe was visibly upset, not just because we had become friends but, no doubt, because it would mean a disturbance in his working pattern. The history of previous cowmen had not always been so cordial.

I continued my job as cowman to the best of my ability, not wanting any reason for complaints. The routine of milking becomes automatic unless broken by an unusual incident. It became a good time for mental ruminations. How pleasing to find a farm position that ticked all the boxes that I thought the college would require of me. How convenient that it would still be in Essex. It came suddenly, like an 'unusual incident', as quick as if a cow had kicked off her milking cluster. I had prayed for God's guidance. Similar to my worry about my eleven-plus exam, here I had needed a specific job and no way of finding it. God had graciously answered my prayers. Confirmation of this would come later but peace had descended upon me. No more anxiety, and a confidence that Jim would be the right employer and mentor to further my career.

I moved all my belongings straight to Claydon Farm with the help of Mum and Dad, who left about 3 pm that Sunday to return home. I had arrived. Harvest was looming, and both Jim and I needed days to settle in. I would need to familiarise myself with the farm and jobs that I could do unsupervised, and Jim and the two men would need to teach me their ways. I had been given a spacious bedroom shared with Robert, Jim and Margaret's ten-year-old son. He was on holiday from his boarding school but I would be on my own during his term time. I joined the family for my first meal around the kitchen table. It was as natural as if I had lived there a year.

## Meeting the Men

I was up in good time, keen to start on an arable farm with all its variety of jobs. I joined Jim in the kitchen for a mug of tea and collected a packet of sandwiches that Margaret must have made the previous evening. We walked across the yard to a large workshop where Doug was waiting.

"We have a new man for you," Jim announced, as if Doug were the boss. "Peter, this is Doug."

"You look a good'un." Doug extended a hand.

Just then a motorbike swooped into the yard.

"Here he is," Doug observed.

"This is Tony; new man for us – Peter." Jim was brief.

He assigned Tony and me to sack-mending whilst he took Doug to do some mechanical task.

Tony led me to a brick-built barn and we opened the large double doors and pegged them back. He had already been sack-mending; all the kit was there. Tony explained it was best to sit on a large round of timber and to hammer on a smaller one with a pile of sacks placed on each side. He demonstrated by examining the sacks in the right-hand pile for any holes that would let grain out, and mended them by gluing a patch of hessian on the inside with Copydex and hammering it all over on the small log between his feet. He then pasted a second patch and repeated the hammering job.

"We usually cut several patches from a starky[14] to mend the rails[15]." He handed me a large pair of scissors and an old starky. "Cut them big." Tony indicated a picture-frame size with two hands. "Cut all that sack up so you don't have to keep changing tools. I'll do the sticking for a bit," he instructed.

There was soon time for conversation once we had settled into a routine. Tony told me he was nineteen, a year my senior; a local country boy living with his parents and younger sister only a mile away. We immediately hit it off; he was an exact replacement for my previous workmate, Joe. The motorbike, a Triumph Cub, was his first serious purchase and his key to the big wide world.

At 9 am we had about twenty minutes' break, which I was told could drift by five minutes without Jim admonishing us. It was reminiscent of my White Court days but with better and more abundant sandwiches.

Tony volunteered Doug's character, saying, "He always has an opinion and it is always right... even if it isn't. He's loud but doesn't mean any harm." Tony looked around in case Doug was in earshot. "He tells the boss what to do as if it's his place. But Jim takes no offence. Doug wants the best tools and Jim wants the best results, so they get along fine."

We started the sacks again with Tony finding fresh bundles from the darker recesses and bundling up the checked and mended ones in groups of twenty. The morning was broken by a lorry-load of empty sacks arriving from the corn merchant. This was in readiness for harvest and had been checked over already

---

[14] a softer lightweight sack
[15] heavy-duty sacks used on the railway

as free of holes. We stacked the bundles all along a wall at the far end, making sure they were not mistaken for 'holey' ones.

"What's that do?" I pointed to a large machine with metal sieves.

"It dresses corn," Tony replied casually. Then seeing my puzzled expression he continued, "Grain comes in here from the pit outside and it flows down the sieves as the whole thing shakes; it sieves the grains for size and chaff is blown out here." He pointed out where the sacks would hang to be filled.

Lunch was 12.30 to 1.30 pm and only a few steps away. Margaret had cooked a full hot lunch, something I was told never to be late for. It was a time when all the local farmers knew they could contact each other, whereas at teatime it would be uncertain depending on their workload. Tea would be bread and cake, which were not dependent on time or temperature. In the afternoon we swept and cleaned the various sheds ready for the first grain of harvest. It was reminiscent of my first day at Fair Oaks Farm. I had been a year as a farmer's boy and was becoming aware of the recurring seasons. This emphasised our closeness to nature and dependence on the weather.

After tea Jim asked if I would like a trip round the farm. Naturally I jumped at the offer. We drove to the first wheat field and walked into the corn.

"Always walk the same way as the drill," Jim instructed. "Your boots shouldn't tread anything down, because the rows are seven inches apart."

Jim saw me look at my feet.

"The seeder drills at seven-inch spacing," he added thoughtfully, pulling off a couple of ears and rubbing them in his hands. He blew the chaff away and selected a grain. "I just bite it to check if it's ready to cut." He offered his cupped hand to me. "Bite it in half."

"It seems a bit soft," I said tentatively.

"Quite right, not ready yet; got to be like shot."

We drove to two more wheat fields and tried the grains there. They tested a little harder.

"I reckon another couple of days if we don't have any rain," Jim said as we drove to the field of peas, again with a running commentary. I was receiving his thoughts as if a recording of his brain were playing for public consumption.

We stepped into the pea field. The soil was hard and the crop, yellow and straw-like, was lying on the ground.

"It looks dead," I ventured.

"No, that's fine." Jim pulled up a plant and pulled off a few pods.

I copied him, opening one to find greenish yellowing peas. A second pod was just the same.

"They have died and are almost too hard to bite." I was puzzled. "What happens now?"

Jim smiled. "We let them dry some more." He explained they need to be completely and evenly dry. "We will probably mow them tomorrow, or at least give it a go."

On the drive back Jim said the peas would be cut and left to dry like hay, then put through the combine like wheat.

"You mean the same machine harvests both wheat and peas?" I asked.

"Yes, and many other crops." Jim saw that I was incredulous.

Back at the yard he led me to the combine where Doug had been doing final cleaning and chain adjusting. The covers and guards were all off. Jim pointed to the cutter bar.

"All crops go through here," he said, walking towards the back of the combine. "Through the threshing drum," he pointed out, "then the sieves... up into the tank." He indicated an elevator and the large tank behind the driver. "Go up the steps and have a look."

I took in as much detail as possible and then sat down on the seat.

"Don't let Doug see you there," Jim chided. "He thinks the combine is his!"

I was excited at the prospect of seeing it all working; then a moment of concern – would I be mending sacks whilst all this was happening?

The morning came and the weather was fine. A lorry was already in the yard. Jim, Tony and I would unload the bags of fertiliser. Doug had disappeared to the combine. Tony opened a Nissen hut door and started laying a stack of old empty paper bags on the floor.

"We stack them flat," he referred to the lorry load, "and have them in a stack of forty, making two tons. You'll soon see. Just take them on yer back, like me."

I followed Tony and soon took the hundredweight bag across my right shoulder, steadied by my right hand. The driver slid the sacks to the lorry bed as we each presented our backs to the edge of the bed. In the Nissen store I copied Tony's practised 'stoop and flick' to land the bag flat. He instructed two bags be placed head to tail along the wall but not touching it; then three at right angles, making a 'square of five'. We had to nudge them square and tidy, up to eight high, the idea being making them countable two tons to the stack. By the end of the load, both we and the driver could readily agree that the number coincided with the delivery ticket.

It was midday before Jim accompanied Doug to try the mower in the pea field. I joined Tony in the yard and we fitted sides to the trailers, making them ready for carting corn when harvest started. There was some minor engineering required to make them grain-proof.

After tea Jim took me to the pea field to see how Doug was progressing. As we waited for Doug to come up the field, Jim explained the mower was adapted from an old binder, as he wanted to lift the peas before the cutter bar and leave the row of pea stems[16] back on the ground. This would aid drying, like haymaking.

"How's it going?" Jim shouted.

"Like a bad dream," Doug called back, stopping the tractor and always having a sharp retort.

"Fair, I suppose, considering this is home-made and I'm going backwards as much as forwards," Doug added.

The difficulty was getting the lifters to raise the haulm for the reciprocating knife to cut the base of the plants without them digging into the undulations of the soil. Jim rolled over some of the swath finding only a few strands of plant not cut.

"OK, do as much as you can this evening," Jim shouted to Doug as we got into the van. Turning to me, he said it was going well. "If Doug doesn't swear, it means he is satisfied. He will never suggest it is a good job."

### Second Harvest (1958)

It rained. The peas were wet and nothing could be done to hasten their drying. Harvest, I had learned, was like that – promising sun and delivering rain, which dampens not only the crops but the spirit. The expectation of continuing ideal conditions and quality produce was now downgraded to second best and delay. Farmers are matured by these humblings, realising God is sovereign and nature is His. This often leads to old men remembering, "That field had plants washed through the gateway and soil was filling the ditches," some even recalling frost in June that cut potatoes, a foot high, off at soil level; then the regrowth from the seed tuber rising to produce fresh growth and a harvest. Such a sage may well conclude, "If everyone suffers a poor crop, the market price is good" (due to scarcity).

The next morning was fine with a stiff breeze which sent Jim to the wheat field. Feeling the straw and biting the grains encouraged him to think about combining wheat and leaving the peas to nature. I spent the day with Jim showing me the corn dresser and what I would need to do as barn boy. Jim showed me the pit outside the barn where trailer loads would be tipped and also the 'cup' elevator that would carry the corn up to the top of the corn dresser. All the machinery was driven by a Wolsey petrol engine using a flat belt driven by an overhead wheel. It was like a Dickensian factory but suited the farm well.

Jim showed me all the checks: engine oil; water level on top for cooling; and all the grease points along the grader. He primed the carburettor and swung the starting handle on the engine.

---

[16] known as 'haulm'

"Started first time; not bad after nearly a year." Jim straightened and looked with pride at the vibrating engine and the dancing water in the open reservoir on top. Turning to me he pointed to the idling wheel on the shaft.

"Always have the belt on 'idle' at starting and stopping." Jim waited for it to sink in. "Always move it to idle before stopping the engine," he reinforced.

"I've got it." I nodded.

"I'm going to set it going," he warned.

The machinery vibrated into action and Jim got me to practise clipping sacks onto the six bagging outlets. He explained that the chaff heads came down the first chute, the full grain next, then the cracked grain for animal feed. I would get a working demonstration when harvest started.

I felt like an athlete at the starting blocks of harvest, but Jim took everything as it came. His experience told him nature worked best with patience; when the straw was dry and the grain moisture was no more than eighteen per cent, then it was time to start. The day came. Wheat took precedence over the peas. Tony reversed the first load from the combine and tipped it into the pit. Jim led me through the dressing machine 'start-up'. Harvest was suddenly in full swing. I was shown how to watch the filling sacks, occasionally pulling up the wrinkles to make sure the 'feet' were filled; sharply shutting the chute and opening the next one to start filling the empty sack next to it. Jim slipped the sack truck under the full sack whilst I replaced it with an empty one. He now grabbed the top of the full sack and wheeled it to the scales, showing me the balance bar gently lift up indicating eighteen and a quarter stones. This was tied tightly with binder twine, already cut to length, and wheeled off to the corner of the barn.

I was left to practise each part of the procedure whilst Jim kept a masterly eye on the operation to avoid any spillages or hold-ups. After lunch, now reduced to half an hour, it was deemed I could manage on my own. Jim's parting instruction was, "Don't panic!" Then, "Any problem, shut off the grain coming from the pit. Shut the chutes to the main sacks. Deal with the problem."

He chalked them on the tinwork in front of me. It seemed simple enough… except the "Don't panic!" bit. Tony kindly popped in when he came with the next load, looked things over and straightened the finished product along the far wall.

At teatime, Margaret's daughter Linda arrived from the house with a pack of sandwiches each and an orange squash bottle full of tea. She walked to the field with the other 'tea towel' packs for each worker. I had been told we didn't stop for tea but had to eat or drink "on the go". After all, this was harvest time.

I would have to continue until the last load arrived, which would be left to be tipped first in the morning.

The next day Tony and I started moving the completed sacks to another adjoining shed. He used the sack truck again and deftly jolted it right into the corner. The bulge of the sack was tight into the right angle, the two 'feet' touching each adjacent wall. Tony said this was important so that not even a rat could get behind it. The next exercise was to use the 'sack lift' to stack a second layer on top of the first. The 'lifter' was a very substantial copy of a 'sack truck' with a winding handle and ratchet to lift the sack vertically according to your carrying height. I steadied the hoist.

"Be careful to take the weight mostly on your shoulder and steady your legs. Turn and flop it exactly on top of the bottom layer," Tony demonstrated. "If there are two of us it is quicker to use a loading stick."

He produced a broom handle cut to just over two feet long that had stood in the window recess. We grabbed the top of the sack, standing either side and, holding each end of the broom handle with our free hands about a foot from the floor, pulled the sack onto the wood and lifted it onto the top of the ground-level sacks. The work was physical and, looking back, no doubt harmful to my still-maturing spine. At the time we quietly thought of it as making us men and being par for the course.

I was reminded of this bodybuilding a year later as I ambled through a fairground during a weekend at home and saw young men trying to prove their strength. The test was a marked pole with a bell on top. The graduation marks on the pole indicated the strength of various professions, starting with clerk, grocer, coalman, navvy, miner and topped with farmer, thus ringing the bell. A group of young men, obviously fortified with a drop of beer, had tried to impress their female friends by ringing the bell. However, they had difficulty in striking the plunger on its own, let alone with sufficient force.

As they moved away, I paid my three pennies and swung with the requisite force needed to settle a fencing post. To the astonishment of the stallholder the bell rang out.

"Would you have a free go – it attracts people here?" he asked.

I had been put on the spot and had to risk my new reputation. I had to concentrate on the plunger and the force needed. It rang the bell again.

The stallholder confided, "That is the farmer's mark."

As I walked away I told him, "I am one."

Doug managed to combine two fields of wheat that were ripe but the rest needed another few days. Our attention turned to the peas; they needed turning in order to dry; this had to be done by hand. It meant all four of us, including Jim, taking a row each and, using the back of a pitch fork, rolling it damp-side up. There was no 'hay turner' gentle enough to avoid shattering the pods and losing the crop. It requires a deft flick to roll the continuous row without turning it 180 degrees. The field was twenty acres, about the size of twenty football pitches, and, due to inclement weather, needed to be turned five times that year before being ready for combining.

The method of finally combining was to mount a pick-up attachment, like that of a baler, in place of the usual cutter bar. This gently fed the pea swath into the elevator and threshing drum with the concave set wide enough to separate pea from pod. By this time the peas had to be so hard that one could actually stand on them without harming them. The peas were cleaned through the dresser and weighed off in four-bushel sacks at seventeen and a quarter stones. This was a little lighter on the back than four bushels of wheat at eighteen and a quarter stones. A bushel was like a huge bucket with a handle on each side and, when full to the brim, was a volumetric measurement. The sacks used could contain four bushels by volume, hence the differing weight of full sacks shown below.

| Crop (weight in lbs) (14 lbs = 1 stone) | | Bushel 4-bushel sack | | |
|---|---|---|---|---|
| Oats | 42 | 12 stone | = | 1.5 cwt |
| Barley | 56 | 16 stone | = | 2.0 cwt |
| Wheat | 64 | 18¼ stone | = | 2.25 cwt |
| Kale seed | 70 | 20 stone | = | 2.50 cwt |

I settled to being a barn boy although it meant working inside rather than in the harvest field. It was hard work and dusty, nevertheless satisfying. The barn became my own little domain; I had grown in confidence. I had dealt with minor emergencies satisfactorily without seeking help. There was a certain pride in being responsible for packaging the finished product. It was good to be part of a team, with each member, including the owner, contributing to the success of the job. In addition it was valuable pre-college experience and would be useful when instructing future employees, "We do it this way."

Gaining entry to college was never far from my mind and this repetitive job gave me time to think. I had to pass Chemistry 'O' level to be sure of a college place. My only chance was to go to night school. I would ask Jim if it was possible to have a little time off. I found out my previous GCE results qualified me for an evening course in Chelmsford, about twenty miles away, on Thursday evenings, 7 pm till 9 pm. My problem would be transport as the bus from Dunmow left at 5.30 pm. I would need a good hour to clean myself up and cycle to town.

Jim readily agreed that I could have an hour off to attend night school. Two problems remained: where to hide my cycle, and the timing of the last bus back. A little research on a free evening revealed the only place out of sight and reasonably secure was a narrow alley between two shops. It was a blind end, apparently for the delivery of goods to the shops. Fortunately, there was a convenient 'downpipe' that I could use to anchor my cycle. Unfortunately, the last bus for the return journey left at 9.15 pm. I would have to leave class immediately it ended and run for the bus.

I enrolled and started in mid-September. The classmates were mostly a few years younger and treated it as an adjunct to their social life rather than an education. I was there to achieve a pass mark.

All went to plan for a few weeks until I missed the last bus. The few people still about at that time of night didn't know whether the bus was late in arriving or had already departed. We could only agree it was not visible. I walked up to the next bus stop, looking around in case the bus overtook me. I decided there would be no bus that night and the only alternative was to thumb a lift. This was not a good prospect on a cold October night. The few cars that passed were not interested in picking up a lone male even in the well-lit town. I could not afford a taxi and was wondering if there was any Plan B, when a large van turned into the road from the traffic lights. I thumbed with my whole arm as if some terrible tragedy had occurred. It stopped.

"Are you going near Dunmow?" I shouted across to the driver.

He nodded. "Hop in mate."

My relief was palpable. He asked what I was doing out this time of night. I shouted back details of night school. The van was empty with nothing behind us except a rear roller door. In front, our only separation was a noisy diesel engine, competing with the rattle of the rear roller.

The driver asked what my job was and why I needed night classes. I explained and then asked him what his job was.

"I'm collecting orders from Lowestoft," he shouted.

My only interest had been securing transport but now my nose identified the heady mix of fish and diesel fumes. By the time we approached Dunmow we had established a rapport, seemingly based on fishing and farming and a kinship of struggles with the elements. The driver, known as Sam by now, said he could probably make this journey a few minutes earlier and would look out for me at the same place each week. He said he appreciated the company and I would save the bus fare. I watched Sam disappear noisily and retrieved my bike, fortunately still chained to the downpipe.

As weeks passed by I looked forward to my Thursday outing. The Chemistry lesson was much more interesting than it had been at school, and my journeying with Sam was a view beyond all things farming. The lecturer soon knew the students who were serious about the subject and readily accommodated the keen ones by answering their questions. It soon became more like a tutorial, which encouraged me further.

My social life had been virtually nil as a cowman but now there was time to attend a church and perhaps the Young Farmers Club (YFC). Jim suggested I ought to get a driving licence as I would need one sooner or later. I could drive a tractor and take a test to drive that on the highway, but if I learned to drive a car it would cover both vehicles. This sounded promising and Margaret was prepared to loan her car to a learner. The arrangement worked both ways: I suddenly had use of a vehicle and she had a chauffeur in the making. The willingness and cooperation of the family was in stark contrast to my previous employer.

# 10

# Potatoes and Poodles

Once the corn and peas had been harvested, Doug spent days ploughing in preparation for sowing winter wheat. Tony and I worked on digging potatoes with Jim's supervision. A field of second early potatoes had been harvested and sold before my arrival at the farm. Now we were starting on the two fields of main crop, King Edwards, for storage and later sale in the winter.

Jim had sprayed the potato fields with chemicals to kill the tops and prevent blight spreading. He had shown me during the evenings how to determine the timing of the operations.

"You need to know what's going on underground," he insisted.

He walked twenty yards up a row of potatoes, me following with a fork and bucket. He took the fork and carefully dug up a complete plant.

"You see, they're big enough." Jim pulled the tubers off. "A good plateful."

"Two plates-full." I smiled.

We were on our knees examining every detail. Jim rubbed the skin off a large tuber.

"See, it won't rub off; it's set."

I must have looked puzzled.

"New potatoes, the skin rubs off, means they're not mature. The skins are protection for keeping them through the winter."

Jim heaped the tubers into the bucket to take back to the house.

"I'll give them a few more days to make sure they're all set." Jim was thinking aloud.

Tony and I had fitted the potato elevator behind a tractor, which would dig under the ridge and shake the potatoes along a conveyor of metal rods, depositing them back onto the ground again. The impressive result was a row of clean potatoes on top of the soil rather than under it. By this time, Jim had turned up with four women from the village; two more had cycled over. They arranged themselves in pairs, putting their lunch bags and coats where they started and working toward the next pair. Tony had thrown hessian potato sacks every few yards on top of the next undug row. When they had a full bucket of potatoes, they tipped them into a sack. The idea of working in pairs soon became evident when one held the sack open and the other tipped her bucket. Struggling as individuals could easily result in half the potatoes needing to be picked up a second time. Time was money as they would be paid by the number of full sacks at the end of the day. We were kept busy distributing sacks and collecting full ones with another tractor and two-wheeled trailer. Tony had to be aware of their need for both fresh tubers to pick up and empty sacks to put them in. Either failure resulted in the less-than-ladylike shout, "Sacks!"

I had to keep a record of the number of sacks each pair picked. Tony had quickly given me this responsibility as I was a 'scholar'. I soon found the scholar also had to be judge and jury when one pair argued which sacks were theirs, the adjacent pair equally insistent they were the rightful owners. At 4 pm the women counted their sacks, or more correctly tried to correct my accounting, and went home. We collected all the remaining sacks and emptied them into the potato shed at the top of the yard. The trailer was reversed into a large Nissen hut with a line of bales either side to stop potatoes rolling under the wheels. The sacks were emptied as gently as possible over them. Bales of straw were also put along the side walls as insulation. We filled the shed to a depth of five or six feet with a foot of loose straw on top to absorb condensation from the roof and to protect the potatoes from frost.

I soon mastered, at least in practical terms, driving the Austin Countryman. The finer points of satisfying a test examiner might take a little longer. To help me in this, an occasional visit by Jim's brother, an ex-police driver, was a huge bonus. I also had plenty of practice, as Margaret preferred a chauffeur. Her interest in dog breeding necessitated visiting potential customers, trips to poodle coiffures, and vets. It also gave me plenty of reading time, which I gathered was par for the course for taxi drivers. I had to agree with Jim that poodles and farms were not an ideal combination. However, I was grateful for the free driving experience, including a little professional tuition from Jim's brother.

Occasionally poodles would be left with Margaret for short-term kennelling at mating time. Jim had no room in farm buildings that he could spare or make dog-proof; or at least, none that satisfied Margaret's criteria. At the back door of the farmhouse was an old washroom that became a dual purpose poodle 'park' and boot store. This was a satisfactory arrangement as it kept mud out of the house, suiting Margaret, and kept poodles from being "everywhere" as far as Jim was concerned. The downside was the unknown 'poodle count' which differed with the hour – some deposited, others departing; it could equally be named a transit lounge. One time, during the winter, I opened the door as usual to remove my work boots, and out shot a poodle. It could only be related as the perfect storm – the conjunction of a homesick visiting poodle, an unsuspecting intruder (me) and dusk. My first task was to inform Margaret; she would know which name to call out. She immediately called "Mitsey" up and down the yard. She then called me names that are best not recorded! I was deputed to calling "Mitsey" myself, around all adjoining fields in the increasing gloom.

All efforts to find the dog failed. I apologised profusely. Margaret calmed down and tried to think rationally of the next move. An uneasy peace descended. By 9 pm she phoned the owner to enquire if Mitsey had travelled the nine miles home. It was a long shot; a fit greyhound might have managed it, if travelling in the right direction, but at least the owner had been informed the dog was missing.

The sad saga continued for months with no resolution. Although concerned, I privately considered Mitsey must have emigrated. Margaret must have come to some sort of resolution with the owner but certainly felt no compulsion to inform me.

It was over five months later that Margaret thought she saw Mitsey on a lead in the local town. She followed at a distance trying to be sure it was the right poodle.

"May I ask, is your dog called Mitsey?" she had to enquire.

"Well, yes!" was the surprised response.

Margaret related the whole saga, pointing out the name was on the inside of her collar.

The lady admitted it was a stray and she had tried to find the owner. The happy conclusion was that the dog was returned to the real owner and Margaret was congratulated on her diligence.

## Autumn Sowing

The strong clay content of the soil demanded it needed to be ploughed and worked to a seedbed quality before much rain fell. Doug was sent to work, ploughing the pea field and then rolling it with the 'ring' roller; this had the effect of breaking and fracturing the furrows rather than using the 'flat' roller that would be used on grassland. Tony did the rolling whilst Doug, the senior man, prepared the corn drill. This largely meant cleaning out any debris that had accumulated since spring and greasing the bearings. I was then required to check that all the moving parts inside the seed and fertiliser boxes actually revolved whilst Doug very slowly drove it down the gravel yard. I was soon to be 'drill boy' and responsible for constantly checking that the flow of the seed and fertiliser was not impaired.

As soon as a field was ready, ploughed, rolled and cultivated[17], it was sown. We loaded sacks of seed wheat and bags of fertiliser onto a four-wheeled trailer, which Doug insisted was called a 'dray'. Tony commented that Doug, who was about forty, was old-fashioned.

"Horses pulled drays and tractors pull trailers," Tony emphasised.

"You wouldn't remember, but we had men in those days, not just boys," Doug retorted.

---

[17] that is, deeply raked with a set of what looked like steel spring 'question marks'

The banter was good-natured but there was still a hint of pecking order similar to that at Fair Oaks Farm.

As drill boy I had to stand on a plank or running board at the rear of the drill and hang on to the lid handles of the boxes into which the fertiliser had been tipped. My ride depended on how rough the ground was and the speed of the tractor. It must have been akin to riding a horse and bending down to inspect the tightness of the girth every minute. I had to keep an eye on the bouncing disc coulters and the flow of fertiliser from its box, down a flexing pipe to the disc, which cut and covered the seed. This was necessary, as a 'walnut' of damp soil could be thrown up and lodge in the flexing pipe. This would result in both seed and fertiliser being wasted. If unnoticed, this would result in a glaring gap in the neat rows of germinating crop. I had been warned to be vigilant or else be cast as a poor workman by the 'inspecting committee'. This committee was composed of head tractor drivers, including Doug, from neighbouring farms, who felt it their business to monitor the skills of other local farm workers. This Sunday group would walk across several fields, ending up at the local pub to discuss farming proficiency.

Once the field had been drilled or sown, it was usual to pull a set of light harrows over the field to make sure the seed was covered in. Sometimes the harrows could be attached behind the drill, saving an extra cultivation. If the seedbed was too rough, and there was a danger of the drill boy falling off his plank, then it would be a separate harrowing operation.

Autumn was a time of change, not only in the glorious colours of the trees and skies, but also in the weather. The changes in rain or shine, wind or lack of it, seemed to fight for the upper hand. There were some days harking back to summer and others hastening to winter. This would hamper work plans and test farm management. Often slight variations in soil type or even aspect, facing the sun or shaded by a wood, meant conditions dictated a change to us working in another field. Wind became important for drying the soil before sowing could continue. This would make all the difference between a good seedbed and a cloddy one. Once the seed was sown it would have to survive or fail, to exist or prosper, according to the soil conditions at the time of sowing. In order to achieve these optimum conditions, drilling the winter crops took precedence over other activities.

# 11

# Sugar Beet Harvest

The less conducive conditions enabled the start of sugar beet harvesting. This was a new crop to me and a harvest less dependent on fine weather. Jim was helping out a neighbouring smallholder with only a five-acre field, prior to him selling it and Jim adding it to our much larger field. Unfortunately, the old man insisted on the old hand-harvesting method which, in his words, "didn't run half the crop down with them harvester machines". There must have been some business arrangement with the old man, as we wanted the field cleared in time to sow winter wheat whilst the owner could see no haste. He would plough out the 'gangways' which would allow a harvester to turn without running on the crop. We would act both as contractor and labour force, and then machine-lift the remaining rows. The old-fashioned method used a 'lifter', being a pair of opposing plough shares, drawn by a tractor, which lifted the beet half out of the ground. They were then pulled up fully manually, one in each hand, knocked against each other to remove any soil, and dropped into a row. On the next wet morning, our own wheat drilling gave way to handwork on these sugar beet.

We all tied sacks around our waists as aprons and helped the old man. I was introduced to this back-breaking routine of pulling up cold wet beet by their tops, and clearing four gangways over the field before the harvester could start work. Each of us taking a row again, the next operation was to cut the tops off the beet. Like most manual farm jobs, I found that particular details, honed over the years, had to be adhered to. This had been stressed at my first efforts to sweep the barn floor, later the sack-filling, weighing and stacking, and now at hand-harvesting sugar beet.

We each had a row, and proceeded to pull beet up by the crown[18] and swung them hard together, so releasing most of the soil. These were dropped back in the same place they had grown, and stretched like 'piano keys' as we proceeded up the field. This completed, Doug handed me a 'beet bill'[19].

"Use the point to pick up the beet; it saves bending. Grab it with your left hand and chop the leaves smartly off with the right."

---

[18] where leaves meet root
[19] wooden-handled carving knife with the end turned down to a sharp point

Doug was succinct and immediately demonstrated what I had to do. Having done one, he went on to do several more in a dance of hands and arms, keeping his eyes focused on the beet. The tops fell to the ground and the beet he lobbed, without looking, the three or four yards ahead to the centre of the five men. After a few minutes the piano keys had become a line of beet heaps. These were later to be forked onto a cart and taken back to the yard.

The work was strenuous and the weather freezing. We all felt the cutting east wind but the job had to be done. One particular morning we had only been working for an hour, and our bare hands and wet clothes were already slowing us all down. I could not focus, and leaned on the rear wheel of the tractor, not for shelter but to be against something solid. My ears were stinging and my head was throbbing.

"What's the matter, mate?" Doug had noticed I was not behind him.

I couldn't answer.

Jim came across and pulled one of the sacks off the tractor seat. It was standard practice to sit on a couple of sacks; apart from insulation from cold metal, they were the 'must have' item for any eventuality. They were containers for anything: a stretcher for small livestock; a cushion against barbed wire; even oven gloves for lifting off hot exhaust pipes; and much else.

"Hold onto the steering wheel," Jim instructed as the two of them hoisted me upward. "Just stay there and have a blow."

'Blow' was the opposite to 'working' and was used for bait-time, the end of a task before starting the next, or just straightening your back and expecting others to do the same. I leaned my head on my hands, still gripping the steering wheel, and Jim just threw the sack right over me.

The dispatch of beet to the sugar factory was controlled by permits stating the date and tonnage that Jim could deliver towards his annual contract. At the start of the season there would be 'free loading', meaning delivery could be at our convenience. The final sugar beet job was cleaning them over the elevator into the farm's Bedford lorry and Jim driving it to the factory. Jim explained one evening that our beet were grown on a slightly wider row width to accommodate tractor wheels travelling up the rows. The job could then be mechanised by the machine, cutting the crown off whilst it was still upright in the ground, easing them up chain elevators, allowing any soil to fall back to the ground, and to be dropped straight into an accompanying trailer. This was music to my ears.

During the sugar beet harvesting, autumn passed into winter. The corn drilling was behind us and it was gratifying that there were no disastrous gaps left by a negligent drill boy. The straight lines of young green plants should withstand frost and snow. There was a tidiness restored to the land as a badge of professional workmanship that had even been noticed by the committee. The ploughing of the first sugar beet ground had incorporated the tops and smartened up the field. This seemed in accord with the leafless trees, stark and smart, groomed for winter.

## My Second Winter (1958-9)

My first winter farming had been a rude awakening with icy kale and freezing pipes. The second winter had its rigours when exposed to the elements but with the compensation of a variety of jobs and friendly company. Harvests of potatoes, peas and corn were safely stored and awaiting a suitable market. Daily work was increasingly spent around the farmyard and workshop. Salesmen and reps were calling on Jim and his brother Ed who lived in his own bungalow a mile away. Ed was a man of mystery in the family; a bachelor footloose and fancy-free. He had a few chickens but that was surely not his main income. He would turn up at the farm most days and with no discernible purpose, but apparently always busy. Ed had a wooden shed in the yard, about fifteen-foot square, that was called his 'office'. The 'furniture' consisted of an extension from the house phone, a battered desk and two folding chairs better suited to a barbecue. Here he met people, but his car was the real office or at least the repository of papers, invoices, address books and half-consumed snacks. Ed was always smiling and would be the centre of attraction of any social group; the mystery was, which groups?

When Ed turned up at the yard, within thirty minutes so did Bill. They both had connections with chicken and eggs; Ed in minor sales and Bill in procurement. In fact, Bill seemed to be able to procure anything given a little time. He considered himself as a 'general dealer', unashamedly his profession. As we approached Christmas, Tony and I would spend an hour or two 'helping Ed' or else at weekends he might even pay us for helping him. December was their busy time, dealing in Christmas trees, capons and turkeys. Bill had a van that carried most things most of the time. Currently a few trees were aboard plus a baker's tray of capons on the front seat. Ed had especially asked Tony and me to spend Saturday helping him to pluck his birds. I was shown how to tackle the job without tearing any flesh. Soon the four of us, sitting on bales around the walls, could hardly be seen for feathers. Ed would take the finished birds and lay them on newspaper in the back of his Ford Zodiac estate. Bill's birds he did himself and placed them back on the front seat, returning with another one with plumage.

Jim had shown me how to draw[20] a pheasant, which he thought every farmer ought to be acquainted with. He worked on the simple principle that everything inside needed to be outside without bursting any organ. He showed me where to cut each end and not to worry about getting my hands dirty. This I managed without concern. The lesson proved useful as Margaret refused to have anything

---

[20] gut

to do with birds except putting them in the oven. I was therefore delegated to practise my acquired skill so that Jim could eat what he shot and Margaret could cook the prepared bird providing there was not a trace of blood or anything else "left dead" in the kitchen.

In the run up to Christmas we seemed to be seconded to Ed, and capons gave way to turkey-plucking. Ed was always jolly, and working with him and the ubiquitous Bill, crammed into his 'office', was akin to a party without the beer. We all suffered good-humoured ribbing, particularly Ed because of his bachelor status and mystery excursions. Bill enjoyed being a similar character on a more parsimonious plane. It was more like playboy and pauper. Ed smoked Senior Service; Bill rolled his own. Ed's Zodiac estate, wastepaper basket that it was, was valeted quarterly, whilst Bill's van just 'was'. This implies a state of unending mystery as we could hardly see through the dirty windows and nobody had never ridden in it. That was true except for the reports that Mrs Moses, "just a friend", had been taken shopping a time or two, generally acknowledged as weekly.

This Christmas I had no responsibilities for livestock and looked forward to spending it with my parents and sister in London. In fact, I took two days' holiday entitlement in addition, which enabled me to share some of the seasonal preparation and have quality time together with my family. Transport was proving difficult, but Margaret kindly agreed to ferry me to and from the nearest town. I used buses to London, walking the last three miles home. I counted my blessings at the difference in relationship with my employers two Christmases apart. Indeed, the 'porridge' encountered in life had changed from stodgy coolness to nutritious warmth. I had wondered about the real meaning of 'buckets of porridge' or to what the suited gent had been inferring. I had assumed it was a reference to my stature; although not slight, I was needing to put on four more stones to emulate a farmer's son reared on hearty breakfasts. Now I wondered if it was a metaphor for life, particularly farm life. I had indeed experienced the ups and downs, even hardships, of Goblets Farm. Now life at Claydon Farm was of a different order. Work and life were smooth, if strenuous. There was a purpose and achievement; a willingness to work as a team. I had been accepted as part of that team and was being taught the relationship we have with nature. I was understanding that as farmers we are only tenants, the freehold belonging to the Creator. Our duty is to leave the land in better shape than we found it, the reward being the harvest that working with nature provides.

# 12

# Social Relations

Winter morphed into spring. In January and February we alternated between selling stored crops and preparing for the new farming year. In practice this meant dispatching sugar beet to the factory as permits allowed. This was interspersed with potato and corn sales as the markets became favourable.

In order to sell potatoes, three or four days were needed to make it worthwhile. The clamp in the shed had to be opened up and the straw covering forked back, exposing the potatoes. These would be covered again every night with a large tarpaulin to keep the light and any frost out. We were all involved, including three women from the village. Jim collected the ladies whilst we pushed the potato grader up to the clamp.

"The carnival is starting," Doug announced.

When he was grounded, as distinct from what Tony referred to as "sitting on his arse", Doug was very loud. Being the principle tractor driver, and all of ten years older than Tony, he acted up with great self-importance. Egged on by the three women, it always became a carnival of leg-pulling and banal banter. Tony and I would take turns at forking the potatoes into a small hopper, elevating them onto the reciprocating grader which shunted them across a sieve onto a metal conveyor to the bagging-off point. The operation was driven by a small petrol engine which added pale blue fumes to the noise of the scrapping of metal slats, which had to be overcome by shouting. Small potatoes, known as 'chats', dropped through the sieve into a bushel, and the larger ones passed inspection into the sacks. The women threw out any green, diseased or badly misshapen tubers. The bags were weighed at 112 lbs and tied up with string. It was important for the two men handling the sacking, weighing and tying to clearly stack the finished product in one ton lots (20 cwt x 112 lbs = 2240 lbs = an imperial ton).

The next part of the carnival was the departure of the women at 4 pm and the arrival of the potato merchant's lorry. The ladies were always keen to oversee which good-looking cockney was driving that day and to ask if he had a spare seat for a trip to London. The usual reply was that he could take all three and share with his mates. The driver had already done his daily deliveries to sundry greengrocers and chip shops, and arrived at farms to collect eight tons for Spitalfields market the next morning. We worked straight away in pairs, using a loading stick to swing up the sacks. These the driver stood five across the bed, like 'soldiers', and three horizontal on top to tie them in. The result was a neat load to be roped down securely. Unfortunately, the driver would usually find he was a sack short.

"One more, mate," he shouted.

"You've got eight tons; they were in ton stacks," came our reply.

"See for yourself, mate," the driver invited.

Whoever loaded would walk around the neat load and count the rows, then make sure each top row sat on the one below.

"See mate, there is one missing at the back 'ere." The driver stood exactly where the gap was.

"How many are in the front row?" Doug enquired in desperation.

The driver walked over the top of his load and peeled the front horizontal sacks back to reveal five neatly-tied soldiers across the back. Defeated, we threw up an extra sack from the next ton stack awaiting the next day's collection. The way a sack could regularly vanish without a trace was a mystery akin to the Marie Celeste.

Margaret had suggested my joining the Young Farmers Club and my new acquaintance Brian suggested the same. He worked with his father half a mile away and I had stopped by twice on my way to an old chapel on the top road. Brian had suggested the belated New Year party was just the occasion to join; belated as always, I was told, because there were too many festivities and too much drinking already over Christmas for Young Farmers as they concentrated on their own partying. The January evening 'do' was still considered party time, consisting of slides showing the events of the previous year coupled with a copious buffet. As I had no idea who or what was represented on the slides, it was impossible to join in with the laughter and the in jokes. Brian occasionally leaned over and whispered names and places, but that hardly helped. Later he introduced me to one or two young men, who were polite but busy with their friends, male and female.

"Just be careful what you say because they are all related," Brian confided, adding, "Don't say much about Claydon or it could get back to Jim."

That was the last straw; I felt right outside the circle.

It was during that time of year, with darker evenings and less land work, that some farmers made time to attend business meetings. These were usually trade or sales meetings informing growers about the latest 'must have' product or innovation. The other meetings were for National Farmers Union (NFU) members, but sometimes open to non-members, covering union activity and government legislation. Jim asked if I would like to attend with him and learn what was going on. It was an offer I could not resist. Apart from practical farm work, I would need to learn the management behind it. In fact, I would need to be acquainted with planning and budgets before receiving more detailed instruction at college. Jim was treating me like a farmer's son who would have grown up in such an atmosphere. This turned out to be the case as, driving back from meetings, Jim would comment and enlarge on any topic I chose. What better introduction to farm management?

I had little inclination to attend another Young Farmers meeting until Sigrid turned up. I had no idea Margaret was getting an au pair as a general help until, coming in for tea one evening, I was introduced to a tall blond from Frankfurt who would be sharing Linda's room. Jim showed her around the farm the following evening and Margaret acquainted her with household duties. At this time I had just failed my driving test for not using the mirror sufficiently and being overconfident. Douglas, the ex-police driver, offered to give me a couple of extra lessons.

Life was getting busy. Spring land work was starting and Margaret was increasingly wanting poodles chauffeured. Additionally, she suggested I took Sigrid to the Young Farmers Club. Whilst I was not too keen on the YFC following my New Year party experience, it seemed a very good idea that I might help foster 'international relations'. I had already been able to show Sigrid places on the farm that Jim must have omitted and I regarded it as a duty to take her to Young Farmers. I asked Brian, who had a full driving licence, to take us to the next meeting. Our appearance at the 'Preparations for Easter' meeting was much more welcoming than my first visit. The lads immediately wanted to join me in my mission of improving international friendships. And after the initial rush, the girls too became good hosts. My 'street cred' had soared to the extent of being offered drinks (they regarded beer as a good currency), and I was even offered trips around their farms if Sigrid could manage it as well.

Sigrid was finding her feet quickly, and comments were being made in the farmhouse. It was suggested that she was not too keen on housework and rather too keen on me. One evening, when Jim and Margaret were at a dinner party, Sigrid wanted to drive the Austin Countryman. She insisted she could drive and that we could drive around the farm. I thought it a bad idea, especially as Margaret had not been consulted. Sigrid insisted there was no reason to worry, and why couldn't she drive an English car? I eventually compromised and, doubting she could legally drive, said she could only drive on the grass meadow next to the buildings. I sat in the passenger seat, she tentatively started the car and we crept forward into the meadow behind the yard.

Once past the first line of hen coops we shot forward. It was not a matter of changing gear but flooring the pedal until the engine screamed.

"Take your foot off!" I yelled. "Slow down."

She was deaf or, more accurately, intoxicated with speed. I was no longer concerned about the revs but the steering. We were heading for one of the hen houses. I pulled the steering wheel against her grip to avoid it. Fortunately, we missed it by a whisker... but were speeding straight for another. The steering wheel, with four hands on it, was flashing from nine o'clock to three o'clock. I wrenched the wheel my way and turned off the ignition. We stopped immediately.

"Why did you grip the wheel so tightly?" I managed to gasp.

"I was frightened," she admitted.

We changed seats and I placed the car back in the yard hoping it was none the worse for the experience.

I set my eyes on farming and the sowing of sugar beet. The two fields for that year had been ploughed before the winter frosts, and the soil was dry and friable. Tony had cultivated it – what Jim called "pulling down the furrows". A contractor had spread two tons of lime per acre. Doug's job was to follow with the fertiliser spreader, adding sulphate of ammonia, superphosphate and muriate of potash. This heady mix was cultivated into the soil giving a fine tilth. The final flat rolling left the fields looking like brown billiard tables.

Doug took pride in getting the rows absolutely straight. This would be a mark of professionalism and favourably judged by the Sunday committee. To start the job, great pains were taken to set up three pitch forks, with a paper bag tied over each handle, in the longest stretch of the field. These were 'eyed-up' in line to appear as one. Doug set off with the four-row seeder as if looking down gun sights. The drill units were set to place a seed every ten inches with the gap between rows being eighteen inches, to achieve an optimum crop density and yield. I was only involved when the seedlings were about an inch high and needed hoeing. Any weeds between rows could be cut out with the tractor hoe, great care being taken by driver and the steerage man sitting on the back of the hoe frame. Failure to keep straight could be disastrous, cutting out part of the crop and leaving the weeds growing.

'Hoeing down' the row of beet was usually done by piecework; this entailed chopping out the weeds within the row for six pounds per acre, and was followed a day or two later by 'singling' the same acre. This involved cutting or pinching out the doubles, ensuring all that remained were singles, and which was paid at two pounds per acre. Traditionally the farm worker would 'chop out' with two strikes of the hoe and his wife would follow pinching out any double seedlings, leaving the strongest. Jim demonstrated two chops leaving a seedling every ten inches and watched me attempt the same on my row.

"Keep your eyes on the plants all the time," he instructed.

I had just chopped out a strong single plant and left a double next to it.

"Look for the best single about every nine or ten inches." Jim offered a little flexibility if there was a healthy single in the vicinity.

It was easier said than done. "Whoops!" Another nice single had been cut out.

"Don't worry about a few doubles; you'll get those at singling. Just keep on walking."

We set off abreast, a row each; this made for conversation and made a monotonous job less boring. I was trying to keep up with the other three when Jim's hoe connected with my ankle.

"Yer don't have to rush. Do it clean." I received Jim's subtle message and concentrated harder. There was no substitute for practice. After an hour my back was aching and we stopped for a 'blow'. I was only five yards behind the others.

"The cleaner yer chopping, the less singling." Doug weighed in with advice as usual.

"He's doing alright," Jim added.

With that encouragement, and the thought of eight pounds an acre, I started again.

It took two days to do a total of four acres and we started again singling every fourth row, so matching our own 'chopping-out' handiwork. It soon became clear who had done the most accurate chopping-out as they spent less time singling. The working together in a line had been for my benefit and for Jim to keep an eye on me. The rest of the field had been marked out in acres so that the first to complete his acre moved on to the next. My motivation now was to do as 'clean' a job as possible and cover the acre in the shortest time consistent with accuracy. I achieved two acres per week which doubled my pay – and doubled my back.

The 'second early' potatoes had been planted just before the beet. Now we started the main crop, King Edwards. During the winter the Scottish seed had arrived and on inclement days was tipped into chitting boxes, one sack to three trays. They now had strong green shoots and were tipped as gently as possible into the hopper of the Ferguson potato planter. The planter was mounted on the three-point linkage of the tractor and the two operators sat on metal seats at right angles to the direction of travel. They had to gather a few potatoes in each hand and drop them down a tube in front of them. This was done to the tune of a single-note bell. The wheel, the size of a dinner plate, had several knobs arranged to measure inches of travel. According to the required spacing of the seed potato, the knobs would strike the bell – *ping* – the theory being that at each ping, a potato would be dropped down the tube as the ridging bodies opened and closed the ridge. It only took one pass up the field to amass several hundred pings and a lifetime aversion to bells. In practice the tractor driver often subtly went slightly faster if wide spacing was required and slower for closer.

*Ping, ping, ping* became a torture worse than dripping water. The bell attachment, by general consent, could be done without and was left on the headland. Thereafter the operator's hands adopted a steady rhythm and test digs confirmed they were sufficiently accurate.

## Seed Crops

That year some of the wheat was grown for seed production. This meant special care and attention to detail was taken from harvest time onwards the previous year. The fields selected had grown second early potatoes, being a year free from any cereals; additionally they were ploughed early, burying any germinated weeds. The crop was grown for a seed merchant on contract, securing a 'known' market should it meet all the quality criteria at harvest. We were meticulous in cleaning the grain drill so that not a single grain of any other variety could germinate in the crop. Throughout the growing season Jim was inspecting the wheat for disease and weeds, spraying it with the appropriate chemicals. The greatest concern was to eliminate wild oats, which were a noxious weed but similar to cultivated oats in appearance.

"Better wear boots today; we are going rogueing[21]," Jim announced. Seeing my quizzical expression, he had to add, "We're pulling wild oats."

It soon became clear as he instructed me in the field. Tony and Doug were with us and knew the job.

"Bend down to eye level with the ears." I could see they were just emerging. "See the taller plants?" Jim asked.

"Yes," I said hesitantly.

"Pull 'em right out of the soil, roots and all," was his definite instruction.

Doug naturally felt the need to comment, "That goes for you too, Tony."

"I've done this before," Tony shouted back.

"I am telling you not to sow your wild oats!" Doug laughed as he lowered the tone.

Together we walked down the lines of wheat looking to left and right some three yards apart.

"You've missed one," Jim called to me, pointing a yard behind.

I dutifully turned and added it to my bundle.

"You'll soon get your eye in," he assured me.

At the end of the rows we made a heap of our armfuls of wild oats, which would be collected at the end of the day and burned. We traversed up and down, with pulled wild oats in one arm and plucking the next weed with the free arm. It was a much better job with social banter than attempting to rogue a field alone. It was yet another job in the tapestry of the farming year, the sun and open air adding pleasure to what some would find boring. The importance of growing a seed crop was that the merchant could confidently sell it on to other farmers as free of wild oats, not introducing the noxious weed to his holding. Achieving this purity would enable Jim to sell the crop for much more than cereals to be fed to livestock.

---

[21] removing rogue plants injurious to seed crop

I was beginning to appreciate the 'team' of young farmers with similar outlooks of caring and embracing the countryside. The initial coolness I had felt was as much my fault as theirs. Perhaps it was something of the gulf between town and country; we each were products of our environments. We all grow up in competition with our peer group much like plants competing for the sun. They had learned as infants that they were striving to cooperate with nature because that was in their best business interest. Town-dwellers have a multitude of other businesses, mostly totally divorced from nature.

As I got to know some of the young farmers, they were much advanced in the business of living in the countryside. They were self-assured in buying and selling livestock, knowing the criteria of quality and its worth. My dealings were pocket money proportions, theirs the size of three months' wages. This reflected the amount of risk they were prepared to take. I was understanding that farming was both risky and rewarding on a scale foreign to me. The cost of a heifer would buy me a car; one would appreciate in value, the other would depreciate. A mutual freedom and respect was growing between us. I was no threat to them as they jockeyed the size of their parents' farm or combine harvester with their compatriots. Equally, I was under no pressure to emulate, only to learn from them. I was soon included in minor tennis tournaments and tug-of-war competitions, and much fun was had by all.

It was about this time that I began to notice my partner in the mixed doubles. She was a tall and attractive blonde with no apparent attachments. Her other attributes were a powerful service game, much better than mine, and being from a farming pedigree. I grew friendly with her brothers and was soon a regular guest at their farm.

# 13

# Agricultural College

I had been accepted at Writtle Agricultural College in the February, having fulfilled the entrance requirements: I had passed the required Chemistry exam and had the three years' farm-working experience. The interviewing panel had run through my farm experience and congratulated me on its variety. It was satisfying to have answered any sceptics about the staying power of a Londoner wanting to farm. I had been asked what my ambition was as I had not come from a farming family. I had always understood owning a farm was out of the question, even if my mother had won the football pools, but I hoped to work as a farm manager. Asked to enlarge upon that I had replied, "Hopefully a thousand acres." Not surprisingly they thought this was a tall enough order and wished me success.

My first ambition had been to reach agricultural college. I trusted in taking one step at a time, and through all the journey thus far the Lord had been faithful. This was my first day; it was to be all academic study now. The front elevation of the main building consisted of two storeys with wings each side of a magnificent central doorway that any visiting dignity would be proud to enter. As a student I was required to use the rear entrance where the cycle racks were. At last I had arrived.

We were directed to the assembly hall and welcomed by the principal. After introducing heads of departments, we were separated into various courses. We were given a plan of the building and introduced to our main lecturers who in turn outlined their curriculum for the autumn term.

The next day lectures started gently, skipping through basics to get everybody to a common level. Each lecturer had a reading list for us to at least browse through in the library to become familiar with the introduction to his speciality. We were immediately sifting the 'browse' suggestions versus the 'devour' option, realising it would be difficult to actually carry all the books let alone read them. Botany, obviously a major subject, required us to start as soon as possible on assembling some two hundred weeds; identified, pressed and mounted by the end of our first year. By general consent in the common room, this was likely to be addressed later on the basis that weeds start growing in the spring. However, Dr Mason, who had obviously experienced the students' work ethic before, insisted it was wise to make an immediate start on the mammoth collection. He also pointed out the weeds needed to be mature, demonstrating their inflorescence or flowering.

I had decided to be an out-student; more correctly, my finances suggested it was prudent. The cost of living in the college was much more than 'digs' in town and would surely have many distractions that would inhibit study. The temptations of joining fellow students at the local pub, when following the herd and the consumption of beer was almost obligatory, did not appeal. I was conscious that, especially in my first year, I needed to make a good academic start. The out-students soon made their own friendships and felt free to come and go as individuals or small groups as the mood took them. One or two were living at home within easy travelling distance, and a few mature students had families, therefore requiring 'digs' during the week whilst having the weekends free to return home. I had been used to living in full-time accommodation and would return to London during the holidays. This flexibility would enable me to take part in extracurricular activities such as rugby.

I soon palled up with Chris who cycled from home and shared a similar sense of values and humour. We both had come from a town environment and were keen to be fully rural. He too had a regard for careful financing and would only very occasionally visit a pub. It was some surprise when he arrived at the college one morning in a Rolls-Royce. He had merely mentioned in our first lecture that he had come by car, which I had taken to mean his father had dropped him off. At our morning break in the common room he said there was just time to see his car; there it stood, next to the cycle shed.

"Chris, surely that's not yours!" I gasped.

"Sure is," was his simple reply.

"Have you won the pools?"

We broke through the small knot of admirers and Chris unlocked the driver's door, surely the proof of ownership, and started the engine. The gathering crowd stood back. He opened the driver's side bonnet and we peered in: a quiet genius of engineering; there was even silence from the knot of admirers.

It was lunchtime before I could speak further to Chris about his acquisition.

"Where did you get it? I mean, what's the story?" I was lost for words.

"I blew my whole travel allowance," Chis replied. Apparently he had been awarded a travel allowance as he lived just over three miles from Writtle Agricultural College. "I get fifty pounds a year to travel from home and thought a car was better than bus or bike."

"Cor, that's an understatement!" I exclaimed. "But what did it cost?"

"Fifty pounds," he said, adding somewhat coyly, "It does take a lot of petrol!"

We examined the inside; the rear seat had ample leg room even with the fold-down seats in use.

"You could have a whole team in here," I enthused.

"We could have a party," suggested Chris more thoughtfully. Then he reflected sadly, "Realistically I won't be coming in this every day. The garage were quite pleased to sell it; it seems an old Rolls doesn't have many takers. Probably the cost of fuel is a major issue, not to mention possible repairs."

That evening a few of us had a tour of the village in the Rolls, Chris proudly at the wheel... and its bulbous brass horn alerting the whole neighbourhood. Having roused most inhabitants, it was surely worth parking prominently at the pub and sinking a pint.

I had found 'digs' with a retired couple only a mile into Chelmsford. They had no family but treated me as one of their own. I had a room that I could sleep and study in, and a hot meal with them in the kitchen/diner. Mary was made like a mother even if she had not had the pleasure of being one, at least until I arrived. George was retired in every sense, invalided out of industry on account of his lungs.

"'Mum' speaks and I listen," was his favourite phrase.

"Get on with you," was Mum's retort.

I never discovered whether they had a family and somehow lost it, or whether Mary 'mothered' everything she came across, including George and me. Although George's thin frame and damaged lungs gave the impression he was not long for this world, he continued to 'roll his own' and cough.

## Books Galore

The college had a good library but rarely the titles on our reading list; perhaps it was inevitable that they were either in great demand or had disappeared into private hands. I needed the text books that were suggested but frankly were too expensive in total. Each lecturer impressed upon us the necessity of their particular subject, and the course could not be done without copious research. Chris had obviously chosen transport as his priority; I would need to dig deep into my savings for books. The head of Animal Husbandry was a canny Scot, an acknowledged master yet practical in his subject and economic with his prepared handouts. He brought to our notice a national essay competition sponsored by an agricultural feed merchant. I took special note that the prize was a hundred pounds' worth of books, surely worth the effort of an essay. Chris thought he had enough books to research but I was motivated by the prize. Entrants were guided to extol the benefits of good farming and intelligent use of manufactured feedstuffs.

My subject reflected good pasture management and quality concentrate feeds for calves. I made reference to André Voisin's research into paddock grazing and creep feeding. To my astonishment, I won the prize; to my relief, I received my library of choice. I had to suffer the embarrassment of the presentation by a beaming principal and his recommendation for fervent study, hence the reputation of a 'swot'. Whatever the flack, I had wonderful books that I could never have purchased. It occurred to me that the prize was worth about two Rolls-Royces. In making my choice I had covered more or less every aspect of farming and management for my complete course. I believed the Lord still had His hand on me. Whatever branch of farming I had missed out working on practically was now covered comprehensively in books. Although students were not required to do any practical work, the college farm demonstrated good practice. I soon introduced myself to the head of the Poultry Unit and gained valuable basics without getting dirty.

## Rag Day

Care was taken to securely pen sheep on a trailer without giving the impression they were imprisoned. The students from farms within the county had done well to clean and groom sundry sheep on their parents' holdings; a couple of goats and two Shetland ponies were also deemed manageable. The local police had insisted no highly bred point-to-point horses were allowed but offered their only mounted officer as a substitute. Other floats gaily decorated and advertising veterinary surgeries and animal feed companies were keen to be included. The committee had managed to involve an infant school to have cheery youngsters, suitable penned, under the banner "all creatures great and small".

Great fun was had by all and considerable money collected. The only incident occurred after the main event as we returned to the village, high on excitement and crammed in or on cars to the 'Golden Fleece'. One of our members chose to sit astride a student's Austin A40 which had to stop suddenly, pitching him into the car park. The 'A' of the Austin's badge retained some of his trousers and very nearly much more. The resulting injury to his person needed several stitches and could have affected his marriage prospects. To his embarrassment we were all reminded of the event as he carried a cushion to every lecture for the rest of term.

# 14

# Summer Holidays – Farming

As the summer holidays approached we were told to add to our practical experience if at all possible. I felt in the enviable position that I had been fortunate in my varied experience, but realised I needed to earn money for the next year. Scanning the noticeboard of "Holiday Vacancies", I took the details of an arable farm.

"I was going for that job." My course friend, Roy, was leaning over my shoulder and noted the address I was writing.

"Bad luck, mate," I said, recognising his voice.

"I'm desperate. I haven't done any arable; you've done plenty," he added, justifying himself.

I had some sympathy because Roy, a farmer's son, had only worked at home on his family's dairy farm.

"You just want some cash, don't you?" Roy was in earnest.

"I suppose so," I admitted, giving way for him to apply rather than contest the vacancy.

"Dad would pay you well and I'm jolly sure it would be different from your experience." He had heard of my exploits as cowman.

"OK, can you fix it up?" I relented, having in mind the little I knew about his farm and the thought that his father would be pleased of a student with some experience. It was a reasonable arrangement for us both. The happy outcome was that Mr Herbert took his son's recommendation and agreed to take me on without interviewing me; and Roy got his arable experience.

I arrived at Easterly Farm about midday and was welcomed by Mrs Herbert. She was the picture of a farmer's wife, used to the outdoors and generous by disposition. The plate of sandwiches and mug of tea, verging on a two-pint measure, attested to 'plenty'. She had a convivial air of authority, not overpowering but definitely leaving little room for debate. I had no doubt there would be no emergency she could not handle.

Mr Herbert was out on the farm and would be coming in for his usual cup of tea before the 2 pm start of milking. I rose and shook hands when he came into the kitchen; we had never met but I was about to work for him and live in the farmhouse.

"Thank you for taking a chance on me," I boldly introduced myself.

"I guessed if Roy said you were OK then you would be." He smiled, adding, "I've been training him for long enough."

He was slightly shorter than his wife but wiry and strong in hand. He was a ruddy-faced farmer throughout; his wind-beaten face had long been shielded by his cloth cap. There was such a dividing line from his white scalp that he appeared to be wearing a mask.

"You know a bit about milking, I hear."

I wondered if this was a bit in the interview I had missed. "I have a lot more to learn," I assured him, "but I hope I'll be useful."

"We'll make sure you are." He laughed so loudly, I wondered what he meant.

"I'm sure you can look after yourself." Mrs Herbert took my side.

"Best use Christian names; I'm Alf and the missus is Sarah. You can settle in this morning and then take a look round this afternoon."

"Fine, if you don't mind. I'd like to see what happens so I know a bit before morning milking," I offered.

In the morning we started at about a quarter to six with a mug of tea and a few instructions. Milking was expected to be going by 6 am. There were eighty-five cows in milk and two of us, Alf and me, to share the job. I imagined I was exactly replacing Roy. Alf was a stickler for routine but not a slave driver. The great aim was to be in tune with the cows; they were the important ones, even regarded as "the governors". Alf recognised this as giving the maximum yield, "putting the cream on top". The cows went to pasture and we cleared up much as I had done at Goblets Farm. The big difference was the ample pasture and the sleek cows. Nine o'clock was breakfast time, and Sarah was as generous as she had been with lunch the day before: two eggs, bacon and mushrooms, with toast offered ad lib. Saturdays I could expect to finish at noon, with Alf's other son Adam doing the afternoon milking with his father. He was a quiet man and content to fall into any job that Dad required. Adam was married to Janet with a young son and lived one field away in a new bungalow. They were independent of the farmhouse but near at hand.

Adam was the principle tractor man and general mechanic, but quite happily fitted in milking whenever called upon. He rarely left the farm, seeming to be hefted there as much as the livestock, possessing an instinct to remain on the same piece of unfenced land as a result of having been bred there for many generations. On Sundays we started an hour earlier, apparently so we could "have time off". I found this to be simply moving the clock forward as no item of daily routine was ignored; no shortcuts, every detail as usual. This of course meant five hours' work before breakfast on Sunday – and how I longed for it. Sarah's speciality was toast like I'd never experienced before. She toasted her home-made bread by simply laying it on the Rayburn's hot plate and slapping the lid down on top of five doorsteps (meaning very thick toast). This was offered on a plate, dripping with butter, whilst she finished off cooking the breakfast. I could only presume she anticipated one of us might collapse without something to go on with.

## The Island

The farm was right on the edge of the east Essex coast and part of the seawall was bordering the yard. Beyond a narrow stretch of salt water was a two-hundred acre island that was used to graze dry stock. The dairy followers spent a lot of their young lives there before their first lactation. It took maximum low tide and 'all hands' to first encourage them up and over the grassy seawall. The next challenge was to patiently ease them to the edge hoping one would test the water, whilst ensuring there was no panicking retreat back to the farmyard. A couple of neighbours were needed to bring up the rear. Care and quiet were the watchwords, as a second effort that day would rarely be successful.

The return from the island, after many weeks of freedom and only sighting humans at fifty yards, presented an even greater carnival. The method was to pen two or three cows near the water's edge on the home-side as a lure. Being low tide, two men could stand mid-stream as 'long stops' for errant heifers testing the bathing. The next step was to corral the loose cows gathering on the island-side. This relied on an inquisitive heifer leading the charge home. Total failure and a full rodeo 'break-back' on the island necessitated the next day penning three cows on the island-side in a small corral before they sighted any relations across the pastures. In the event of no inquisitive heifers, the three cows would have to be released homeward, hopefully encouraging the herd to follow. Alf had learned that patience was a necessity.

Adam had a rowing boat and would cross the water whenever needed, whatever the state of tide, enabling inspection at any time. At lowest tide we could stand in the sea in Wellington boots. He showed me how to 'tickle' dabs[22] by bending mid-stream and gently gliding one's hands just over the seabed, hardly touching it. I stood watching, bucket in hand.

"There." Almost immediately he held out a dab the size of his palm, dropping it into the bucket.

"How did you do that?" I asked in astonishment.

"Just feel the seabed like tissue paper, then when you glaze across a dorsal fin, push it into the mud so it can't escape."

The instructions were simple enough. I tried in vain, then suddenly a fish scurried away. I excitedly told Adam.

"You must push down instantly," he insisted. "*Snap*, it can't wriggle when pressed down hard."

---

[22] a flatfish like a plaice

After a couple of minutes I had one. The joy of achievement. So easy when you know how! We ended up with five or six flatfish like miniature plaice.

"About enough for Mum to cook for supper," he said smiling, and we returned to the yard.

I was fascinated with the twenty-five yards or so of sea and a private island.

I was given permission to use the boat providing I secured it firmly to the pole on the far bank. Alan showed me how to tie a clove-hitch knot and made me repeat it a time or two.

"And always ship the oars." He was very insistent.

When I had a chance at the weekends, I slipped across to another world. There were no regular fields, just some areas of better pasture and others with more wild flowers. Here and there were scraps of rusty fence that had been boundaries and even dried-up ditches. There was an old Dutch barn that was hardly any shelter for the stock. Nature had largely taken over; there were no paths except for those made by the regular ramblings of cattle.

I was not concerned with the cattle; they were in the distance and not worried about me. They were just part of the landscape. There was no sound except the hum of nature getting on with its own business. Bees and other insects were on the wing. Birds were vocal, occasionally a disturbed skylark calling out. I sat on the edge of a dry ditch to observe the scene. In the eyes of most people nothing was happening, but as I lounged there, doing nothing, I simply felt part of the picture. I was vividly aware of the Great Creator. I found myself saying, "Thank You, God."

*Thank You for the beauty and the awareness of Your mighty hand in such diversity and subtle colours.* It was as if God Himself had drawn me across that short water to show me His picture. Away from all distraction I was reminded that His hand was on me. He had answered my stuttering prayers. He had journeyed with me through thick and thin. I was part of nature as much as all around me. I remembered that in the Bible, God examined His work several times and declared it was "good". What affirmation, what love He has for His creation!

I walked further, not along a coastal path but in nature itself. This was surely why I was drawn to farming. I had been given the privilege of being part of food production. Then it struck me: it was more than food; it was a responsibility for tending the environment. He was teaching me to care for all around me. I completed a circle of the island and then rowed back to the mainland.

# 15

# Serious Study

The return to college, after a pleasant change, was an awakening to serious study. The lectures became more focused, requiring a hunger for depth. The training was for the practical farmer, able to deal with any situation due to knowing the science and improvising when no other help was available. This was exemplified by a visiting lecturer and practising vet. He bounced into the room as if the wind had blown him gale force, then stripped off his jacket, displaying bright-red braces over his tailored shirt, holding up cavalry twill trousers. Sticking his thumbs behind the braces he announced, "These do not necessarily denote my voting intentions, but they may come in useful for restraint of most animals smaller than a cow. That is lesson one."

He certainly had all our attention, but what was lesson one?

"Don't jump to conclusions," he answered our thoughts. "Observe the patient carefully. Contrary to popular opinion, animals do talk."

His arrival had proved his professional credentials. We had all noticed that vets scarcely had time to pull on the handbrake before leaping out of the car. I had assumed the concern was to arrive before the animal died but later understood 'time was money'. Maybe that was lesson two?

The vet had introduced himself as Harry and mentioned his practice address. Now he was dispensing valuable knowledge.

"I always appreciate you watching the patient carefully before lifting the phone so I am briefed as accurately as possible before arriving." Having our rapt attention he continued, "What will you be thinking about having called the surgery?"

"The bill," came an anonymous shout.

"Ah, I bet your father taught you that." Harry was not to be outdone. "You will be thinking how will the patient be sufficiently restrained?" he said, adding, "I hope Dad answered that and has all the latest equipment to aid the vet. Private medical care for an injured vet will certainly add to the bill."

This ready wit was received by us all, impressing the need for our personal safety and that of all those coming onto the farm. Having established a rapport with us, Harry's weekly lectures continued through various animal ailments in a very practical way. We were left in no doubt where our responsibilities ended and the timely intervention of a vet started. It instilled a mindset of clear thinking and the need to use specialists in other aspects of management as the need arose.

In spite of Harry's self-assured start, he soon became a favourite among us for his down-to-earth approach, often against himself. This was soon evident when he dealt with pigs, announcing they were not his favourite animals as they were capable of dying before showing symptoms. Nor had his veterinary training equipped him with all the answers. He recalled that his first solo visits on farms often required returning to the boot of his car several times. This was to thumb through a textbook on symptoms and treatments. His dislike of pigs was based on them squealing as soon as they were touched and their death wish. In his estimation, if a pig was ill it would be unlikely to need a visit the following day. He also admitted that the limited treatments available in 1960 amounted to little more than an antibiotic and hope.

Although academic study and passing exams was increasingly the main focus, I had to make time for some social life. I was a member of the Young Farmers and lived near enough to take part in their activities. My friendship with Hazel (more of whom later) was growing, and I regularly joined her and the family at the weekend. I could not afford a car but had a scooter which was an advance on cycling. Further freedom came with the use of her farm's pick-up, which was offered as "safer than two wheels" in her mother's eyes. I was also conscious that my ongoing 'weed collection' had been sadly neglected. This happy conjuncture proved to be much more appealing when two of us were hunting wild flowers.

Farm management came into prominence in the final year, joining husbandry subjects together. I was thrilled with reading around the necessity of balancing the business and cash flows. The use of contractors and agronomists as a resource in addition to regular staff could free up the manager to run the farm business. It was even impressed on us that if the manager did not manage, then nobody else would. He was responsible for the direction and profitability of the business.

Amid all the activity and learning, the exams loomed. It was like a fog clearing and the real world coming into focus. We had to sit the College Diploma exams, which were intended to be a stiff prelude to the national qualification. This was taken as a matter of the college's academic rigour and proudly maintained.

I managed to pass this hurdle due to my varied farm experience and prepared to sit the National Diploma in Agriculture at Leeds University. The college had made all the arrangements for the agricultural department students to sit the exams, including booking accommodation. My group of friends thought we would stick together and opted for a large house able to take six. Double rooms with twin beds were apportioned by the landlady as we mounted the stairs and peeled off in twos. I had paired up with Oliver and took the last room across the landing.

"This has only got a double bed!" Oliver exclaimed.

"I can't offer you anything else." She looked surprised.

Oliver and I looked at each other with blank expressions.

"It's a big bed," she proffered.

The exam was the next morning; we could not afford to be choosy.

Oliver, who was tall, said, "It will fit me... if you don't mind sharing."

We dumped our overnight gear and all took the landlady's recommendation of a reasonable restaurant nearby. She was used to students and we found it was reasonable value for the financially challenged. The meal over, the discussion was, where do we hit town? Not knowing anything of the area, the majority vote was for a pub crawl. Oliver and I were reluctant and decided to do our own thing. We wandered a couple of streets and settled on a coffee bar.

"I think those two are eyeing us up," Oliver murmured.

"I doubt it," I said taking a nonchalant glance. "Anyway, I prefer Hazel."

"Well, I am married," Oliver announced.

We both agreed we didn't want any distractions – we had come to Leeds for a purpose.

We moved to another coffee bar. The talk was mostly about future employment, avoiding all thought of the next day. One coffee led to another until it was reasonable to return, thinking of bed. We didn't see our mates until breakfast, bleary-eyed and asking the landlady for aspirin. The idea had been that Oliver and I would not be in such a state, but in fact we had hardly slept due to the quantity of caffeine innocently imbibed. We learned from our mistakes and completed the week in Leeds.

Back at college things were quickly running down. The air was relaxed, the exams were behind us and lectures and reports were completed. Remarkably, all six of our group passed our exams and were free to conquer the world. We discussed in the common room, "What next?" It didn't seem right to just go our separate ways and join the employed straight away. We needed a holiday, something appealing to us all before returning to the home farm or job applications.

# 16

# New Life for All

Oliver had to return to his family. Chris suggested touring together but there was no agreement as to where to tour. I suggested the common link we had was farming, so why not see what Russian farming was like; none of us had been there. That was voted such a bright idea that I had better arrange it. It was soon evident that one did not waltz into the USSR as one does Butlins. In-Tourist had to agree to every aspect. My letter had been passed around various offices and returned stamped in red. It seemed we failed on every point. Four young men in a car with no specific purpose, although I had mentioned educational establishments, had no chance of entry. Naive as we were, what was wrong reaching for the moon?

More realistically we arranged a six-day trip to Denmark and the Netherlands, thinking one country would not be enough. We again sought universities to advise on places to visit bearing in mind we were agricultural students just postgraduate. I had specified that our main area of interest in the Netherlands would be the use of polders[23] and in Denmark aspects of the pig industry. I can only imagine this audacious approach, without any real knowledge of the work they might have been engaged in, must have been passed around various departments like a hot potato. In spite of my best handwriting and assumption they would forgive the use of English throughout, I received a reply: something could be arranged if we specified the area of interest and the day of arrival from a list that they offered. This, although welcomed, made us apprehensive that we were launching ourselves into the unknown. What we had envisaged as a jolly trip seeing foreign farming at the end of our studies was getting out of hand. We met round a pint and maps of the Netherlands and Denmark, away from common room banter and 'helpful' suggestions.

"The first thing we need is a car."

Robert had always been part of the out-student group but there in the background. Now he had voiced the obvious that nobody else had dared to state.

"We could use Chris's car?" Robert suggested.

"Never afford the fuel; anyway, what would they think, us turning up in a Roller?" I interjected.

---

[23] land recovered initially from the sea

"It's gone." Chris announced.

"Gone where?" I was surprised Chris hadn't told me.

"Back to the garage it came from." It appeared a sensitive subject. "I couldn't afford it."

"Well, that answers that," Robert concluded, his suggestion quashed.

"None of us has a car." I stated the obvious.

A moment of reflection. We realised public transport was out of the question, being too slow and expensive.

"It's just possible Dad might lend me his car," Roy added tentatively.

We all looked in amazement.

"Really?" Chris was a little brighter.

"Mind you, I can't be sure." Roy was backtracking.

"The next thing is money." Robert was excelling himself. "It will cost a lot with bed and breakfast and fuel."

The whole idea was being called into question. It was not a trip we had to make and I did not have endless funds. We noted the most direct route in both countries and measured the distance to travel. It certainly would stretch us. Roy promised to ask his father that evening, and we folded the maps. We were all disappointed.

Roy announced the next day his father had agreed to lend us the family car. We were all amazed.

"Mind you, we've got to be really responsible; it wasn't easy."

We all in turn clapped Roy on the back as if he had won a marathon.

"He said he knew Peter from the summer job and hoped – no, *expected* – the other two to be steady," Roy announced.

I was ribbed as "steady Pete" but could put up with that after Roy's father, Alf, had been so generous. I had only worked for him for about nine weeks in place of Roy as he had needed arable experience. It later emerged that Alf wanted to show how pleased he was that his son had achieved the arable training he never had had the chance to experience himself.

The trip was arranged in detail and we all turned up at Easterly Farm, our bags packed as soon as possible on leaving college. I had seen the car before, but Robert and Chris were staggered. They were packing their bags into the latest Vauxhall Velox Cresta and we were all insured to drive it. We set off to the ferry with great care not to scratch any part of the car. There was a general air of elation; exams were behind us and ahead lay days of new interest. It was as if all burdens had been lifted. We stayed in pensions and wandered through villages when we had covered enough miles in the car. The plan was to arrive at the university on the third day.

On the evening before the visit we found a suitable restaurant-cum-bar and the conversation turned to what to expect.

"I guess they will show us around the labs and maybe some trials," Chris suggested.

"What did your letter say?" Roy asked me.

"Well, I just said we were interested in water use and glasshouse crops." I was rather embarrassed that I hadn't consulted the others or been more specific in our request. At the back of my mind had been a general understanding of Dutch farming and any modern developments.

"That's OK, but what's in it for them?" Although Robert had always been the quiet one, he had a reputation of thinking outside the box.

"What do you mean? It's their job." Roy added his weight.

I was concerned we had been selfish. Here were four students, not connected to the university, asking for favours outside term time. At least, it could be seen that way.

"We weren't asked to pay," Chris offered, but Robert interrupted.

"We need to give the main one something at the end."

The question now was what to give and what that would add to our meagre budget. We discounted flowers, although perhaps that would be appropriate if the lecturer were female.

"If we gave flowers it would look as if she had won something." Roy was on shaky ground.

"She may think you fancy her," was another unhelpful suggestion.

"I wrote to a male professor," I added. "This could arise for each visit and some are farmers."

Robert surfaced again with, "What about a bottle of whisky and cigars?"

"We can't afford all that." Chris was the sort who expected a Rolls-Royce should only cost fifty pounds.

"If we have a bottle of whisky and cigars in the car, we can quickly pop and get the most appropriate thing as we are saying thank you." Robert didn't mention flowers as they seemed fraught with innuendo or wilting tendencies. We managed to purchase both at the restaurant ready for the morning.

We were cordially welcomed at reception by the professor, who spoke perfect English, and being so used to students, he put us at ease. He conducted us through various static exhibits demonstrating damming and draining processes that had reclaimed land from the sea. These had become fertile polders in a country where much of the surface area was below sea level. He also gave a great resume of Dutch cropping practices. We were surprised at the size of the national glasshouse sector and its ability to export worldwide. Unable to establish whether cigars were appropriate or not, we ended up presenting him with a bottle of whisky and many thanks.

We motored on to Denmark, starting in Copenhagen for a day or two of tourism. Accommodation was difficult to find at our sort of price. Eventually we found rooms above a shop. The landlord showed us up a staircase on each floor, eventually arriving at the fourth. This we assumed was it, but he indicated another flight of stairs into the roof. The room had the contours of the roof rather than side walls. The four single beds were comfortable, provided one did not sit up quickly. We were shown the exterior fire escape and probably the best aerial view of Copenhagen.

Our visits to Aarhus and a bacon factory gave us a background to the importance of pig production and their drive to economic efficiency. The visit to two family-run pig units astonished us with their attention to detail and was our practical introduction to what is now called 'factory farming'.

The trip ended and we naturally thanked Roy's parents with whisky and flowers. Indeed, their generosity and sheer faith in four students testing their car will never be forgotten.

## Finding a Job

College and educational trip behind us, employment was essential. We went our separate ways; some to firms serving agriculture, others to practical farming. Some went back to the family business. I had to find another route. I looked at vacancies in the *Farmers Weekly* but could find nothing that I felt would advance my career. Equally, I was not qualified for jobs at the start of the management ladder.

I had to ask the Lord for help. My spiritual life had been neglected. I recognised I had only attended church spasmodically but that did not mean I could not pray. God had heard my calls for help from the toilet back in my childhood. The truth was I had relied on my own judgement without any spiritual thought. I knew the Bible teaches the need for faith and a relationship with Jesus. Just expecting my needs to be met in a fire-fighting mode wasn't good enough. I had to ask for forgiveness, being truly sorry that I had neglected Him. I remembered the Book of Jeremiah tells us God has plans for faithful believers (Jeremiah 29:11). I recalled that through thick and thin He had provided me with all I needed to get my qualifications, so why falter now?

"Jesus, please keep Your hand on me. I know You have never promised life would be easy. I can't manage it without You. Please find me the right job, the one You want me to have. Amen."

The answer came a week later. I felt I should ask the agricultural college for their suggestions. The head of the agricultural department looked at my experience and noted my exam success.

"The problem you have is there is no accepted route to farm management. Indeed, the manager of one farm may not be successful on another. The only person who might help you is our farm's manager, David." He gave clear and positive advice that I would act upon.

I made an appointment to meet David who ran the farms as a commercial business but within the constraints of demonstrating good current practice. He told me his career path from student, to some laboratory work, and a spell running a farm for ex-offenders. I listened with interest but was thinking I would have to go back to the Situations Vacant page. David ended with a question:

"Would you like a job here?"

"What sort of job?" I was wide-eyed.

"General farm work, all enterprises… really, helping me."

I accepted immediately.

"I'll clear it with the principal. Consider you've had the interview."

David smiled. So did I.

That evening I praised the Lord, thanking Him with a full heart. Out of nothing, I had not known there was a vacancy, nor had the head of agriculture, but then he was in charge of academic studies. I phoned David's house the next day asking when he wanted me to start so that I could arrange for new accommodation.

"All is OK," he confirmed. "The principal was pleased I had engaged an ex-student."

"Great, when do you want me to start? I need to find some 'digs'," I asked.

"Oh, there is a small cottage vacant in the village if you want it."

Unbeknown to him, David had answered all my prayers – or, I should say, the Lord had. I moved in that week and started work the following Monday. Surely God had not only answered my prayer again, He had put His signature on it! A job without even an interview; helping the manager, although that was not in the job description; house provided; timing immediate. Not a detail missed.

I joined four others: the cowman milking on the dairy farm, two elderly tractor drivers and a general farm worker. We looked after the pig unit and arable work, and there was a separate poultry unit. My job was varied and I was kept abreast of management decisions by David. I was able to attend the local Methodist church and settle into a less frenetic working week. There was adequate labour for the farming and the extra brush and pan work expected on every demonstration unit.

I settled into the cottage, and the freedom to cook and eat what I liked. It was easy to shop in the village or two miles further on in town. I took up a minor hobby of home wine- and beer-making, and gratefully accepted Hazel's culinary offerings when we met many a weekend. The only thing I missed was the open views and wildness of nature on the more rural farms I had lived on.

The cottage did not have any garden, which was a plus in my bachelor existence, but I did have neighbours which was a novelty. After a few months the pensioner from the other half of the 'semi' knocked on my door bearing an apple pie. I thanked her profusely, admiring the shortcrust pastry and offered to pay for it.

"No, I wouldn't think of it," she insisted. "But I would just say we have a funny smell coming from our cupboard under the stairs."

Before I could offer to check her drains, she added, "My son thinks it's beer."

The awful realisation dawned that I had my beer-making kit under my stairs. I leaped to the cupboard; the yeast had performed very well, indeed exceeding all expectations. I felt as if I should give the pie back. The dear widow looking after her son and minding her own business had not come to complain but to make peace with the offender. A loving reversal of roles.

I was embarrassed, not knowing what to do except of course remove the beer. I returned the plate with a box of Maltesers, thinking a bottle of beer or wine would be inappropriate. The lady accepted it graciously but had another pie "just out of the oven" which she insisted I take.

On Sunday evenings I had taken to regular church attendance and cultivated a friendship with John, a trainee accountant. He was thoroughly urban and I regarded myself as a 'country man' by adoption. Maybe our friendship stemmed from my roots being urban London or perhaps it was the attraction of opposites. We would join together at the back of the church by the wall, summarising the week. The services were traditional and we enjoyed each other's company.

On one occasion there was a visiting preacher who was lively and spoke in a very down-to-earth manner about the essentials of the Christian life. At the end of the last hymn he asked the congregation a surprising question: "Do you really love Jesus?" Then he said, "If you do, come down to the front." It struck me as an impossible request, because why would we be there if we did not love Jesus? In addition, how did he expect the whole congregation to move to the front?

I turned to John who was just impassive.

"Come on."

He didn't move.

"Well, I'm going," I said.

I thought it was the only honest thing to do. Jesus had proved Himself real and answered my prayers; of course I loved Him. It wasn't easy; hardly anybody moved. I had to push past about six people to get to the central aisle. I looked back but John was stood eyes to the front, not moving. I walked down to the front where there were a couple of teenagers.

The minister repeated the question and I looked back, but nobody else had budged. I wondered why nobody joined us; perhaps I had misunderstood.

We were led through to a small side room and asked if we believed in Jesus and really loved Him. I said yes to all this and a little more about how He had answered my prayers. The minister then prayed over us and gave us a small booklet, *The Gospel of Mark*. John must have gone home, so I went back to my house. I didn't feel any different but was proud that I had stood up for Jesus. If

I hadn't obeyed the minister I would not only have been dishonest but would have disowned Jesus.

My time on the college staff was easy physically and engaging academically. It rounded off the side issues of practical management, revealing the necessary compromise between the theory of optimum production versus personal or institutional aims. This would be useful later in my career when landowners insisted they required maximum profit from their holding. Practically it was often the case that shooting, fishing, 'rare breeds' and other interests were at least equally important.

After about eighteen months I was thinking of a move to progress my management ambition. David agreed there was no opportunity internally but he would support me with references.

# 17

# Assistant to the Owner

David had suggested the likely first step for me was to work as an assistant to a manager. He had provided something of this experience and now it was time to go further. It was difficult to find this sort of halfway step into management as the farm or business had to be large enough to warrant such an employee.

It was interesting to read the Situations Vacant pages in the *Farmers Weekly* and imagine the reality behind the gloss. It is much the same as buying a house but at least one has a photograph of the bricks and mortar. I sent my CV to likely appointments and waited for letters or a phone call. Letters mostly came from consultants employed to find the right person. They would be once-removed from the business and more dispassionate in connecting the two parties.

Phone replies were the usual 'farmer' mode of contact. This had the advantage of being able to exchange questions before either party committed to an interview. It was often the background sounds that gave hints, even colour, to the situation at the other end. If there was a baby crying in the background, it might indicate the age of the farmer, whilst two kids fighting in the kitchen being separated by an irate mother would indicate a degree of chaos. Equally, a farmer breaking off to shout some obscenity to a tractor driver across the yard gives a negative impression.

I was always pleased to get an interview where first impressions of the farmyard said a lot about the business and its owner. The state of any equipment spoke of the attitude of the employer, which usually meant his appreciation of staff would be similar. The age of the machinery was a good indication of the amount of capital available to the business. If there was a chance to have an extended interview or even a trip around the farm, it showed promise that at least I was worthy of the time spent. The state of the crops and livestock told their own story.

Consultants often favoured the 'party' approach with up to ten candidates interviewed at the same time. There would be the trip around the farm on a trailer for the group. This would demand each candidate rising above the others to be chosen for the final shortlist. Depending on the type of job on offer, did one jump off the trailer at the first closed gate to show willingness in opening it for the tractor driver or studiously ignore his plight as it was his job? It is even more embarrassing when two or three of the ten interviewees jump off at the same time to open the gate. Have they lessened their chances by covering their shoes in mud or enhanced them by showing themselves willing?

I applied for an assistant's job on a six-hundred-acre Lankly farm  in Oxfordshire and got an interview. It was a dull, wet day and I was seen separately. The farm was fairly flat with large fields, the buildings large to accommodate the tonnages involved. There was little clue about machinery but I assumed it was elsewhere. The farmer was workman-like with a hands-on approach, which I took to be a good sign. He drove across fields in a Volkswagen pick-up which would be more economic to run than a Land Rover. I was offered the job and was shown a bungalow on the farm as my accommodation, which needed a new floor in the bedroom.

I started after working out a month's notice at the college farms. The bungalow was in the same state as I had seen it, but with only myself to please, I slept on a bed in the lounge for the first few weeks. I had experienced less than ideal situations in other houses and felt I could put up with a little inconvenience.

My first job was to get acquainted with the hatching egg enterprise. The farmer showed me the two fields of portable chicken houses and how to collect the eggs from the laying boxes on the side of the huts. There was also a small pack-house where I would rub the eggs clean with sandpaper and store them, two and a half dozen per tray. There were also washing facilities for scrubbing and sterilising the metal nest box parts. The only other employee was a shepherd, Tim, whom I had not seen when interviewed. He also doubled as a tractor driver.

After a couple of weeks I found it reminiscent of Goblets Farm where I had been cowman. Tim became a friend in need much as Joe had been. He was slim, wiry, about forty and a bachelor. The open-air life shepherding had weathered his appearance, and his eyes were small and dark as if peering into the distance. His flat cap covered most of his forehead as if resting on his eyebrows. Importantly, his nature was one of being the patient shepherd and able to stand up to the boss, Mr Thomas, when necessary. It was a month before Mr Thomas announced he was going to "do" the bedroom floor. He did it all himself without Tim or me being involved. The first day he spread hot bitumen all over the concrete base and six inches up the walls. Two days later he concreted the area leaving it to mature. About a week later I had the use of the room, bare concrete, and moved the bed into it. This was an improvement but cool to my feet, coolly reminiscent of Mrs Baker's but without the lino.

In the cold and wet winter months I had to sterilise the galvanised plates that assembled into metal boxes for the laying nests. This was achieved by lighting a fire under an old-fashioned boiler to get hot water. The next process was scrubbing the plates on a draining-board arrangement until spotless. The hot water was as much as my rubber gauntlets could stand, but it was a warm job in an otherwise cold existence. Mr Thomas looked in on my second day of the big clean, obviously not in a happy mood. He examined the cleaned plates, draining on the side before being stacked away, unable to find any fault.

"You should have done more than these," he growled.

"I did all that lot yesterday." I pointed to probably a couple of hundred stacked by the wall.

"Put more vigour into it and more wood on the fire," he ordered.

I turned to check the fire and was knocked into the heap of chopped wood.

"What was that for?" I gasped as I picked myself up.

"You slipped."

"You pushed me!" I retorted in my shock.

"Just get on, and fast." He raised his voice.

"Just a minute, Mr Thomas. I know when I am pushed."

"You said you played rugby; what are you complaining about?"

"I did, and I know a shoulder charge." I was trying to restrain myself, knowing this was a fight I could not win. I fancied my chances physically but knew my CV would be blotted.

This was not the first time Mr Thomas had urged greater vigour and output, which I should have seen as a character trait before joining him. I confided in Tim, who said nobody could do enough to satisfy him.

"Is he the same with you?"

"He has tried it on," Tim conceded.

"Have you confronted him?" I asked

"I don't think you can change him. I have never found out his problem; after all, there's only the two of us on six hundred acres," Tim observed.

"You put up with it then?" I felt angry; Tim was a good worker.

"I am a shepherd and do a fair bit of ploughing and tractor work," said Tim. "He and I both know I am too valuable."

"That doesn't make it right or fair," I steamed.

"I like the village and get plenty of overtime," Tim reasoned. "Besides, I keep out of his way as much as possible."

In the slack times Mr Thomas would take over the egg collection and I would be sent stone-picking. Most of the arable fields were 'brashy', from small pebbles to stones the size of saucers. I was given a tractor and ex-WWII bomb trailer without any sides. The task was to drive onto the young barley crop and pick off the surface stones, leaving only pebbles. I worked round both sides of the trailer and then moved on. This was back-breaking and totally boring, relieved only when the trailer was full and its contents were to be shovelled off onto an adjacent concrete pad. The stone was to be used as hardcore when need arose. I was able to push myself to fill two loads in the morning, have my sandwiches, and then fill a further two in the afternoon. This gave a little incentive with only the thought "Another half hour and it will be full" or "Only another ten minutes and it will be full". I expressed my boredom to Mr Thomas, asking how necessary it was. His repost was he could do five loads a day.

I refrained from suggesting that he would therefore do better if we swapped jobs but the seed had been sown; I knew I had been sucked into the wrong employment. I had not achieved any advance in learning or experience and it was time to move again. I had given it a respectable time that should not have harmed my CV. I had to scan the newspapers afresh. I realised I had been struggling through porridge, the sort that is lumpy and sticky. It had made me stronger and wiser.

By a refreshing turn of fortune, I quickly obtained another job interview. The problem was to have a weekend off from collecting eggs and attend the Saturday interview without arousing Mr Thomas's suspicion.

My transport situation had greatly improved; I now had a car. The days of my bicycle, and then the scooter, were sufficient at the time but now a car was essential for the country dweller. I had looked for something reliable and within my budget. The local garage near the college had about six or seven assorted vehicles and I expressed interest in a Ford Popular. It was not an exciting choice but would probably fit my requirements. "Nothing much to go wrong," the mechanic said which warmed my interest, but at £120 it was at the top end of my budget. After a little bargaining and nothing to part exchange we agreed on £110.

I loaded my suit and clean brogues the evening before and set off Saturday morning in casual attire for a weekend off. Littlehampton was about a hundred and forty miles away and I had listed the towns that I would need to pass through, to save map reading. I would need to hurry to make the interview by one o'clock. Mid-morning I found a lay-by and hurriedly changed into my suit and shoes. It was beginning to rain and the Saturday morning shoppers further slowed the journey. By 11.30 am I was anxious that I would be late. The car had one fault that had not been disclosed: the windscreen wipers were pneumatically driven from the engine. In practice this meant the faster the car travelled, the slower the wipers. When I put my foot down on a clear road the wipers would stop altogether. This may have been a cunning ploy by the road safety engineer at Fords to limit the driving speed on wet roads.

I became more concerned that not only would I be late but the excuse "My windscreen wipers were not fast enough" seemed lame. I looked out for a telephone box to inform the firm of my hold-up. This too I discounted as a further delay. I had asked the Lord for guidance in finding a new job and had been rewarded with an interview with my first application. Now it seemed to be unravelling minute by minute. Surely it was a cardinal sin to arrive late for an interview, especially when I had asked it be moved to a Saturday afternoon.

# 18

# New Horizons

Eventually I drove into a private road leading to the office entrance of Mayhurst Farm; it was all shut. What else could I expect; I should have left Oxfordshire earlier. There was an elderly man hoeing the roses in front of the office block. "Excuse me, I'm looking for Mr Morris." The old man straightened up.

"You'll be Mr Jennings," he said.

"Yes, sir." I was staggered at hearing my name.

We shook hands. I could see now he was dressed in a pinstriped suit and black shoes. I followed him into the reception and along to the main office which he unlocked, ushering me in. Putting the hoe next to a coat rack, he sat in the plush chair behind a huge polished desk with nothing on it except a telephone and a Bible. I was offered the chair opposite him, astonished at an office with no paper, pens or paraphernalia normally associated with commerce.

"I am so sorry I'm late, sir." I would have apologised earlier if I had realised who he was.

"I expect it was a difficult journey." He was softly spoken and without a word of criticism.

He opened a drawer and pulled out my application.

"Tell me more about yourself. I see you were at school in London."

I listed my journey from leaving school, filling in a few details of my farming experience. It seemed he wanted me to speak, probably learning more about me than the face value of the list of farm jobs.

"Are you a Christian?"

I was surprised by his straightforward approach. "Yes, sir." I hesitated somewhat.

"We are a Christian firm," he announced. "You don't have to be a Christian to work here, but we do enjoy Christian fellowship as much as possible."

He reached for the Bible and read from Hebrews 10:25: "...not giving up meeting together, as some are in the habit of doing, but encouraging one another – and all the more as you see the Day approaching."

"Some of us worship at the Brethren chapel and you would be welcome at our gospel service." Mr Morris smiled and turned to his own history. "Let me tell you a little about the firm. We – that is, my parents and I – came from Devon to farm here and we brought the whole farm up on a train; the animals and machinery, all sorts of feed, some hay, all on the train, to start afresh here."

Mr Morris explained some of the other businesses they were involved in, but quickly returned to the farming operation.

"I will show you the yard here and then the farm," he said as if it were his passion.

We left the office and turned to the side of the building, and got into a sedate Rover saloon. Instead of driving down to the main road, we turned to the left and into a complex of corn merchants' buildings and large areas of concreted yard. Without getting out of the car, Mr Morris waved his hand, pointing to the seed-cleaning plant and, on the other side, "The animal feeds are made here." He turned in a large circle towards another huge building with most of its roller shutters down. Under a roofed area, which he called a Dutch barn, were about a dozen Thames Trader lorries, which seemed to be announcing, "This is our wholesale vegetable department."

It was so unexpected. I had met an elderly man hoeing roses, before noticing he was in a smart suit. We had sat each side of a desk with only a phone and a Bible. I had been asked if I was a Christian and been told he was a farmer. Here he was showing me an empire. I had no questions to ask Mr Morris, but was simply trying to digest what I had experienced.

"The workshops are behind us," he continued.

The Rover purred out of the yard to the main road and ten minutes later into a farm drive. We stopped at a modern farmhouse and collected the farm manager.

"This is my nephew, Mr Wells," he introduced him as he climbed into the rear seat.

I made as if to get out and offer Mr Wells the front seat.

"We are only going up the lane." Mr Morris's arm restrained me.

The meeting seemed so tidy and prearranged. No knocking at the farmhouse door or going around to the back entrance. In fact, no farm litter or pieces of machinery to be welded. No children's bikes or prams, only a small lawn and tidy hedge.

A quarter of a mile further and we were in the farmyard. I got out of the car with Mr Wells, Mr Morris saying he was returning to the office.

"I'll run you back to the office later. I take it your car is there. And by the way, I'm Paul."

The younger Mr Wells was taking over the interview. He was refined and well dressed, little doubt public school, but with the quiet air of benign authority, which soon turned to friendly informality.

"The dairy is here."

We walked in. Milking was just starting.

"Fred, we are just showing Peter the farm," Paul called out.

It seemed strange that Paul should mention me by name. It was as if I was already known or had been there before. We left the 'eight abreast parlour', which looked an advance on the traditional cowsheds I had been used to, and walked on to pasture each side of the lane. Paul said they were young leys[24] in place of what had been permanent pasture. It was to increase milk from grass, part of the new vision in their dairying. He asked about my dairying and how it compared. I was able to say without wishing to flatter that it looked much more progressive as well as cleaner and tidier than my experience.

"We try to keep the whole operation tidy or it is a poor witness to customers of the firm." Paul and the farm were obviously part of the whole business.

We drew up to a level crossing just as a train passed by.

"That was a coincidence." I could have said 'surprise'.

"This is a very busy line." Paul laid serious emphasis: "It's the main London line." Then he added, "I wanted to show it to you because it is so busy."

He opened the level crossing gate, ushered me through, stood still and closed the gate behind us.

"We must look both ways very carefully... then look again," Paul insisted. "Straight over," he continued as we made haste. "Then open this gate," which he secured open. "The idea is to keep cattle shut behind the gate until the opposite gate is fixed open. Then, with men each side on the track to stop escapees, you can finally walk them across."

I could understand the caution.

"Actually, we very rarely use the water meadows for milkers because it is dangerous to get eighty across in one go." It seemed strange that he should give such detail as if I might have to do it the next day.

We walked across two leys to an arable field. It was smaller than the Oxfordshire fields and stood neatly ploughed. I bent down and took a small sample of soil, rubbing it between my fingers.

"It's good to see you do that." Paul was impressed.

"I am interested in how it compares with Oxfordshire and Essex."

I was genuine, having been taught, "It's your heritage, bor," by Mark way back at Fair Oaks Farm. No doubt he, having walked acres behind a horse, could feel through the plough handles when soils differed.

"I suppose you call it medium loam?" I enquired.

"Yes, but a bit of clay in it; most of our fields are similar," Paul replied.

We went through another field, a little higher, with open land and an expansive view to the west.

"That's the Arun over there and the sea to the left." Paul was selling the job to me.

---

[24] fields untilled for some time

We returned to the farmhouse and Paul drove me back to my car at the office, or should I say 'headquarters'.

"Will you take the job here?"

I turned to look at him. "You mean I've been accepted?"

"The governor phoned me before you came up. He was satisfied."

"Yes, please!" I was excited by everything I had seen and it was endorsed by the attitude of both gentlemen. There was no mistaking their integrity; I knew their word was their bond. Paul would surely be easy to work under, and the outstanding character of the owner – managing director, gardener, even in a suit – it spoke volumes.

I thanked Paul and we shook hands, saying I would give my notice in on Monday morning. Paul in return said he would confirm the appointment by letter. I drove back to Banbury in a totally different mood. Gone was the anxiety of being late and apprehension of even having an interview, now replaced by the elation of securing a job that promised just what I had hoped. As I mused over events, I was aware God had answered my prayers again. How did I know that? It was His signature assurance. I had become used to the Lord operating in His perfect timescale. I had been through a difficult testing time but strengthened by it. Now I had been offered a job, after a cursory interview, and no reference from my employer, and additionally asked if I would accept the appointment before even leaving the farm. The outstanding confirmation of His hand was the Bible on the desk. I had never seen an office with not a paper in view, not even a tray of files, only the Word of God and a phone. I laughed out loud, shouting, "Thank you, Lord!" Then a naughty thought: was the phone a direct line? I believe God has a sense of humour.

Mr Thomas did not have a sense of humour. I had written a formal letter giving one month's notice and handed it to him on Monday morning. He open it and read it in front of me.

"I won't take any notice of that." He stuffed it into his pocket and told me to go stone carting.

I had phoned Hazel on the Sunday to tell her the good news. I was back on track with my career and had what amounted to a foreman's job. Things are rarely formal or governed by strictly demarcation in farming. When the unusual happens, there is rarely a rule book to consult; it is expected that whatever your rank you are there to use your common sense in the interests of your employer. Mr Morris had impressed me by being servant-minded. With time on his hands he had not written a memo to the gardener, if he had one, but had used a hoe himself.

I asked if I could visit Hazel the following weekend and stay the night with the family. I had often done this when her father was needing extra help, if only for the weekend, whilst I had free time from college. I had been accepted as a member of the family, as would be common between farming families with cousins helping out in busy periods. Her brothers were my close farming friends but it was obvious there was a great personal attraction to their only daughter. Hazel, being the only girl, had been expected to help her mother rather than her father. She was an inch taller than me and strong enough to compete in most jobs, but there were enough 'boys' about – four in total. Hazel and I had simply grown together rather than having a whirlwind romance; a coming together of common interest.

It had started at Young Farmers. Hazel was nearly three years younger than me but mature and able beyond her years. The YFC had competitive sports as well as dances and stock judging, and I was called on to join her in the mixed doubles. Tennis was not my strong point and I had no training from school days, but how could I refuse to be her partner? My sport had majored on rugby but that was not played by young farmers at that time. Similarly my tennis owed more to strength than finesse. Hazel on the other hand was accomplished and could beat most girls older than her. It was with trepidation that I partnered her as the weaker half of the double, but we won two rounds and reached the semi-finals of the competition. By the following Saturday, and after a morning's practice on her home grass court, I was as ready as I ever would be. Hazel had a powerful service and I was agile, if a little erratic. We won the mixed doubles in the competition and a small cup.

Hazel's family were keen on point-to-point racing, which provided an opportunity to inspect the course together whilst others were engaged in keeping the bookies in business and discussing the potential during the Paddock Parade. There was much to enjoy, not least the picnic lunch in the car park. Hazel and her mother, Joan, had always put together a hamper that only the strong could lift. There were sandwiches for every taste: cheese and cucumber, salmon and cucumber, assortments of tomato, French stick, sausage rolls and fruit cake. Whilst some in the car park competed with popping champagne corks, we were satisfied with Thermoses of coffee.

Hazel's father, Douglas, was keen to the extent of having a couple of his own horses which Raymond, the eldest, jockeyed. The others were keen followers of the hunt and would attend when work permitted. Those were fun days and a great relaxation from farm routine. I was a little more confined to the farmstead if the others were busy with seasonal work or 'contracting' elsewhere. It allowed Hazel and me to be together and steal the odd game of tennis, wander a field or two nearby, or tend the horses. I was prepared to ride the quieter of the horses but nervous of saddling them. I guess this amounted to feeling safe astride but less so at ground level. Whilst I was happy handling cattle, even bulls, horses were dangerous at both ends: either biting or kicking seemed possible without any prior notice. My fears were fed when dragooned into clipping off the bottom half of their coats in spring.

The clipping took place inside the box with Douglas handling the clippers, a neighbouring farmer holding the bridled head, and me as the 'electric' motor. The clippers were run by a cable driven from a portable tripod. I had to turn the handle on this tripod which tuned a solid wire connection activating the clippers. In fact, *I* was the electric motor. The faster I turned the handle, the quicker and better the result.

Unfortunately, the mare resented her box being crowded out with three grown men, on top of which she could remember the episode a year earlier.

The circus began with the noise of the clippers. I was stationed in the middle of the ten-foot-square box, holding the tripod in one hand and turning the handle like fury with the other. It was necessary to hold the tripod in order to dance quickly enough as the mare swung around the box. Douglas was not a man of great patience and would swear every time she flinched. This exacerbated the horse's fear as we cavorted together in circles. My real anxiety was the occasional lashing out of the hind feet which had the power to take planks out of walls. My abiding thought was, is this the cost of love?

I hoped the horses with the bottom half of their coats removed felt more comfortable, and that my part in the job would hopefully be earning 'Brownie points' with Douglas.

The weekend following my successful interview seemed the appropriate occasion to formalise our intention to become engaged. Hazel had alerted her mother and she would try to ensure Douglas would not be out anywhere that evening, not even taking on any pressing job in the workshop. At the end of the evening meal there seemed a suitable moment for me to grab the initiative.

"I would just like to say something." Looking at Douglas I came straight to the point: "We would like to get engaged, and I ask your permission."

There was simply an outburst. "What?" he roared. "What?" He didn't need it repeated, he was incandescent. "Do you think I'm going to let my daughter marry a cowman?"

He strode out of the room and we heard his car start up in the yard. There was silence until it had gone.

Joan started crying and Hazel went over to hold her mother tight. We knew it would be difficult and the answer might well have been "wait". However, Hazel was nineteen and I was twenty-two, with reasonable prospects, and we were not contemplating imminent marriage. It was Douglas's extreme aversion that seemed so shocking. I was not deemed good enough. We had expected to have to wait but this was a disaster. I put my hands both on Hazel and her mother.

"I am sorry." It was all I could think of. "I am going off now. I can't stay till the morning."

Hazel came outside with me and we just hugged and kissed.

"I am so sorry. Take heart. We'll manage, my love. I'll phone you when I get back."

"No, it will be late and we can't be private on the phone." Hazel was so sensible even in this situation. "Let's write to each other."

I agreed and we parted.

On the journey back there was a lot to mull over. We had thought the worst response would have been, "Wait until you are twenty-one." Legally we could get married, but realistically we wanted to please our parents with their concept of 'a decent age'. This, we thought, coupled with my new secure job and house, was an appropriate time. However, it was now proven I was not of the required breeding to be a son-in-law. This did not bode well for family relationships.

Back in Oxfordshire the last month was tense. I did my best to work as if nothing had changed, so that no arguments could arise. It was also prudent to avoid arousing Mr Thomas's temper. If that happened we might both have said things we would regret. I told Tim that I was leaving and he wished me well.

"I guess this isn't the place for you, but I am sorry." There was nothing more Tim could say, as Mr Thomas was crossing the yard. I continued to fill the tractor with diesel.

"There's no time for talking." Mr Thomas was not happy.

"I'll be off right now," I said.

"I expect you to clear that field today."

"I'll do my best, Mr Thomas." I screwed the fuel cap back on the tank and set off with the bomb trailer for more stone picking.

On my last Friday working at the Oxfordshire farm, I turned up to the back door of the farmhouse just behind Tim. This was the usual procedure at five o'clock, whether there was overtime to do or not. Tim received his wage packet and turned his head towards me as he walked away.

"All the best, Peter!"

"Thanks." It was all the chance we had. There was no problem with our somewhat distant relationship, it was simply that we rarely worked together. We had not rehearsed a longer goodbye. It was probable that our employer had not let us get any closer. Whilst I waited on Mr Thomas, Tim mounted his bike and was off.

"You haven't got any wages," Mr Thomas announced.

"What do you mean? I have earned them." I was too surprised to say more.

"I will pay you next week," he said.

"But you know I will not be here next week."

"I told you, I'm taking no notice of that scrap of paper." He closed the door.

"Please forward my wages." I made it sound authoritative just as the door slammed.

I washed and stowed my belongings in the car and wrote my parents' address on a piece of paper. The key to the cottage was wrapped with the address and put in a sealed envelope.

I knocked on the farmhouse door to hand the envelope to Mr Thomas, but there was no answer. I returned to my house to write a note on the envelope: "I have locked the cottage and here is the key." I had rehearsed this simple statement, wanting to make sure the package was handed over, but had to drop it through the letter box. I was leaving that moment, whatever Mr Thomas had in mind.

# 19

# Success – Promotion

After a week at home I started at Mayhurst Farm. I had been allocated a semi-detached house on the farm which was ready to move into, and I was itching to see it. My wages had not arrived from Mr Thomas, but I was starting a new job as trainee foreman in West Sussex. I expected that in practice I would be more of a linkman between workforce and management – something that I never achieved in Oxfordshire. Paul was effectively managing the farm, but there would be times when he was on other business that I would have to make decisions. The very nature of farming requires an overall plan to be known by the workforce, but played out as conditions and situations change. These can change within the hour.

I arrived at Paul's house on the Sunday afternoon and met Ruth and the family. Ruth immediately suggested a cup of tea, whilst Paul filled me in with expectations for work on the Monday. Ruth returned with not only a pot of tea but a tray of sandwiches and various cakes. She announced that they would be off to chapel at six and I should take the plates with me "so as to settle in".

My car was so full, passenger seats and the boot, that Paul had to walk the two hundred yards to open the door to my new abode. It was a modern semi-detached house built sideways to the main road, and I would occupy the semi at the field end. Paul entered first, showing me each room, starting with the living room. I noted the modern 'picture window' overlooking the small paddock across to the farmhouse; the dining room looking out to the field at the rear. The kitchen was larger than I had been used to and surely a delight to any woman. I noticed a cooker and refrigerator and a tray of groceries on the worktop.

"I can't believe it." I must have been open-mouthed.

"Ruth thought you might need cereals and bread before you could get to the shops." Paul opened the fridge door revealing a jug of milk. "She would like the jug back when you've finished," he simply added.

"Of course. I'm overwhelmed!" I confessed.

"We get our milk from the farm but I know the milkman calls, so ask Mrs Schumann next door and she will tell him to call on you too." Paul was almost apologetic that I would not be entitled to milk from the farm.

"Yes, and thank you for everything. Let me pay you for…"

Paul interrupted, "Ruth certainly won't take anything."

He gave me the spare key, saying the other one was in the front door, and departed.

I unloaded the car before it got dark. I had my sleeping bag and two folding chairs, two saucepans and a frying pan; belongings indispensable for any bachelor. I unloaded a couple of odd casual chairs that I had acquired into the front room, one upholstered and the other wooden with arms; exiles from student days. Finally, my radio and a box of opened groceries that I had not been prepared to leave with Mr Thomas. It flashed through my mind that I had not received my wages in spite of threatening legal proceedings. I settled down in the front room, which had carpet and curtains and plain emulsion on the walls. Well, this was home. I didn't mind the sparsity of furniture and I could get a bed in a week or two, but mostly it felt much better than where I had come from. There were all the signs that the Lord had answered my prayer and guided me to where I should be.

The next morning I walked past the farmhouse and through a small yard to the main dairy and farm buildings. Dennis was already there waiting for Paul to arrive at 7.30 am.

"You're my next-door neighbour," Dennis greeted me.

I nodded. "I'm Peter." We shook hands as Paul drove up.

"You've met, I see. Peter only arrived last night," Paul addressed Dennis.

"Yes, Carol doesn't miss much; she saw you go in." Dennis had in mind the picture windows. "Do you want the milkman to call?" he turned to me.

"Oh yes, I was going to ask; I guess, a pint a day."

"There, fixed already." Paul smiled. "Now, Dennis, can you get all you want for the fencing job and I'll just introduce Peter to Fred."

"Most of it is still on the trailer but I'll get more stakes," Dennis said as he went off.

In the parlour Fred was halfway through the milking. Amid the background of the vacuum motor and the sucking and syphoning, he stuck his hand out.

"Good to meet you. We'll have to chat later." He was well built and had a rosy complexion; the hallmark of plenty of milk and sun. The air of friendly ease from all three was in contrast to the strained relations in Oxfordshire.

Paul drove off and I joined Dennis on the tractor as he came through with the fencing trailer. We both dismounted at the crossing gate.

"We have to be really careful here," Dennis cautioned.

"I know. I had a lecture when I was interviewed," I smiled.

"It's OK with just a tractor; it's stock that's dangerous," Dennis went on undeterred. "Look up and down and then open the far gate."

I took care and obeyed, then shouted and waved him across.

He got off the tractor safely beyond the gate.

"You look carefully and close the farm side," Dennis instructed.

We pushed the field gate shut together.

"Yer have to look every time… Never cross without making sure no train is in sight." It was a repeat of Paul's caution, but then Dennis added, "If you have an animal escape, you must run to that box." He pointed to a white box about twenty yards away by the side of the track. "Just lift the phone and speak. It goes straight to the signal box."

We returned to the trailer.

"These are the water meadows and we mostly have dry stock or make hay here," Dennis continued.

"Are they really water meadows?" I asked.

"Dunno, they may have been once… Not now," he replied as we moved along the cart track.

The old barbed wire was rusty due to the sea air and was broken in many places. It was going to be a big job to replace the fencing in all four fields. The pasture was a mixture of old grasses peppered with docks. Dennis had obviously spent some time taking down the old wire; the job was now replacing the unsound posts and straining up new wire.

It was strangely quiet; no road noise, only the sound of nature if one listened carefully. We seemed suddenly cut off from the world. The trainline between us and the farm had fenced us out of civilisation, like a zip closing a suitcase.

We stopped at nine o'clock for breakfast, which Paul had alerted me to and Ruth's provisions had prepared me for. What a kindness!

We settled against the rear wheel of the tractor and better introduced ourselves. I told him about college and the farm there and then outlined my experience in Banbury.

"How long have you been here?" I asked Dennis.

"I used to drive a van and then did a bit in the mill here. My father worked on a farm the other side of Arundel. When we got married we needed a house and I was lucky to move up here from the mill."

Dennis was open and I was sure we would get on as neighbours.

"You're not married," he observed, or I guess his wife had.

"Not yet. I've got a girl and expect to fairly soon." I was choosing my words carefully.

"Is she expecting?" Dennis enquired.

"No. NO!" I gasped at his train of thought. "It's a bit delicate; her father is not keen," I admitted, but did not want to go further.

"Our youngsters are ten and twelve, and Carol does some part-time work in Arundel." Dennis filled in more detail.

The rest of the day was spent steadily banging in posts, at which we took turns. We finished at five as overtime was not required on this job, and I went straight to explore the nearest shops. That is to say, by 'exploring shops' as a mere male I meant finding out where I could get some groceries. I have since found that ladies would expect to examine the contents of a shop in greater detail than a detective. They would then report back that there was "nothing in the shops". I had been on a few trips with Hazel to arrive at this conclusion. In fairness, she had been looking for clothes whilst I was hoping to find the nearest grocers that would replenish my new kitchen. I found a number of shops by the head office and mill that saved a trip to Littlehampton and all that might entail.

I phoned Hazel that evening, having feasted on bangers and mash, which required my trusty frying pan for the onions and sausages and one saucepan for potatoes, done to a turn and mashed. It was essential to phone and excite her about the modern house and reassure her that all was going so well. The phone in her parents' farmhouse was just inside the front door at the bottom of the stairs which meant at least one side of a conversation was public knowledge whether upstairs or down. Privacy could only be maintained between an engaged couple by letter, which would hopefully be exchanged within the first week. The engagement had been a taboo subject because of her father's total objection. We had agreed that nothing could stop us getting married legally on Hazel's birthday, but that would not improve family relationships; indeed, Hazel was nervous of wearing her engagement ring.

I explained about the friendliness at work and especially Paul and Ruth at the farmhouse. Hazel was interested in the novelty of having a close neighbour, so close we shared a common wall. Her near neighbour experience had only been at a distance of four hundred yards and on the other side of the road. She was excited about a house of our own and the exhilaration of freedom in a new area very near the sea.

Back on the farm I was settling in, getting to know my way about at Mayhurst and the mill. The cows were confined to grazing fields around the farm with more distant fields growing cereal crops and roots. At the mill there were some old pigsties and a fattening shed together with a small acreage of rhubarb and cabbage. Fields further beyond the mill and office buildings grew mostly cereals. The retention of pigs seemed to have been a convenient way of disposing of surplus and 'tired' vegetables from the wholesale greengrocery department.

John was the main tractor driver and looked after the farm equipment there. He was always jovial and ready to see the lighter side of any situation. He was ready to do any job and never afraid to have a shovel in his hand rather than a steering wheel. He could use the workshop facilities or get one of the full-time mechanics to help maintain tractors or weld machines. He was as jovial with any of the mill or veg employees as with the farm staff. Many a time John would enlist the help of the mechanics without the need to tell Paul.

"I've got a bit that fell 'orf," said John as he ambled between two lorries that were filling the workshop.

"Don't bring it here," Walt shouted from the inspection pit, without so much as a glance at the object.

"We need it straight away," John grinned, cloth cap at an angle and shirt unbuttoned to within an inch of his waist.

"I've got two lorries to get out," Walt shouted.

The other lorry jumped into life with a blue plume enveloping John.

"Blimey, is it something I said?" John was still good-natured.

"What's dropped off?" Walt was resigned to looking.

"The hoe," John said simply.

"Blinking big hoe," Walt gasped.

"Tractor hoe," John answered without exasperation.

"Well, you're lucky; it seems Fred has finished the other vehicle so he might look at it."

"Look at it! I want 'im to glue it," John insisted.

The interdepartmental banter might have gone on longer but Paul walked in.

"Long handle 'as sheared 'orf the bracket," John explained.

"I want Walter or Fred to weld it." Paul turned and walked out having resolved the issue with one sentence.

I had breakfast with John before helping him to feed the pigs. We settled down sitting on the feed bags in the store next to the piggery.

"How do you get on with Paul?" John's question took me by surprise.

"Fine. I've had plenty of worse bosses," I replied.

"Oh, they're all good to work for." John turned to me, "I mean they are religious."

"So am I… I suppose you'd say." I hadn't thought of it as a label.

"No, you're ordinary; it's like they are super good," John added.

I took 'ordinary' to be a compliment.

"I go to chapel and pray, because God has been really good to me. It doesn't make me super good," I volunteered.

"Maybe they're a cut above us but I try and be good." John seemed to want more explanation.

"It's not about being good; it's about believing in Jesus Christ." I didn't want to give a sermon.

"What's 'believing'?" John wanted to pursue it.

"Well, being good doesn't get you to Heaven but believing in Jesus does; it says so in the Bible." I could see I was not making headway. "Believing means trusting, having faith in God. All I can say is, Jesus has answered my prayers even when things were hopeless."

"I mean, they look down on us for smoking and having an occasional drink," John returned to the 'them and us'.

"I'm the same as you, John, but I know God has guided and helped me and that's what He wants: me to trust Him. I'm sure Paul could explain it better." I felt I had not helped, but at least I was 'ordinary'.

We turned to feeding the pigs whilst the repair was done. Life rolled on for John; he had a council house just off the main road and was content to rent that rather than seek a tied cottage. "A tied cottage goes with the job," which to him meant if he lost his job he would be homeless. He would rather scrape by without any real prospect of advancement, able to keep his wife and have enough for modest smoking and perhaps a visit to the club on a Saturday night. Whatever the circumstance he would see the bright side, which endeared him to all.

## Married! Hurray!

We had managed to get together essentials for the new house by visiting shops and department stores at weekends in Essex. The purchase of a double bed was a precious moment as we confided to the salesman we were getting married. Having looked at several, which really amounted to different headboards, we asked if we could try one.

"Of course," came the reply.

We were a little nervous about whether to take our shoes off or not.

"Don't worry, it's plastic-covered," the salesman said.

We laid flat like two dummies, suddenly conscious of a number of shoppers looking on. The salesman, obviously gifted in his job, saved the day.

"It is alright as long as you don't enjoy yourselves!"

The sale was made and we asked for the nearest branch to deliver the bed to Mayhurst Farm. Hazel was going to keep her old dressing table which her brother would deliver in the horsebox. We also chose a three-piece suite and a dining-room table. All other items would, we hoped, be received as presents or we would purchase after the wedding as funds permitted and necessity demanded. The horsebox was well laden but all arrived safely.

On the farm, fencing the water meadows was completed and the grass mown for hay. Although all four fields over the railway line were destined to be hay, Paul told me to instruct John to cut only two and to 'make' them until the forecast promised sufficient dry weather for the other fields. The hay was turned and baled; it smelled beautiful. I had been used to newer pastures, especially short-term leys which produced bulk and, when made well, smelled fresh. These old meadows produced less quantity per acre but were strong on quality. The sample held to the nose was a collection of herbs evoking thoughts of summer days and picnics. I wondered if cows could sense the same? Farmers tend to think in terms of which sample will produce the most milk and researchers quantify the sugar and protein; the old hands seemed to get there with the right smell.

Observing cows grazing, they pull off grass and wander on a pace before swiping another mouthful. Sheep nibble, preferring short grass, but are just as selective. There is no doubt they choose what they like best with no thought of what tomorrow will bring.

My thoughts were very much on the future, rather than the imminent harvest, be it hay or cereals. The thought of being married, the anticipation of living with the one you love, the novelty of setting your own agenda together. At times I thought of life being simpler, no journeys to meet each other, no thought of others' convenience. And yet, was not a bachelor existence total freedom? I settled with the notion that 'freedom' could be confused with licence. Surely the joy of life is of one shared; isn't that what God intended? I swung between concerns for various wedding preparations, although the bride would be dealing with almost all of them. We had talked around the changes she would experience: leaving the job of a school's domestic bursar; a drop in our joint income. What sort of employment would be available here? On the other hand, there was the beach and sea right on our doorstep, a friendly church nearby and a whole new countryside to explore. We could hardly wait.

The Wedding Day arrived. It was all arranged, leaving from Hazel's home to the Congregational church; a great gathering of her family and her many uncles and aunts, together with cousins whose names I had quietly to enquire as we noticed them in the distance. They were nearly all in, or associated with, farming. Roger, my old school friend, was my Best Man and of course was even less acquainted with Hazel's relatives. We were mostly reduced to friendly smiles that implied, deceitfully, recognition.

My family was there in full but, without being so numerous, was a much smaller contingent. It was a warm October day, and Roger and I settled in the front row. Hazel was suitably late and I kept glancing towards the main door. Finally I spotted her and her oldest brother Raymond in the doorway. Douglas had threatened not to attend his daughter's wedding but Joan had not mentioned anything about it since.

The organist struck up with the 'Wedding March', and Hazel and Raymond were at my side. We smiled and silently ignored the lack of her father. We were united as husband and wife, and nobody could gainsay it. The wedding breakfast was a happy event with Raymond taking his father's part as if it were the most normal occurrence.

We settled down to married life with the house full of every modern convenience and gadget due to our guests' wonderful generosity.

# 20

# Everything New

My life was immediately different. I no longer had to make my own sandwiches or wonder what was for dinner. The quality was also greatly improved. My long period of bachelorhood was over and I had somebody to share my life with, both the good and the bad. Hazel soon sorted the house and domestic routine and was scanning 'Situations Vacant' columns. It was more fruitful when she cycled into town and read small ads in shop windows. After a month or so she got a job as a shop assistant in haberdashery and ladies' fashion. Although this was a far cry from her domestic science qualifications, it was an added interest and a small income.

On reflection, my wage was now a fraction under ten pounds per week, we had a free house and a modest car. Hazel's money was a great help and life was happy. We seemed to have settled and the hardships of the past had slipped into memory as 'growing pains'. Our routine was becoming established as a couple, although this did not mean there would be no downside now and again. We had become regular members of the congregation at the chapel on the new estate near the mill.

On Fridays we attended the evening prayer meeting and had made new friends mostly outside the farm environment. We had just sung the first hymn and sat down when a lady who always finished work late burst in.

"There's a man in the Ladies." She was badly shaken; all eyes were on her. The leader asked if she was alright. By this time the women either side were supporting her and two of the men had gone to investigate.

"There's nobody in there now," they quickly confirmed.

Peace was restored in the knowledge that nobody had been hurt.

As the meeting was closing, Hazel rushed up to me.

"My wages have gone!" She too was shaken.

"Are you sure?" I knew it was a daft question as soon as I uttered it.

"Of course. I was paid as I left work; the packet was in my coat pocket, which I'd hung up in the cloakroom in the Ladies." There was sympathy all around and questions asked if the original lady could describe the intruder. Other women were searching their own coats to see if they had lost anything. There was a sense that they had all been violated… but not as much as Hazel.

At home at about 9 pm there was knock at our door; it was the chapel leader, Mr Barclay. He stepped onto the doormat but would come no further.

"The fellowship want you to have this; you can't afford to lose your wages." He handed an envelope to Hazel who could only say, "But…" as his hand closed on hers.

He quickly retreated to his car and was gone. She opened the envelope; it was not her stolen wages, but a replacement. On the outside she saw written "From the chapel" and burst into tears. They had obviously had a collection and their generosity had even exceeded her wage.

Hazel had an immediate rapport with Ruth, Paul's wife, and often spent her spare time at the farmhouse across the field. Ruth had a boy of seven and a girl two years younger. She had been a teacher and was all things domestic; her generous heart and lively mind fitted well with Hazel. The overarching attraction was their Christian faith which permeated the whole firm. The Christian ethic within the firm was no soft option but provided an environment of honesty and integrity that boosted efficiency. Many employees were prepared to go beyond the call of normal duty to get jobs finished, feeling ownership of the business. Mr Morris himself seemed to have set the style with his hoeing the rose bed ethic rather than standing idle.

Also new was my growing responsibility on the farm. I was entrusted, within the limits of Paul's direction, to adjust labour and task to maximise efficiency. A small example was to send help to John so that the pig work for the day was achieved earlier and the main work such as haymaking attacked with extra vigour. John could then mow the grass earlier in the day and another man could turn or ted[25] the swath by mid-afternoon.

In the spring I was entrusted to organise cultivations and the barley drilling.

Mr Morris was still a farmer and delighted overseeing operations whenever he could get out of the office. This overseeing was not taking away Paul's responsibility or mine but was seen by all as a benign interest in farming. Indeed, I think it was his suggestion to Paul that a little responsibility was the best teacher I could have.

Mr Morris regularly drove to the Corn Exchange in London to deal in cereals, beans and peas. On one occasion he turned up at the field on his way up to London, dressed in his pinstriped suit and carrying his usual stick, just as I was examining the ploughed field. This stick appeared to be a conventional walking stick but at ground level had a straight steel blade about two inches square. I had kicked a furrow or two which was quite dry and friable[26]. He prodded the furrow with a similar effect. He then pushed the stick a little deeper making a cut in a clod.

"What do you think?" he asked.

---

[25] fluff up
[26] crumbly

"It seems it will probably work tomorrow." I was a bit measured, expecting some advice.

"You know, it's for barley so we need a fine, firm seedbed." He turned and went back to the car.

I had in mind the forecast being reasonable but with the possibility of a shower. But we had really planned to drill the seed the next day. I thought we should lightly cultivate the ploughed furrows and see what the soil looked like. Dennis was going to work the ploughed ground with spring tines on the back of his tractor. I let him make a couple of runs up and down the field.

"Is all the field similar?" I was asking if, in his experience, the soil type was consistent.

"Yes, just the same," Dennis confirmed.

I prodded another untouched furrow and rubbed a bit of deeper soil in my hand.

"Bit marginal," I suggested.

Dennis remained silent.

"Do the rest of the field but don't go any deeper," I told him.

I returned to the field about 4 pm; Dennis had just finished. Mr Morris had arrived back from London at the same moment. We looked at the field together.

"This won't do, Peter," was his immediate verdict.

"I was hoping it would dry if it was moved." It was a forlorn excuse.

"If it rains it will become a mess."

Mr Morris was right. I was really deflated.

"Leave it and we will see what the weather does." It was his final comment, made without rancour or recrimination. It would have been better never to have cultivated that day. In fact, the field remained untouched for another three weeks.

I had learned that patience is a virtue and if there is any clay in the soil-mix, leave it until dry.

Perhaps the most important lesson was to be humble. Nature is wonderful and, I had to learn, totally in control. This episode taught me that we have to work with nature, not imposing our agenda of speed or convenience. Furthermore, what we think we know for one field can be different in the next. I had ignored for the moment what the 'old boys', who had worked at the pace of a horse, had learned from birth: a relationship with nature that understood she was in charge and with her own timepiece. The reward was a crop, good or not, depending upon obedience.

Fred, the cowman, had served his employer well and at sixty-five was wanting to retire. His torrid complexion indicated a heart problem, and fewer early mornings and less responsibility beckoned following a mild heart attack. It would mean moving house, leaving it free for the next cowman, but health and life were paramount. Fred managed to find accommodation and a new cowman was found. The new man was a young Scot, full of ideas and rather full of himself. For a start he wanted to build the herd up to a hundred cows and would not need a relief milker. In other words he would not have a day off and he would ensure the cows were entirely under his management. Paul must have agreed to these terms and regarded it as favourable. Archie, the new brush, was going to make his mark and was confident to stand by it.

I warmed to Archie over the first month as his brash start mellowed. He was always softer and more open one-to-one. When confronted with two or three people, he felt he had to assert himself as if they were a personal affront. Judy, his wife, was charming and unassuming with a Scots burr that would charm birds off a branch. She was dedicated to motherhood and the rearing of their twins. Archie, no doubt a loving father, was dedicated to the cows. As I understood his total focus on the dairy enterprise, it was plain why Paul had employed him. He 'lived' the cows; their nutrition, comfort, foot-care, vet checks, in fact their total welfare. His first move was to change all the milk liners in the clusters so that the suction was uniform on all four teats.

Dennis, who had relief-milked for Fred, was now spared the job and became the stockman, littering yards and tending about thirty beef animals. He lost a few hours overtime as a result of the change and resented the extra expense the new regime was costing the farm.

"Don't your bullocks want more straw?" Archie dared to suggest to Dennis.

"There's not enough to go round now you've littered yer calf boxes." Dennis's barbed retort hurt.

"Aye, they need TLC cos they will be cows one day." Archie would defend all his actions.

"Yer could sleep in those boxes yourself." Dennis was stirring the pot.

"Aye, and I wouldn't mind that." Archie made his point and war was not declared.

## Paddock Grazing

Even the grazing system was going to be changed. Paul told me Archie was interested in trying 'paddock grazing'.

"Really?" I was astonished.

"Do you know about it?" It was Paul's turn to be surprised.

"Well, yes, I was very interested as a student, but I haven't seen it done in this country."

"You'd better have a talk with Archie."

Paul obviously mentioned our conversation to Archie. The next time I was near the parlour he shot out and asked if I could talk about the system. After breakfast the next day we met at Paul's house.

Archie outlined the idea of the fields nearest the parlour being divided up into smaller areas, being grazed intensively between two milkings and then the cows moving on to graze a new paddock.

"What benefit is that? It will cost a lot to fence smaller fields," Paul said.

"Cows do better on fresh grass," Archie leaped in.

Paul looked doubtful. "What's the science behind it?"

"Voisin did research in about the early 1900s, calling it 'rotational grazing'. He found it made sense; the pasture became much more productive," I enthused.

"How's that?" Paul was looking at me.

"Well, briefly, the cows would be in a small paddock and graze it all off in twenty-four hours. Then, next morning after milking, they would go into the next similar-sized paddock. You need about twenty-eight paddocks so they come to number one again on, say, the 29th day. But it's important that the grazed-off paddock is fertilised every time they leave. The botany is that the first two inches of growth is quicker than the fourth to fifth inches," I explained.

"And the young growth has more sugars," Archie added.

There was a moment of thought whilst it sunk in.

"How big do the paddocks need to be for the eighty cows now?" Paul asked.

"I think about two acres," Archie suggested.

"Have you done this before?"

"I have used a similar system but didn't design it," Archie offered.

"At that rate we would only need about sixty acres," Paul calculated. "Remarkable!"

Although we hadn't long had breakfast, Ruth appeared with a tray of coffee.

"I thought you would be ready for a drink after all the talking."

"It's important stuff," Paul quipped. "We are making acres."

"Well, that's good; I could do with a winter coat." Ruth swept out.

There were more questions coming to mind.

"What happens when the grass grows quickly in May?" Paul addressed Archie.

"You have to leapfrog one or two paddocks and leave them for silage."

"It takes a bit of careful management. Voisin found that when the grass is about five inches long, it is ideal to start grazing the new paddock," I added.

Paul wanted to know the ideal height of internal fencing, assuming it was a single strand of electric wire. Archie offered to find out from his Scottish farmer connection. Paul said he would look at the farm map and draw up possible paddocks of two acres, bearing in mind access for cows and farm machinery.

Archie fenced off a couple of paddocks in the field next to the parlour using a portable electric fence. If it proved too small, being grazed completely in one session, more trial and error would be needed. Soon an appropriate size was determined, and they were made permanent by using wooden stakes and a single tight electrified wire run by a 'mains' energiser. If a paddock grew too quickly, it had to be topped, rather like cutting a lawn, so that it would be an even five inches tall when the cows first entered it. Dennis and I planted the wooden fence posts in straight lines according to Paul's plan.

"Can't say I see the sense in all this work," Dennis grumbled.

"Time will tell, but I expect it will make good use of the grass." I wanted to encourage him.

"There is all the work of fertilising just two acres every other evening," Dennis replied with a grunt.

"We can keep the spreader on the little tractor most of the time," I added. "Look on the bright side: it will be a bit of overtime for you."

It kept him from complaining. By the end of the summer the new rotational grazing was reasonably established.

## A Breath of Fresh Air

Work was not all labour and no reward; there were great times of communing with nature. In quieter times we made preparation for the busier, even frenetic periods. A trailer and bale sledge needed repair and it was prudent to be independent of the firm's workshop for the bigger jobs. Paul told me to take a four-wheeled trailer and a bale sledge to the blacksmith. I left the farm on a sunny morning driving a new David Brown 880 tractor. This had no cab but otherwise a comfortable seat and positive controls; although the top speed was a rather pedestrian 15 mph. This proved to be perfect for my trip of four miles with little to do but enjoy the countryside. The roads starting up the slope of the South Downs were likely to be the medieval tracks of five hundred years ago, now bitumen sealed. Mature beech and occasional oaks stood either side, randomly edging mostly pastures. The views were stunning, getting ever wider over higher fields. These were worked for arable crops, becoming larger and flatter. The slight breeze and glorious sun showed off perfect pictures of rural England with even a castle in view. Finally, I could just make out the Isle of Wight in the distance.

I found Burpham and the Smithy as if time had stood still for fifty years, if not longer. The blacksmith was in keeping with cloth cap and leather apron. Taking up the entire forecourt, I pointed out that the drawbar connecting tractor and trailer needed remaking in heavier steel than from its horse days and finishing with a modern 'eye' that would be picked up by a tractor hook. The trailer needed cleat hooks for ropes and strengthening. The bale sledge needed new tubular metal piping where friction had worn it through. I reversed the trailer down a track at the side and unhooked it. The return journey was a similar delight, drifting through Yeoman England and being paid for the privilege.

We continued to become part of the chapel and helped out at the youth club, which was an amalgam of the church in Littlehampton and ours on the nearby housing estate. There was glorious mix of ages, extending to the 'young marrieds' who helped in the running of events. In the summer months we often had games and activities in the woodlands north of Arundel. The age groups spread out and the younger ones were often given a list of things to find in the woods. Older ones had games like rounders or cricket. Transport was provided by one or two lorries from the vegetable department, courtesy of the firm. The evenings would always include refreshments provided by the adults. Once or twice a year there was a BBQ on a farm, which was a cause of great excitement. The final act of the evening was a short epilogue, everyone thanking God for everything they wanted to mention. It was also a time when the youngsters could talk privately to a leader if they had any problems. Fun and fresh air was had by all, and several parents collecting their children mentioned the growth in self-assurance and discipline they had noticed in them.

The 'breath of fresh air' had drawn us closer in our Christian belief. It seemed like a spiritual freshness. The chapel people were different from others we knew; they had a self-assurance and ease that we were growing into. My original cries to God had been from fear and desperation. This had gradually been replaced by understanding from the Bible. I had the solid experience of God answering my prayer; it was no longer a calling in the dark. I had proof that He was there and interested in me. As we mixed with our new friends, we were discovering greater depth and increasing our understanding of the truths of the Bible.

As part of the prayer meeting, one of the elders, Mr Dacre, would explain a passage of scripture and link it with other books of the Bible. He had explained the meaning behind Easter and how it was all part of God's plan for mankind. Over the course of a few weeks, he explained how it was necessary for Jesus to die on the cross and be brought to life again. Resurrection. I was fascinated how the Bible was joined together; I simply knew there was a wonderful God and He answered my prayers. I told Mr Dacre this and that I loved Jesus. He asked if I would like to be baptised, as it was a command of God and an outward witness of sins being forgiven.

"I think so; all I know is I love Jesus and he has been such a strength to me."

It was just over a week later that Hazel and I met Mr Dacre and his wife to learn more about baptism. Mrs Dacre would chat with Hazel in a separate room whilst I was alone with Mr Dacre. It was a little more intimate like that, we were assured. The door closed and Mr Dacre started as if we were old friends.

"I am sure it is wonderful that you love the Lord, but there is something He wants from you." Mr Dacre had a soft, reassuring voice.

"What does Jesus want me to do?" I asked, willing to do anything.

"Let's look at the book of Hebrews." He turned to the Bible. "Hebrews 11:6 says, 'Without faith it is impossible to please God.' Faith means really trusting in God."

"I do trust in God; I told you," I asserted.

"I know you *believe* in God but do you have *faith* in Him?" Mr Dacre turned to another part of the Bible. "Romans 10:17 says, 'Faith comes from hearing the message, and the message is heard through the word of Christ.' So we need to study and follow what Jesus says and really believe it," he went on. "Do you understand, God is so great and holy and perfect and we are so tainted by sin that, as we seek Jesus, we realise how imperfect we are – fallible humans? The Bible says, '...for all have sinned and fall short of the glory of God.' Check it out in Romans 3:23."

"I know I have done a lot of wrong things... I mean *sins*." I was crestfallen; it hit me to recall how imperfect I was.

"You just ask Jesus to forgive you... if you really mean it. We have all been there. We have to repent, turn around from bad things," he comforted.

I was taking it all in.

"God wants to forgive you," he added.

"Really?" It was a wonder that God, great as He is, and Jesus His Son wanted to forgive me.

Mr Dacre was turning through his Bible again.

"'If we confess our sins, He is faithful and just and will forgive us our sins and purify us from all unrighteousness.' That's in 1 John 1:9."

"Does it mean all that... is really true?" I asked.

"Yes, absolutely," he confirmed.

I could feel tears running down my cheeks. I couldn't stop them. The more I tried to ignore them, the more they flowed. I felt a hand on my shoulder. A full minute passed.

"One more thing, Peter. Would you like to ask the Lord to forgive you now?"

"Yes!" I didn't look up. "Oh God, I am truly sorry. I know you died on the cross to pay for my sin; I just didn't realise. I mean, thank you! No, Jesus, that's not enough, please forgive me... I want to be honest with you. Tell me what I can do because I do love you. Amen."

"That was great, you don't have to do anything... You just have to have faith; that is, believe in your heart and know that Jesus is your Saviour," Mr Dacre concluded.

I felt worn out, exhausted.

"Sit down; have a rest." Mr Dacre had been so kind. "I am sure you can be baptised but we will have another talk or two another day."

We rejoined Hazel as Mrs Dacre came in with a tea tray. She spoke as she poured out the tea: "We have had a nice time talking and hope to have another chat about getting real with Jesus."

"Peter has committed himself to Jesus; we have had a great time." Mr Dacre was beaming.

At home we compared notes. I enthused about Mr Dacre tying together verses from the Bible. "I had told Mr Dacre I loved Jesus, but he showed me much more meaning about it being real; it was about being committed and asking forgiveness of our sins."

"Mrs Dacre was lovely," Hazel confessed, "but I wasn't sure what 'full commitment' really meant."

"Didn't she talk about Jesus taking our sins away on the cross and how we could be forgiven if we said we were really sorry?" I asked.

"Not really. I am going to have to chat with Ruth about it." Hazel seemed a little underwhelmed.

I told Paul that I had been talking with Mr Dacre and had asked Jesus to forgive me and accept me.

"I am delighted; that's the best possible news. That's what we call 'saved from sin'; the effect of sin is death, Jesus wants you to have life now and forever." Paul was thrilled and made it more simple. I really was at peace and lighter in spirit.

"I really feel different," I confessed unashamedly. "Sort of more bouncy, more buoyant."

Paul laughed and clapped his hand on my shoulder. "I hope I'm 'bouncy' too." Paul had moved from a work-related stance to brotherly.

A month or two later Mr Dacre crossed my path in Arundel as I came out from the newsagent's shop smoking. I didn't smoke much, and never at work, but I was not surprised he disapproved.

Mr Dacre greeted me with one question: "Can you imagine your Saviour smoking?" Without reprimand he passed by.

I was cut to the quick. When I got home I burned the few cigarettes and half ounce of tobacco that I had left. I have never smoked again and never missed it; surely "a word in season" as it says in the King James version of Isaiah 50:4. What a man of God!

Paul knew I smoked occasionally and said he would not have challenged me, suggesting Mr Dacre was correct and helpful but from an "older generation". I loved Mr Dacre for saying it but respected Paul as my work boss.

In his quiet yet straightforward way Paul had revealed some valuable management techniques. He was approachable but had not been matey, not 'one of the boys'. He had plans and ideas in place but was prepared to listen and adapt if convinced. Such was the revolution of Archie's idea of rotational grazing. Paul no doubt was aware of the idea but could not have started it with Fred as cowman. Archie had come up with the idea and was keen to embark upon it. Paul had seen the possibility to start with a fresh man, but with the assurance that Archie had the drive to make it a success. Indeed, Archie would make it a success with every fibre in his body. There could also have been Paul's desire to move to the system but for resistance of senior management in the person of the 'father' of the firm, Mr Morris. Years later I would need similar wisdom.

The paddocks were producing good, nutritious feed from a reduced acreage and, in late spring, even a surplus. We needed to cut and ensile[27] one or two paddocks and leapfrog to a third when it had reached five inches in leaf. Such a small quantity was not enough to put into a silage clamp in the conventional way. Paul had found the answer in a new innovation: a huge plastic groundsheet with a resealable cover over the top. We unrolled a heavy-duty plastic sheet on a grassy area near the middle yard.

"We must be careful not to pierce the ground sheet," Paul warned as he read the instructions.

"What about stones poking through?" I observed.

"Tell them not to!" Archie couldn't resist the odd unhelpful comment; he was high on excitement and determined to be involved.

"I'll tell you what you can do: walk all over the grass and find anything that sticks up." Paul was serious.

Archie was happy to do anything that would avoid puncturing the sheet and letting air in.

"We can't roll this out and then run a trailer over it," I commented to Paul.

"I was wondering about that!" He continued reading down the instructions looking for guidance. "It seems that the bigger of the two rolls is the top sheet or 'canopy', and the smaller roll the ground sheet."

Archie and I started rolling out the smaller roll.

"Wait a minute," Paul shouted. "Only roll out about ten or twelve feet." He paused. "The filling method is to use a fore-loader[28] standing on the ground, front wheels touching the roll, and tipping the material to be ensiled over onto the unrolled area... unrolling a yard or so at a time depending on reach." Paul was relieved at understanding the theory. Practical experience, I expected, would be by trial and error, mainly the latter.

A short conference decided trailer-loads of wilted grass would be tipped against the cattle yard wall and tractor-forked over the rolled end. The two paddocks were completed by mid-afternoon. We then had to lift the larger roll, with the loader, on top of the clamp and roll it out.

"There must be an easier way." Dennis had joined me on one side, whilst John was aiding Paul on the other end of the roll.

"Where is Archie?" John called out.

"Milking," Dennis gasped.

"This was his bright idea," John called back from his side.

"Rest a minute." Paul was not settling the argument but suggesting another brainstorming.

---

[27] convert into silage
[28] loader on the front of the tractor

The roll was heavy and about head height, making it difficult to lift and roll at the same time.

"We need to roll from the middle but can't stand on the sheet." It was good of John to state the obvious, but how to do it?

The brief silence that followed allowed us to take fresh breath.

"If two of us get on top and walk backwards..." I thought Paul was trying to introduce humour or more likely farce.

John started singing, "I'm walking backwards..."

"I'm serious," Paul insisted.

"Come on, Peter." I followed Paul, clambering up the side of the spongy grass to the roll of plastic.

"I've seen it all now!" murmured Dennis.

Paul and I bent over the plastic and rolled it over our feet, recovering with a backward step whilst Dennis and John took some of the weight. It proved successful, adding to the carnival as we descended down the end slope, avoiding being run over by the remainder of the roll. We now had the task of joining together the top and bottom sheets. This was no zip fastener but a concave miniature plastic 'gutter' for both sheets to sit in, retained by a flexible plastic rod. This too was testing, as we struggled with several pairs of hands to hold the gutter and sheets whilst pressing home the rod in a snap fit. Fortunately, Paul left us to collect his children from school. This left us free to express our feelings about the man who had patented the system and our admiration for Paul who had purchased it.

"I hope Archie likes the silage after all our trouble," Dennis said, taking a breather.

"Yer, you'd think he was a cow himself the care he takes with silage-making." John smiled. "Perhaps he has it for breakfast!" He laughed at his own joke; there was no malice.

"He might give us a pint of milk," Dennis joined in. "On second thoughts, it would spoil his record production figures."

When Paul returned, he used a small hand pump which came with the kit to expel the air and thereby start the fermentation process. The sheet settled down tightly to the grass.

A few weeks later another two paddocks were getting ahead of the cows and needed cutting for silage. This news didn't meet with great enthusiasm among the men who had struggled in the first experience. Paul and I considered the prospect of another kit but it seemed expensive and there was no obvious site to put it.

"Could we open the old one and put the new grass on top?" I asked.

"I'll phone the manufacturers," Paul suggested.

Predictably they suggested a new kit, which didn't answer our problem. The dangers were in tearing the plastic and simply not being able to make the top sheet airtight a second time. We decided to undo the 'shallow' end of the wedge. It looked and smelt as silage usually should. Prompted by this we sealed it back up.

"I wonder if we could put the new grass on top and use a tractor to roll it like an ordinary clamp?" I proffered.

"Bit dangerous without a wall," Paul reacted quickly.

"We are not going to get the same amount of grass on without rolling; we relied on natural shrinkage last time," I said.

"True!" Paul agreed.

We were back to brainstorming.

"It's not easy to get grass up high enough over the side now," Paul mused.

"Supposing we dropped grass at the thin end, making a ramp, and kept running over it up to the middle?"

"Still tricky; we couldn't get near the edge." Paul was still worried.

"We could use the buck-rake on the back of the small Fergie, dump the grass, and just go up and down the middle." I was hesitant offering this without any experience of silage without walls.

"Well, we will have to try it." Paul was decisive.

There was no Plan B. We would have to cut the grass before any trial run. Paul got us to put the 'cage' wheels on the tractor, which were extensions to the rear wheel making them twice as wide. This made the operation safer, compressing a greater width without getting near the edge. The day came and the grass was mowed. We left it a day to wilt, turning it once. The next morning Dennis and I pulled the plastic seal apart, releasing the top sheet. With extra help from Paul, we pulled it back over the high end of the wedge and carefully weighted it down.

The loads of grass were tipped against the cattle yard wall as before and I picked up a full buck-rake to drop on the wedge of the silage. Dennis levelled out the clumps and tidied the edges with a long-handled fork. The tracking up and down compressed the incoming loads, making it firmer and safer. Finally, the grass from two paddocks was not much higher than the first two had been without compression. All the grass ended up on top of the first cut and rolled up as much as possible. Dennis and I climbed over to the high end and, with the help of John and Paul, pulled up the top sheet.

"Keep it about knee height," I called to Dennis, just as a gust of wind threatened to return the sheet, and us, to the ground. We pulled harder, walking backwards to the ramp end. The sheet was too short.

"There is no sense in trying to fork any grass off the top," Paul said aloud as if a thought had come to mind and been immediately dismissed. We were about a foot short of the top sheet meeting the lower.

"I'll walk about on top again," John offered his considerable weight. "It'll grab an inch or two."

Paul said nothing, deep in thought. Then, "It is worth a try; pull back the sheet so he can scramble up the grass." Paul surprised us all, including John. "Go back to the other end and we'll try another pull," he suggested.

It came only an inch or two.

"Come down, John."

He was as cheerful as ever. "Thought my weight would have done some good."

We pulled as much as possible and Dennis drove his tractor over and 'stood' it on the end of the sheet. The next morning I was pleased to see the sheet was still as we had left it. The team assembled again and, using two new broom handles wrapped in the end of the plastic, pulled the sheet as tight as possible. Two efforts achieved a promising result. Two of us each side and we managed to clip the plastic tube and gutter back.

John said it was his weight after all, and he would do his best not to slim down.

In fact, it was likely the overnight settlement that did the trick. We all hoped the silage would 'make' not only to the cows' satisfaction but also Archie's.

## Our First Child

Hazel was pregnant and we were expecting our first child. It was exciting and a little daunting. It would be my mother's first grandchild and Hazel's mother's third. Hazel was in close touch with her mother but distance precluded many visits. She had journeyed from home a couple of times but phone conversations were a constant link. Paul's wife, Ruth, wonderfully took on the role of mother and confidant to Hazel. We purchased a cot and pram but did not know whether the baby would be a boy or girl. Excitement grew with each item of baby clothing purchased or equipment filling different areas of the house. Friends calling were aware that corners and cupboards were filling up. It was as if the new arrival was sending on luggage; he or she knew the address but hadn't checked in yet.

Harvest was equally pressing. Both crop and infant were in God's good hands; His was the timing. Hazel would continue her work until the end of June, if there were no complications. Ruth was excited and was Hazel's chief adviser, so I could take a back seat. I was familiar with the necessary preparations for harvest and, with Paul's overseeing, prepared the combine. I knew the main greasing points and examined the condition of the belts. It was a Claas grain-bagger without a bulk tank but with bagging-off spouts to fill sacks as the grain was threshed. I asked Paul why they used sacks rather than bulk.

"I've never seen a bagger before," I said tentatively, giving a chance for an explanation.

"It fits our link with the mill; being in sacks it keeps ours separate from other customers'," he answered.

"But other farmers must sell theirs to the mill in bulk," I suggested.

Paul was having to justify under duress; I guessed he would have liked to have modernised.

"The reason is we have no storage here. It all goes to the mill and Mr Morris says money is better spent down there than on the farm." Paul saw that I wasn't satisfied.

"A customer can come up at any time, go over to the weighbridge, have a sample taken and just tip."

"Ours is stored in sacks or even dried and sold when I choose," Paul firmly stated.

"OK." I wasn't convinced.

"We try for seed quality, keeping it absolutely separate and getting a premium."

"I see," I conceded, but I could smell a tussle between a shrewd managing director and the next generation.

When harvest was ready, Paul drove the combine and I was on the bagging unit with Big Vic. He was not a regular on the farm but an odd-job man around the mill, the vegetable department or anywhere else a hand was needed. The amazing thing about Vic was, he only had one hand; his wrist ended in a single hook. This was never referred to and certainly never joked about. John, who worked at the mill as much as at Mayhurst Farm, had primed me to avoid the subject. Cautious enquiry with other employees met with various ideas of how the accident had occurred. General answers were that he caught it in machinery years ago. I never found out whether it was at the mill or on the farm. It may even have been on another farm. Vic was in no way self-conscious about his hook and could do any task asked of him. Although I tried not to be caught looking at it, he seemed to totally regard the hook as part of himself. When at rest or sitting down, his right hand would hold, even embrace, the metal as if to warm it up. I found myself doubting whether he even took it off at night.

The job on top of the combine was no trouble to Vic; we had our own steps to mount the platform separate from the driver. Space was restricted with two men: one clipping sacks 'on' and 'off' the chutes, the other tying and dispatching them down the slide to the ground. I had been used to doing the job in a barn, but with the motion of the combine, it seemed we were working through a constant earthquake. The dust and noise were much the same, but tying and moving the completed sack to the chute required extra strength and skill. There was no time or room to weigh the sacks, as I had done as barn boy, but just enough to tie the top securely ready for the 'drop': I refer to the lift and nudge to the chute and the gravitational force of eighteen stone hitting the moving ground. Failure of the knot would result in at least half a bushel of corn lying in the stubble.

Vic admitted this was the one job he could not manage as he would have to bunch and tie the neck of the sack one-handed. In fact, he did well to clip and remove the sacks whilst the tractor was in motion. The combining stopped at five o'clock and we had half an hour tea break. This over, we had to collect the sacks scattered over the field before nightfall. Vic never drove a tractor even for this stop 'n' start collection job. He, along with me, lifted them from the ground onto the flatbed trailer. He held one end of the loading stick with his left hand and stuck his hook into or around the neck of the sacks. On the other end of the stick I lifted with my right hand and held the neck with my left. With a lifting and swinging motion the sack arrived, base-first, at the loader's feet. This picking up and carting off operation required at least three men, plus a boy if possible, to drive to each sack on the stubble. Although harvest had been gathered cheerfully this way for some years, it was plain that bulk handling would be a distinct improvement. A combine harvester with a bulk tank could work all the hours that the moisture content of straw and grain was satisfactory. There would be no danger of sacks getting wet during a shower nor of spillages from sacks hitting the ground with force.

A week later the combining was going well, when Ruth drove into the field waving madly, obviously some emergency. She then drove across the field towards us.

Paul stopped the combine. "Hazel's in labour," he called back to me.

I climbed down to Ruth. "You must see the birth," she called.

Paul immediately agreed and asked Ruth to pick up John to replace me on the combine.

She first took me to collect my car. "You must go straight away; you don't want to miss it." She was quite breathless.

I was thinking of having a quick change of clothes.

"You haven't got time for that; they won't mind," Ruth assured me.

I jumped in my car leaving her to find John at the mill. The two-mile journey to the nursing home took only minutes. I apologised to the receptionist for my farm clothes and army boots, but she simply said, "Follow me."

She knocked at the delivery room door and peered in.

"Stand just inside; she is having the baby now." That sounded like an order and then she disappeared. The midwife and two nurses were busy... and then it happened, right in front of me. The baby was passed to Mum for the first time. A nurse waved me over.

"Darling!" I kissed Hazel's forehead. "I'm sorry I couldn't come any quicker."

"It's a girl!" She smiled and beamed up at me. "This is Nicola."

We were left together for about ten minutes. We had planned to be together during the birth but it was quick and apparently without much drama. Although not there for moral support, I was there at the actual birth. I had to return to the combining but managed to visit again during evening hours.

It seemed as if time were suspended. I could think of nothing else all day. Paul and Ruth were delighted for us, and Dennis and Carol from next door came round with a card. Everybody seemed to know the news. Paul and Ruth looked in with flowers for me to take to Hazel.

"Everybody seems to know and are so kind." I was somewhat bewildered.

"Of course." Ruth beamed as if she had had an addition to her own family. "We were all looking forward to it and it's so lovely to have a girl, but I know you didn't mind which." She smiled.

We had talked of possible names and eventually agreed on Nicholas if a boy and Nicola if a girl. As I entered the nursing home, flowers in hand, the receptionist asked me to fill in the birth details and sign and date the record.

It was the next evening that I saw Nichola's first bracelet.

"That's lovely; you won't lose her now." I was light-hearted.

"It doesn't matter but you spelt her name wrongly." Hazel pointed to the minute wrist. "Nicola doesn't have an 'h'." She looked up at me.

"Doesn't it? Nicholas does." I felt foolish.

"I don't think it matters." Hazel said. "I rather like it being a bit different. Shall we keep it like that?"

I readily agreed.

Hazel returned home after four days as there were no complications. The midwife visited daily for about a week, helping the new mother with the details of washing and a daily routine. Both were doing well.

We settled down as a family. The word seemed strange – carrying the connotation of a unit, a responsibility. There was a permanence establishing the marriage. Hazel and I had moved from single to married status and now further, to encompass the next generation. It was an awesome thought that had become a reality; no regrets, but a significant change and a responsibility. I thought about the future. It seemed to hinge on my future action: my earning capacity and my ability to support a family, which might increase in number. Indeed, it was time to work on my ambition, on what I hoped to achieve. The start of a family was the spur.

I started looking for more responsibility. Although I was happy at Mayhurst, there was no prospect of promotion. I needed to get on the ladder of genuine farm management; it had been my ambition from school days. It had started from the first time an adult had asked, "What do you want to be when you grow up?" I could not recall when that question was first asked of me but it must surely have been after my holiday experience in Devon. The serious question had been floated to my class in high school before we settled on the GCE subjects we would major in. My reasoning started from the negative rejection of life in an office. I had noticed my father checking books of figures at home and then taking them to another office two miles away. I had occasionally delivered and collected papers from that office for him. It was situated above shops in the High Street, approached through a dark anonymous door and upstairs.

If I didn't want office life, what were the alternatives? Perhaps the police? They were mostly working outdoors, but I knew I was an inch short of the five foot ten inches the Metropolitan Force specified. Working in the London parks were unappealing as, however high one climbed on a career level, it was really only gardening. Such was my view of the world of work. I realised farming had the benefits of fresh air and purpose, a blend of physical work and business acumen. I knew it was reputed to be poorly remunerated but surely they managed to live more cheaply in the countryside. That was it; I wanted to farm. There was no chance of being a farmer but some large farms required a manager. Strange as it was, I thought I could just leave the East End of London and succeed in agriculture; it must have been the arrogance of youth.

I had always devoured the *Farmers Weekly;* now I always turned first to 'Situations Vacant'. I was looking for an "Assistant Manager Required" on an estate or sizeable holding, or perhaps "Farm Manager" on a smaller farm. I applied for a number of positions where the land belonged to companies and organisations, tailoring my CV appropriately. This resulted in excitement waiting for the postman. A thin envelope was invariably a single page rejection, obvious before opening. However, a bulkier envelope would contain more information about the farm and possibly be granting me an interview.

My interview technique was to research as much of the area as possible and discern the policy of the owner. I enjoyed many interviews, not only to walk and discuss current management in a new area but to observe other candidates. The first impression was arriving at the business and noting the competition by the vehicles in the car park. They ranged from smart saloon to well-used four-wheel drives. It was easy to spot the family car with roof rack and possibly evidence of children's waterproofs. The driver would often be the outdoor man with a crew-necked cable-stitched sweater and clean jeans for the occasion. The other extreme was the smooth country-suited candidate with matching tie and pocket handkerchief, more at home in a shooting party. I hoped to be practical but smart casual, which often dressed me in corduroy or cavalry twill trousers and sports jacket. It was always important to have a clean pair of Wellingtons in the boot of the car to be collected as necessary for a trip around the holding.

The morning would start with the offer of coffee and a whole-group session describing current farming practice and some idea of what was expected from a successful candidate. The next part was to take the group on a brief tour of the farm either by tractor and trailer or walking. I made it my business to be energetic, one of the first three of the party to exit the trailer, and to keep a modest distance from the host or interviewer. There was usually one candidate trying too hard to impress by shadowing the leader and asking all the questions.

Occasionally one could see the guide wishing he had a flyswat to at least injure the persistent pest; undoubtedly that candidate was not improving his chances. I tried to be in the picture sufficiently to be remembered, but not obtrusive. After the farm tour we would be interviewed separately for a few minutes, which enabled a more focused discussion by both sides. This enabled the candidate to assess the employer and his style of managing his workforce. It also helped the employer discover the motives and character of the candidate.

# 21

# Farm Manager

I was twenty-seven and now had family responsibilities; it was time I advanced my career. After a few interviews I applied for an appointment as Farm Manager. It was run by consultants on behalf on an industrialist wishing to enter farming. The initial selection was at the consultants' headquarters in Kent and it appeared that a suit would be the appropriate attire. There had been over a hundred applicants whittled down to eighteen for interview. The smart Georgian block of offices indicated the serious intent of getting the right manager for the industrialist. We were welcomed by the chairman's secretary and offered coffee in bone china cups. The interviews took place in two halves; nine candidates in the morning and a similar number in the afternoon, depending on the distance candidates had to travel.

We were told the size of the farm, where it was, and informed it was a completely new start-up with only one resident employee. There was no machinery or livestock to take to it, and the policy would be largely determined by the successful candidate with quarterly support from the consultants. We were questioned in detail about our experience and told that references would be required later. I returned to Mayhurst exhausted and frankly with little positive expectation. Would they seriously consider a young man my age to be the right candidate to start a farm from scratch? I was told I could expect an answer within a month.

I thought the job would be the marvellous entry I had hoped for, but the competition was huge. In the meantime I continued to look for other opportunities, but the thought of this one would not go away. It was nearly a month before a thin envelope with the consultants' crest arrived. I was already disheartened. The letter simply said I was shortlisted to attend a final interview. I read the letter again; the door was still open. The final six were to meet at the same offices for more detailed questions from the consultant, Mr Smedley, and to be introduced to the general manager, Marvin Campbell, who was the industrialist's son. I did not learn much more about the farm but understood it would be very different working for an industrialist than for a landowner.

The wait following the second interview was interminable. I had prayed from the outset that the Lord would guide the whole process. Naturally, I had committed my future to Him after all the prayers He had answered. Now I asked not to be involved with the wrong employer. Attractive as the appointment seemed, I didn't want to bite off more than I could chew. I waited until I could wait no longer. I was seriously thinking this was not to be mine, but at least I had made the final selection. I phoned the consultants as I had another interview pending. The chairman's secretary, ever polite and professional, said they had been delayed but would phone me in twenty-four hours with the result. She phoned the next day offering me the job, saying a letter would follow for me to sign.

I was overcome with gratitude and confusion. We thanked God. He had answered our prayers again. It seemed that God was still faithful to my original concerns when I fully cast myself on Him. Right from my eleven-plus exam when I had totally relied on God, He had brought me through good times and bad but never given up on me. Now, as I had seen such little hope with apparently over a hundred applicants, He had pulled me through. I was aware that I had landed what appeared to be a plumb job – but what a responsibility: a new farm, one man and nothing else. We were to meet the consultants and the owner on the new farm in just over a week. I had to tell Paul the news and hand in my notice the next morning.

"I'm afraid we have got to be leaving you," I nervously told Paul.

"You've got a new job? Congratulations!" Paul helped me out.

"Yes, really seems good... but we are sorry to leave." I was genuinely sorry to leave friends.

"I will keep your letter until you've seen the house." Paul was marvellous.

Hazel was so pleased I had the job but very sorry to leave Ruth, who had been a tower of strength. We both arranged to take a day's holiday to see the farm and the new house. Beeches Row Farm was in Wessex. We drove through scrubby woodland and bracken banks to a straight avenue of tall beech trees and a large stone barn set back from the road.

"This is it!" Hazel announced. I pulled over in front of the barn complex where there was already a parked car.

"Nice to see you again, Peter." Mr Smedley, who had interviewed me, shook my hand.

"My wife, Hazel," I offered, as they had not met at my interview.

"Welcome to your new home. I hope you will very happy here." Mr Smedley welcomed us as if we were old friends. He hesitated for a moment as if to decide the next move. "First things first, here is the house."

We crossed the road to the only house in view, a white pebble-dashed cottage behind the line of roadside beech trees. Mr Smedley unlocked the door and ushered us in past a utility closet and kitchen to the lounge. We stood taking in every aspect.

"This is lovely." Hazel spoke for us both.

We were standing on a deep-pile light-grey carpet in the lounge with views both sides through large windows, stretching from just a foot above the carpet and up to the ceiling on the one side and a 'cottagey' leaded light casement on the other.

"Who lived here, Mr Smedley?" Hazel was incredulous.

"First of all, call me Michael. We will be with you on the journey. The owners lived here; it is the only real house. I'll show you upstairs."

Michael led us up the open stairs rising from the lounge with the same fitted carpet. There were two bedrooms and a box room sufficient for a child. The bathroom was, in estate agent parlance, 'well appointed'.

"I will have to lock the house but you will have the keys this afternoon once we have met Mr Campbell. I'll drive you round the farm now and then we will have bit of lunch at the hotel with him."

We drove slowly around the top farm of arable fields between two roads, and down a track with ponds at the bottom. We stood looking though a bamboo curtain at still ponds with reeds and a swan with cygnets.

"These are apparently 'stew' ponds," Michael informed us.

"What are they?" I asked.

"Something to do with monks in the Middle Ages; their source of fresh fish." Michael smiled.

"It's all lovely." Hazel was warming to the whole new adventure.

We drove back towards the farmhouse and the track behind it took us to the lower road.

"This is the other farm," Michael said casually.

"I didn't know there were two," I said.

"They simply call this New Farm. I don't know the history but it was possibly added at some time." Again Michael was casual.

We drove through some open yards and past a few sheds down to a wide open view and stepped out of the car again.

"What is this?" I enquired in surprise.

"An airstrip; I believe the previous owner landed here occasionally."

We walked to the side of the airstrip, which merged straight into a crop of lucerne. Michael, although dressed in a suit, bent down and pulled up a plant.

"What's this?" he enquired.

I studied it and the soil it came from. "Not sure; it could be lucerne and clover," I suggested nervously.

"Well done! I had to scratch my head," Michael confessed. He had shed the 'office' and was at home, farming. He took a spade from the boot of the car and we crossed to the other side of the strip to a barley stubble. He handed the spade to me. I accepted the invitation and sunk the spade in with ease.

"It's really sandy," I said with surprise.

"Take another deeper spit," he instructed.

"Sand all the way," I exclaimed.

Michael added, "We'll have to think about what to do on this ground."

The time arrived for our meeting with my new employer at the hotel on the edge of the village. We approached the bar.

"Table for Smedley, please." Michael's secretary had done her job.

Mr Campbell Junior tapped me on the shoulder.

"Mr Campbell is over here."

There were introductions around, all new to Hazel. We moved to the booked table in a recess by the picture window. Sandwiches and drinks were soon served.

"Mr Campbell, this is your new manager," Michael started the conversation.

"I look forward to a long and happy partnership." Mr Campbell Senior grinned rather excessively. He was rather short and lean, with dark hair swept back and well Brylcreemed. He was not my picture of an industrialist and certainly not a farmer, but that is why I was there. Mr Campbell Senior obviously needed a Farm Manager.

"Do you think he could make your team?" Michael, smiling, launched a friendly repost to break any nervousness.

Mr Campbell Junior rushed in, "Mr Campbell is chairman of a football team."

"Peter, do you play football? Mr Campbell asked.

"I am afraid not; I'm a rugby man," I replied, and immediately regretted it.

"I'm sure Mr Campbell won't hold that against you." Michael was saving the situation.

Mr Campbell Senior obviously thought business must start.

"My son, Marvin, will do most of the talking." This appeared to be a rehearsed instruction. Marvin was the oldest of the family and larger than his father in both height and girth.

"We want to tell you about our side of the partnership. That is, the partnership between Mr Campbell's organisation and yourself. You need to know a bit about us and how we operate our other businesses. Mr Campbell employs a lot of staff from our London office with a manager for each of the various enterprises." Marvin was not only formal but pressing the "Mr Campbell". I wondered if he addressed his father in this manner all the time. Would he offer the plate of sandwiches in the centre of the table with the same title? Maybe it was a house rule and Marvin would feel it necessary to bid "Mrs Campbell" good night on retiring to bed. As he was eating his morning cereal, would he welcome his mother with, "I trust you had a good night, Mrs Campbell"?

I was wondering what sort of organisation I had agreed to join. Marvin flowed on, mentioning the car parks and leasing business which was his main concern as general manager, and now the farms. He stressed that farming was new to them but would follow the same management pattern. I would need to send a weekly report, a single page of A4, outlining progress and anticipating future events. It was made clear that I would be held responsible for all that happened in the farming enterprise and be the company's eyes and ears in that part of Wessex. There would be quarterly meetings with Smedleys, the consultants, and Mr Campbell to review progress and accounts.

Michael broke in to engage Mr Campbell Senior and lighten the tone.

"Mr Campbell, tell us about your plan for a house."

"It's all happened so quickly." There was his ingratiating smile again that surely hid a hard business mind. "My wife wanted a house in the country and I've ended up with an estate." He laughed as if it were by some benign chance.

I was beginning to grasp that inflated words were a useful front in high business.

"I sent my estate agent to an auction and his bid won." He grinned some more.

"You were telling me you wanted to move down here." Michael was eliciting more plans.

"We would like to get planning permission, not easy these days. I'm sure Peter will keep me informed."

"Peter is here to do the farming," Michael gently reminded him. He struggled to get back to farming and the expectations, but to little avail. "He will need a vehicle by the end of the month," he tried.

"My son, Marvin, will see to that."

"And they will need to organise moving house. Can I leave these keys or get a set cut?" Michael pressed.

"Get some cut; it's always useful," Mr Campbell said, grabbing the offer. "Marvin, we must go now." It was an instruction; the interview was over.

"Goodbye, Mr Campbell. We'll keep you up to date." We all said our farewells.

Michael drove us back to the farm, giving me a chance to politely ask why it was so brief.

"I think the position is that Mr Campbell's managers are regarded as the experts in their field and he leaves them with the responsibility of achieving the best results. I'll get Sally, my secretary, to send you a farm map and anything else useful. We would like a cropping plan and a gross margin assessment for year one. Also, a list of capital items like tractors and tack you think appropriate, with approximate prices of course. Is that OK?" Michael summed it up quickly. I understood my work had started already.

Hazel naturally was excited about the house and would be planning furniture and colours with Ruth. She would also be collecting Nichola who had been with 'Auntie' Ruth all day. We were sorry to be leaving Mayhurst; workmates, neighbours and friends had all been so kind. Another loss were the chapel friends who had helped us on our spiritual journey, including Mr Dacre, who was not a close friend but a strength and a teacher when we had questions about what the Bible was saying.

# 22

# A Clean Sheet

Everything at Beech Row Farm was new. It was a clean sheet for me to write on; a new house that was a 'farmhouse'. Hazel did not even have to worry about buying curtains as these perfectly matched the carpets and, in the case of the lounge, hung from ceiling to floor. There was room for all our possessions, and the pram could be stored in the lockable shed between the back door and the gate to the road. There was no garage, but an open cart-shed on the front side of the house would suffice. Being a farmhouse, the back door was the only one used; anybody approaching the front door by definition would be strangers.

The day after moving, Michael and Mr Campbell Junior arranged to meet us at the farm; Michael, to better acquaint himself with my cropping plan and the essentials for starting from nothing, and Marvin, to hear discussions and learn the possible 'pinch points'. We met together in an altogether friendlier and less formal manner, and I took it Marvin no longer felt the need to impress his father. We travelled in Michael's car, obviously used to traversing farm tracks, and stopped at nearly every field. We examined the topography and previous cropping, relating it to a schedule for year one.

Our main focus was on buildings and their possible uses. We also examined the terrace of four workers' cottages. They were all unoccupied and in need of a spring clean but little else. Marvin offered to send a couple of cleaners to freshen them up and obviously saw them as a potential 'lets'.

"I'll need at least one of them, possibly two," I intervened before his ideas wandered any further.

"It's about maximising assets," Marvin retorted.

"Don't fight, boys!" Michael rescued the situation.

The huge stone barn by the road had flagstone flooring and was divided into two by barn doors front and rear, accessing a covered yard beyond. Substantial wooden stairs led up to the first floor which covered the whole area. Two dusty bulbs gave just enough light to see the huge water tank covered with loose corrugated sheets.

"This must be the water supply for the houses," Michael assumed.

It appeared to be constructed from heavy iron sections bolted together, forming a 'swimming pool' about 32 x 8 x 4 feet.

"The weight of this!" I exclaimed.

"Looks as if it has come from some RAF airfield," Michael added.

"What can you use this for?" Marvin enquired.

"Precious little these days." Michael had experienced old farm barns before.

I guided them outside to the end of the building and to a complete house without any internal access to the barn.

"This is my office," I joked.

I had already put an old table and chair in the back room. Marvin looked into the adjacent toilet and pulled the working flush.

"It's disgusting in there," he judged.

"I think we'll have to scrap the lot and start again," I said.

"The pan will clean," he asserted.

"Get some bleach round it." I took it as an order, the sort he would have given to slipshod cleaners.

It was resolved that I would immediately advertise for a head tractor driver and Marvin would let two of the terraced houses. He would find the tenants and organise the appropriate agreements, but I would be responsible for the maintenance and daily practical admin on site. Michael's office would be responsible for overseeing the farm accounts but I would supply all the invoices and information direct to Mr Campbell's office.

"That's fine," I agreed. Marvin gave me his card with the head office details. They were just turning towards their vehicles when I added, "By the way, I don't work on Sundays." I wanted to mention it at the outset, but didn't see it as a concern.

I thought for a moment they had both suffered a heart attack.

"What do you mean?" Michael was first to regain his speech.

"I like to go to church on Sundays."

This didn't seem a satisfactory answer. "I thought farmers worked all the time?" Marvin insisted.

Michael was more measured: "What about during harvest?"

"I have done essentials like combing and baling." I hesitated. "I mean, I wouldn't plough or do unnecessary work... that is, not weather-critical." I could see they were still nervous. "I have milked and looked after animals," I continued my defence.

"I'll have to tell Mr Campbell," Marvin said and drove off.

"What has happened in the past?" Michael asked.

"I didn't mean anything dramatic. It worked perfectly on my last farm."

"I guess it will be OK if the men work and you fit in your church." Michael seemed reassured.

Hazel had discovered the few local village shops and more particularly had visited the local town. We felt we had at least arrived. The next days would be consolidating our way around, and finding which cardboard box contained the things we knew we had but couldn't locate. On the Monday at 7.30 am I met

Ernie. He had walked up from nearby Overley Farm where he lived in another pair of our cottages. He introduced himself, hoping we had settled in.

"I didn't know what you wanted me to do." Ernie was one of the old school, always willing and anxious not to be idle but not into great rushes of activity; the school that gives a task thought, measures it with previous experience, collects all the tools and only then starts work.

"I'll tell you what we'll do today. Come with me and tell me all I need to know." I carried a chair and we walked to the office. "Not very posh or clean, but tell me what you have been doing here," I started him off.

Ernie had been cleaning up for weeks prior to the sale and for a few days recently. He had always been left "to do what's needed".

"What did you do when the previous owners were here?" I asked.

"My main job was pigs. We had some up here and some farrowing at home." Ernie expanded a little on the enterprise. "We did 'weaners' and 'baconers' mostly; it depended a bit on what markets were like. All the food was bought in," he continued.

Ernie mentioned other jobs during the year and that they had two part-time tractor drivers to call on, otherwise contractors were used for combining and lucerne hay or haylage[29]. The previous owners had had other business interests which seemed more important than maximising farm output.

I outlined my ideas for the farm now, largely the cropping programme, but stressed there would be a lot of settling in initially.

"Ernie, it seems the new owner wants the farm to be profitable and, I think, will invest money that is going to make more money. That doesn't mean you have to work harder or faster, but we will have to be smarter," I stated.

"Does that mean more spit and polish?" he asked.

"I don't think so; it's not a show place, more smart thinking and best practice." I hoped to encourage him.

Hazel could do without the car, and so Ernie and I drove down to the stew ponds.

"This is where our water comes from." Ernie probed around a ditch with his back to the water. "Hear that?" he asked. "It's the Hydram."

I peered at an iron pipe slopping down into the ditch.

"Water comes under the track, down the pipe fast, slams the waste valve shut, building pressure in the exit valve, opening up the delivery pipe," Ernie explained.

"I think I've got the idea although I'd see it clearer in a diagram," I admitted.

"There is a rubber clack[30] that flexes and makes the noise," Ernie added. "It only sends up about ten per cent of the flow but it is automatic." Ernie grinned, hoping it made sense.

---

[29] silage made from dried grass
[30] saucer-shaped diaphragm

"And that sends it right up to the tank in the barn?" I asked.

"Yep!" he concluded, content with his explanation.

I turned to the two ponds.

"Do these dry up at all?"

"Never change," Ernie simply replied.

"Are there any fish?" I asked.

"I've never fished. I keep bees; never seen fishermen." Ernie dismissed the idea.

I had my mind on it needing irrigation, but Ernie said they had never done any.

We drove on and I took soil samples as we went from field to field, Ernie holding the samples and supplying names of fields and their areas. He would comment on any problem patch or weed infestation, ending up with a general caution about 'burn off' and couch grass. 'Burn off' was referring to crops wilting or dying off prematurely due to drought on the sandy soil. Couch grass, Ernie regarded as being immune to every method of control and taking over the farm. I thanked him for the tip and said we expected to address it.

Mr Campbell's secretary, Brenda, phoned the next morning.

"Hello, Peter. I have Mr Campbell wishing to speak with you."

We had not met but she was sociable, although in office mode.

"I hear you don't work on Sundays." He was straight to the point.

"I didn't mean to shock you, Mr Campbell, but it has been my practice to go to church."

"You didn't mention this earlier." He was curt.

"No, sir. The farms I have been on never suffered at all. Of course, I will see all essential work is done." I feared it had become an issue.

There was a pause.

"I hope there will be no problem. Indeed, there *must not* be a problem. You will have to be on probation. I will discuss the matter with Michael." Mr Campbell rang off.

I returned the receiver but sat there with my hand still on it. What did 'on probation' mean? I understood it to be a trial period, but how long would that last? What trial could there be? The farm would be at no disadvantage. After an anxious night discussing the matter with Hazel, we decided to carry on and tackle the problem if and when it arose. I trusted my hard work would hold me in good stead.

A few days later Marvin left a message that my vehicle would be delivered to the farm.

A grey van arrived by the barn and I crossed the road to see if it was from head office.

"Are you waiting for somebody?" I enquired.

"Yes. Mr Campbell is driving down."

"That will be new to him."

I smiled, but the driver looked blank.

"Do you have Land Rovers elsewhere in the business?" I enquired.

"Some old ones in the Parks department, but he'll be coming in his car." The driver was showing some sign of understanding. "This is for you," he said.

I stared at the 5 cwt Ford van and was about to point out that this was a farm when Marvin drew up. Remembering I was on probation, I knew I should measure my comments.

"Morning, Peter!" Marvin was unusually casual.

"I didn't expect a van; normally it would be a four-wheel drive."

I was cut short. "Plenty of room and it's a sandy farm," Marvin promptly stated, as if trying to sell a second-hand vehicle.

"Yes, but..." I got no further.

"It's only two years old and we change them; and the old signage has been painted out." Marvin was still trying to make the sale; the situation was looking bleak.

"I don't think I will get much in it," I continued meekly.

"I guess you will be buying a tractor for bigger loads." Marvin was not going to budge.

I went back to the house.

"I've got my vehicle," I said to Hazel between closed lips. We went out to take a closer look.

"At least they have painted out the cleaning company's logo," she remarked.

"I'll have to make the best of it," I replied. "I am conscious I am on probation."

## First Pigs

I decided the first job was to start the pig enterprise. I took Ernie to the market and we looked over the pig pens. We agreed Large Whites would be the best breed and found some useful-looking gilts[31]. I had earlier introduced myself to the auctioneer and they were happy to do business with Beech Row Farm again. That afternoon twenty-one gilts arrived and we penned them in the boxes around the yard behind the barn.

I made enquiries with the auctioneer for his recommendation on buying a boar. He recommended a well-known pig breeder near Reigate. Having made contact with him, I arranged to visit and possibly purchase a boar the following Saturday. I considered, if I made a purchase how would he be delivered? A livestock haulier would only consider the transport of one animal at his convenience and certainly at large expense. The pig breeder would be in a similar position, expecting most purchasers to collect their own animals in a livestock

---

[31] young female pigs which haven't yet bred

trailer or at least a long-wheel-based four-wheel drive on the day of purchase. I had a five hundred weight van.

I made a wooden screen out of old planks and trimmed it to fit behind the driver and passenger seats. Taking two bales and some loose straw, I set off for the breeder's farm. Selecting a large white boar was the easier part of the exercise; more nerve-wracking was our joint transport home. He was warranted fertile and penned apart from the others, seemingly calm by nature and ready for a ride westward. I reversed up to his pen and opened both rear doors with three welcoming straw bales as a step.

"It looks as if you have done this before," the farmer said as we stood each side and slightly to the rear, closing any possibility of escape.

The boar obligingly put his front feet on the straw and sniffed the inside of the vehicle. At the same time we urged him forward, encouraging a closer inspection. One bale was slipped behind him and the doors quickly shut. The straw was mostly intended as a friendly diversion to stop him routing around the door mechanism in boredom. The other bale I wedged between the back of the passenger seat and the dashboard, indicating the seat was not vacant nor an easy exit. We congratulated ourselves, and indeed the large pig, on the smoothness of the operation that could well have been fraught.

It was a hot day and the pig settled down contentedly for the journey to his new home. By midday the holiday traffic had slowed to a crawl and I was increasingly anxious that the heat and long journey might be too much for us both, not to mention any inquisitive policeman. The wooden barrier had rattled loose and was now in danger of falling on me or, worse, on the boar. I reasoned there was nothing I could do to improve the situation and had to carry on. I had cut a slot in the barrier so that I could use the rear view mirror, but most of the time I could only see two huge ears and a snout. Fortunately, the van had wing mirrors so I could keep an eye on the traffic tailing back behind. Suddenly two ladies in the car behind stared ahead, hand over mouth. What could that mean?

I checked the rear view mirror; the boar was still with me. In fact, he was staring at the ladies. The sudden sight of two huge ears and a snout peering in their direction must have been a shock. The pig was merely changing from looking forward to looking back. The cargo was no longer a secret; would they inform the police? Even worse, would they inform 'animal rights'? I knew they could read the number plate; if only the traffic would move. At that moment it did, but only at walking place.

A little later there was rap on the nearside window; surely all was lost. I imagined the headlines; even worse, head office being accused of my crimes.

"Your radiator's leaking, mate!" The good Samaritan was a cyclist pushing his bike up the hill.

"Thanks, it will be OK." I tried to sound confident, but could hardly blame the pig for not asking for a urinal.

Maybe the ladies had put pig and leak together, hence the shock. It was all getting too much; there was nothing I could do to improve the situation. We moved again and the boar lay down. I nearly thanked him but reasoned hearing a human voice might exacerbate the problem. I was eternally grateful to arrive at the yard and backed the van up to the pig's new quarters, an empty box. I resolved to mention to head office that a Land Rover and trailer were a necessity now we had the pig enterprise under way.

Pig numbers increased by breeding and further purchases. I aimed to make the unit sufficient for one man, Ernie, and to farrow the pigs in the fields rather than in the buildings. This had the merit of saving a lot of hand work in the boxes whilst providing a healthier environment for the pigs. I designed a simple hut, or 'ark', by making three 'A' frames and cladding them with six-foot-long galvanised sheets longitudinally, with one end closed in. These could be moved anywhere by trailer or fore-loader, rotated around the fields using pigs as a break crop in the rotation, leaving manure where it was needed.

The arks proved an instant success with the sows making them single dwellings with hardly any argument about occupation. The baby piglets were protected from being accidentally lain on by the 'tent' shape, allowing them room away from mum. The number of pigs reared per sow per year improved markedly. Ernie, with a little help, made a hundred and twenty huts in total. Initially we sold weaners[32] and porkers[33], which helped the cash flow, pleasing Mr Campbell. Later we introduced the popular British Landrace boars for a longer lean carcass, fattening the pigs to bacon weight (about 220 lbs).

Naturally there was a good deal of experimentation in the beginning to settle on the optimum size of herd and crossbreed preference for the market. The pigs were contained by electric fence which could easily be moved to fresh fields. As sandy land is generally rather poor and 'hungry' for nutrients, the pigs' manure soon lifted the general fertility of the farm. The rotation became pigs – winter wheat – barley – roots – winter wheat.

The first farm sales were eight-week-old weaners sold for other farmers to take them to pork or bacon weight. I was able to load these small but active pigs in the van to market much more safely than the boar experience. They were easily loaded and released into a pen at market. However, the transport was not without problems. On an early journey to market I was stopped by police. The police car overtook us on a dual carriageway although I was driving with the utmost care.

"Sir, you were exceeding the speed limit." He bent down rather awkwardly looking at the instruments. "You were travelling at up to thirty-six miles per hour."

"But the speed limit is forty miles per hour," I remonstrated.

---

[32] piglets weaned from their mothers
[33] piglets fattened to about 130 lbs for pork

"That is the road limit, sir, but you are governed to thirty miles per hour in a van," he asserted.

"I didn't know that; the van is new to me." I guessed it was no excuse and waited for the next infringement of 'carrying pigs in a van'. Fortunately, the officer was satisfied with 'one cop', immediately asking for my name and address. He wished me a safe journey and was gone. I kicked myself for not noticing the police car behind me, but doubted what difference it would have made. The truth of the matter was I couldn't see out of the rear window. There were no pigs' heads in the way but the combined breath of sixteen weaners had completely steamed up the glass.

I realised I had to inform Mr Campbell before news came from anywhere else, particularly the police. I mentioned the episode in my weekly report.

Mr Campbell arrived unannounced a few days later to see the developing pig enterprise and inspect the possible site for the new house. He and Marvin came into my slightly improved office and I was able to apologise in person.

"I am sorry about being caught speeding in your van..." I was cut short.

"I read your note. I do not require you to exceed the speed limit. You will be a little light in your pocket; it can easily happen." He grimaced in that infuriating way I had become used to which did not lighten the air but finalised discussion.

## Starting from Scratch

It was good to set the pig enterprise in motion but that was only part of the business. We needed to plan the cropping to get the best results, given the natural resources. Mr Smedley had agreed the principle that working with nature was the only way to optimise output and profit.

"Peter, you can't push water uphill; in other words, go with nature." Michael sat back, satisfied that we shared the same approach.

"I think the large sand element makes it necessary to grow root crops as far as possible and fewer cereals; we're not going to achieve heavy wheat yields here."

Michael nodded.

"I think potatoes would do well and suggest second earlies," I offered.

"Fine, but they will need irrigation," he said.

"Ernie has shown me some possible pump places." I hoped this registered as being on top of the job.

"You'd best apply for an abstraction licence and change of name."

I noted Michael's advice.

"Would carrots grow here?" I asked.

"Don't know of any in the locality." Michael cleaned his glasses as if it might help clear his brain. "Plenty in East Anglia!" he observed. It had done the trick.

"Of course, it's worth a trial." I was enthusiastic. "Perhaps we could use the potato equipment?"

"You'll need to do plenty of research if we are going to get Mr Campbell's agreement," Michael warned.

"I would like to grow a small patch and, if promising, more next year," I suggested.

We ended with an emphasis on roots and pigs with barley and wheat in the rotation to enable a four-year gap between successive roots. We would have to trial winter and spring varieties to see which gave the best returns on the light land.

"Michael, before you go, has Mr Campbell discussed my not working on Sundays?" I asked.

"Yes. I said we were confident you would not let the farm suffer and that the harvest would proceed in all the essentials, as I think you were intimating," Michael replied succinctly.

"So he is reasonably happy," I concluded.

"I'm not sure 'happy' is a term Mr Campbell uses much, but he does appreciate effort and results. Don't worry, you'll make it!" Michael was reassuring, we shook hands and he was off.

I spent the evening sifting through applications for the tractor-driving job. A lot could be deduced from the envelope and address before even reading the letter. Whilst allowance could be made for letter-writing not being a requirement, it did signal a degree of schooling. Driving was one element; another was confidence that instructions on spray cans could be deciphered and acted upon. Another failing was starting with, "I have always wanted to drive a tractor." The notepaper was another indicator of whether they might be worthy of an interview. The applicants who had obviously torn sheets from a lined pad and lost the top-right-hand corner were hardly showing a sign of care. Another negative, to be avoided as far as I was concerned in applying for a tractor driver job, was asking, "…and can I bring my dog?" I was half-inclined to reply, "Why the dog; does it help in navigation?"

I was looking for experience of various operations and a history of their employment. The most promising I chose to phone and invite for interview. Those whom I would not interview received a polite letter thanking them for their application. The four whom I wanted to learn more about I invited separately to the farm office and a walk around the buildings on each farm. The atmosphere was relaxed and their conversations and reactions spoke for them. The one chosen was a married man without family but whose wife wanted casual farm work when available. They inspected the house and accepted the job.

My priority now was to purchase tractors and equipment as needed but using a contractor when appropriate. This would avoid too large a capital expense until some income was achieved. We needed modern equipment capable of dealing with the size of enterprise but less sophisticated cultivation tools. The potato harvester would need to be of the latest design but not the plough or cultivator. Initially I purchased two new trailers with conventional drop down and removable sides, enabling the flatbed to take bales, but with extension sides slid on for bulk crops. The baler and combine were on our wish list with a main agent to find before harvest. These would be second-hand but in good order. We were offered a combine two months before harvest which the main dealer had used for two harvests as a 'demonstrator'. This was little more than half price yet capable of many a harvest on our modest cereal acreage.

Our new tractor driver, Ken, was a good ploughman and had soon cultivated the easy working soil to a tilth. Ernie worked with him on the drill sowing the winter cereals, whilst I fitted in the pig-feeding routine. It was soon a joy to see the neat rows of young plants enter the winter in good condition. The fields were fresh and weed-free making the farm looking cared for. I was able to put such notes in my weekly news sheet to head office.

I was summonsed to attend Mr Campbell's house and extensive office suite at the beginning of December. I drove to a very exclusive part of London in my company van, noticeably a tradesman rather than a resident. The other managers of various departments had parked their smart saloons in the driveway. Mr Campbell's secretary, Brenda, answered the door and let me in.

"Good morning. Pleased to meet you at last, Peter." She smiled broadly. "We have talked over the phone and now we have faces! We meet in the boardroom. Follow me."

"Ah! Peter, let me introduce my other managers." Mr Campbell was in top form. "Christopher is my accountant; you have met Marvin, my general manager." He turned to Ray and Edward, who were running car parks and holiday sites respectively, but the other three were unable to attend.

The meeting consisted of updates on the various departments, which made little sense to me.

"I've asked Peter, our new estate manager, to meet you and acquaint ourselves with the resources we share. Obviously if he needs a caravan he will come to Edward; if you need help on landscaping or dealing with landowners, Peter is your man."

The thought that my responsibility might stretch further, not to say beyond my capability, was daunting. When called upon, I gave a brief account of the start made on the farm and plans for its growth in output. I also took the opportunity to invite any of them to call in and acquaint themselves with the 'farm department' if in the area. This appeared to be expressing the mutual inclusiveness I had witnessed. The meetings were always as brief as possible and mostly for Mr Campbell to get across his message on any situation.

I was called aside as the others left, to acquaint Brenda with my accounting ledger. As farming was new to her I had drawn up columns headed numerically so she would understand in which column to place my checked and authorised expense invoices. For example, '1' indicated seed expenses and '2' was for fertiliser, etc. Similarly, the income side had alphabetically headings: 'A' for wheat sales, 'B' barley, 'C' potatoes, etc.

I was the last to leave, accompanied by Marvin. As I was about to find the van, which I had parked out on the roadside, he pressed a set of keys into my hand.

"We agreed you needed a Land Rover," he said, as if the idea had just occurred to them. He opened the garage doors revealing six vehicles, the front one a Land Rover.

"My goodness!" I gasped.

"We realise you will get it dirty but do have it serviced regularly," Marvin instructed.

"Thank you. I certainly will." I was like the cat that had just found the cream.

"Just a minute; your van keys." I gladly handed them over.

Both Marvin and his father visited the farm from time to time but always gave me notice before arriving. This was necessary, not to smarten the place up, but to organise jobs and labour to continue in my absence. Their visit always required my attendance for the duration of their stay. This would cut across meal times or family arrangements without second thought. In early spring they looked at the property at Overley Farm and noticed a couple of horses using the wartime airstrip as a gallop.

"Who is that?" Mr Campbell was quite indignant.

"Oh, that's our neighbours with a stable business." I must have sounded too casual.

"What are you charging?" he asked.

"Nothing," I had to admit.

"It's a facility!" Marvin jumped onside with his father.

"We sell some forage to them and a paddock for grazing when their grass is tight. It's common in the country to help each other and it fosters good relations," I said.

The stony silence suggested their concern would be raised again. I made a mental note to work out some pricing structures and float them with neighbours, Mary and Guy, in readiness.

Mr Campbell looked at some items of equipment in the open cartshed and I explained what they were used for.

"It's nice to know what you are spending my money on." Did he now seem more amiable? "What's that one?" He pointed to the rear of the otherwise empty Dutch barn.

"It's a combine harvester." I could hardly disguise the surprise in my voice. "It cuts the cereals and the straw comes out there."

"It's got a flat tyre," he observed.

I had hoped this would have gone unnoticed. It had been delivered a week before and driven off the lorry apparently in perfect condition.

"It's only a flat tyre; if it is a puncture they will certainly mend it." I referred to the main machinery dealers.

"Send it back and buy a new one." Mr Campbell was adamant.

"We can't afford to buy new with our relatively small acreage," I pointed out.

"I'm not in the habit of buying second-hand." I understood that made it an order.

I spoke to the sales manager the next morning.

"Jerry, you know the combine you delivered last week? I want another one." I waited for his reaction.

"Are you going into contracting?" he hesitated.

"No. Can you take it back and supply new?" I asked.

"What is wrong with it?" he enquired.

"It's got a flat tyre," I replied.

"You're kidding."

"No, it really has," I asserted, keeping the joke alive.

"I have never had a customer do that." He knew my employer was an industrialist.

"Jerry, I have not educated my employer yet, but I still need a good discount on the new one."

The low-loader arrived the next day with a shiny new combine, and the second-hand one, tyre inflated enough to drive it onto the lorry, was taken back.

"Jerry, that was very quick; it's very shiny." I wanted to confirm it had arrived safely.

"I was frightened your man might change his mind," Jerry joked.

"I am trying to manage an industrialist; it must look right but so must the price!"

"I will do my best. You keep coming to me and I will help you out. Rather you than me." Jerry wished me well.

In the spring we trialled growing a small acreage of carrots. They were drilled by a local contractor with a root drill. The three acres had been well cultivated, fertilised and rolled; all looked well. Although only a trial, it would show whether the crop would be viable. Similarly, the second early potatoes had closed over in the rows and were in flower. I had done trial digs to check size and weight; they were ready for harvesting. The second-hand potato harvester had not been 'discovered' by Mr Campbell. I intended to use it on potatoes and change the 'digging', and maybe other webs[34], to use it for the carrots. Such trials

---

[34] moving belts made up of equally spaced steel bars

were needed before committing to a new machine. The potatoes were bagged and weighed and sold through the wholesale vegetable market. The yield and price per ton were quite satisfactory and established their place in the cropping plan for the following year.

I had planned to sell the carrots to the wholesale market but we had no washing facility; it would be trial and error this first year. The first job was to top the carrots as they grew in the field. I asked a contractor to use his various pasture toppers and experiment on doing the best job; that was to cut off the top as near as possible to the crown without harming it.

I was able to borrow, at a small price, an old potato grader and inspection conveyor. The carrots were dug fairly successfully by the potato harvester and hand-sorted by ladies from the village; the sandy soil readily separated, presenting a soil-free sample, although unwashed. There was a limited demand in the wholesale market as they were competing with the washed product. Some were sold directly to greengrocers as unwashed and natural. The only real point established was that the soil was excellent for growing carrots. We needed to research what markets existed and what they required in presentation and packaging.

There was another immediate problem: the disposal of the oversized and damaged carrots. These were heaped up in the covered yard behind the big barn, amounting to about fifty tons. There was a limit to the amount Ernie could feed to the pigs but they seemed very happy with the varied diet. A number of local horse enterprises were pleased to pay for nets of carrots, but it hardly reduced the pile. Ernie approached me one morning with his wife's recipe book.

"Would you like to make 'carrot wine'?" I looked at the tonnage and looked at Ernie.

"Are you pulling my leg?" I didn't want to upset him.

"I could give you some crystallised honey," he offered.

As a keen beekeeper he had already given us some beautiful honey. The honey in question couldn't be sold as it had crystallised, but it might make mead.

"Ernie, even if I had time, we are not going to make any impression on that heap of carrots," I argued.

"Mead is made from honey but can also have a fruit base... like carrots!" Hazel suggested. "You ought to help him; he is so kind and gentle," she persuaded me.

We made as much carrot wine as the honey permitted; needless to say there were still carrots for all. It turned out to be the best full-bodied white wine, or should I say 'mead', I have ever tasted.

Having established that the soil was very favourable for carrots, I now had to match growing them for a definite market and customers. I had to find amenable farmers in East Anglia to research the necessary details of husbandry and sales.

# 23

# Building the Business

Starting the farm had been a very busy period but it was about to get much busier. I had only just got the ball rolling and discovered what the land was capable of producing when Mr Campbell stepped in. It started at our third quarterly meeting with Michael Smedley and me; we met at head office and reviewed progress at Beech Row Farm. The accounts showed reasonable progress.

"It depends what you call progress, Michael." Mr Campbell was obviously in strident business mode. "I see no surplus yet; I have spent a lot of money and have no return."

"Come, Mr Campbell, you are establishing a farm; there will be no real return for a year." Michael was smiling as if he needed to 'tell grandma how to suck eggs'.

"I can get two and a half per cent in the Post Office." Mr Campbell leaned forward as if to emphasis the point.

"The average sort of return in agriculture nationally is about one per cent as landlord and one and a half per cent for tenants. Being owner and farmer, it's about two and a half per cent. But of course that does not take account of land values increasing," Michael stated authoritatively.

Mr Campbell had certainly known the position before investing, but in present company had laid down the marker that we must strive for significant returns.

"Peter has made a good start and I'm sure we will see good growth for you." Michael was used to dealing with clients and, no doubt, acting as referee in any match of two sides. He now changed tack. "Tell us, when will you be building your house, Mr Campbell?"

"My architect has drawn up a nice first plan." He added his ingratiating grin which signalled money. "But it's a bit expensive at the moment."

He turned back to the farm business.

"I mentioned to Peter about a modern Atcost building somewhere opposite the big barn, a sort of new complex." Mr Campbell was now proposing spending more money.

"It would be very handy; there is only the tin workshop at the moment," I rushed to endorse the suggestion. "There is chance of a horticultural grant with the carrot enterprise starting," I added.

Brenda knocked and came in with a tray of sandwiches. "If you could kindly hold the door open, I'll bring the drinks."

I moved quickly, expecting it to be my job.

She stood back, mouthing, "All OK?" and a supportive smile.

The soft drinks were put on the table with the sandwiches.

"Do help yourselves." Mr Campbell showed the way by taking two sandwiches, leaving us to be more modest.

A few days later Mr Campbell wanted to meet me on the farm for a site discussion on both the house and the new building. At two o'clock sharp we walked to flat open ground at the far side of my garden and to the tin workshop.

"I thought the best site would be alongside the workshop with the entrance about level with the workshop doors." I indicated with my arms and stood in the proposed entrance. "We need this as a grading shed for both carrots and potatoes so it will be truly horticultural," I added.

"And you have room for further expansion." Mr Campbell waved to the seventy or so yards between us and the only other building – the corn store by the track to Overley Farm.

I drove Mr Campbell in the Land Rover across two fields to a sandy depression of heath bracken and stunted silver birch.

"We thought something could be done here." Again, he waved his arms as if casting a magic spell. I could only imagine it would take magic to do anything with the area. "My architect has in mind the house sitting in a saucer." More waving.

We walked about a hundred yards to the lower road and indicated a possible drive back up to the planned house. He fumbled in his briefcase and, to my surprise, produced a plan.

"Wow!" I wished I had chosen a better expression. The front elevation was of a property only seen in magazines of tropical islands owned by the super-rich.

"It would look down this way with the farm behind," Mr Campbell demonstrated.

I looked around and found it difficult to imagine, especially in this rural location with nothing remotely like it in the vicinity.

"Of course, we must wait for planning permission, but I hope that will be through in a month or so." He said this as a matter of fact, bar the short wait. "You can get water to us, Peter?" He meant it as an instruction rather than a question. "We'll have to sort out electricity." He discounted main services as a matter of just switching them on.

Six weeks later a large Clark-Michigan bulldozer arrived. Mr Campbell phoned to inform me to keep an eye on it.

"I know you are busy, Peter, but pop over now and again. He is scooping top soil aside and digging down about ten feet to where the foundations will be. You're my site manager."

I said I would keep an eye on the project and the phone clicked off.

I noted the quick promotion and added responsibility, wondering if it could be a poisoned chalice. I reported all this to Hazel.

"How are you going to manage all that and the farm?" She was not pleased with today's promotion.

"It shouldn't take much time, but I don't know what I'm supposed to do." I felt out of my depth and dared not mention engineering a water supply to the site.

"I don't see much of you now," she retorted.

My job got a lot busier with trips to East Anglia and Kent. The carrot enterprise needed a lot of research and learning on my part. Fortunately, I had a contact in the machinery business dealing with root crops and he, smelling a sale, offered to help. David was a very practical representative who earned sales without pressure. With the patience of an angler, he tried different flies until a farmer found one tasty and then he reeled him in. He had found growers needing particular machines and worked for a firm that made them; why not join the two together?

David took me around large vegetable holdings to whom he had supplied equipment for some years. There seemed to be a willing fraternity of growers who shared ideas and had advanced as a band in developing ways to satisfy supermarkets and processors. I noted the systems they had devised to supply particular markets and the attention to detail required. I was introduced to a freelance engineer who had worked for a number of large growers, designing and making their plant[35]. He relished solving problems and made bespoke machines. Colin was a true son of the soil, living and breathing farm equipment. I found his trademark was strength of product in contrast to mass-produced machines. His were heavier, more durable and totally unbendable. Any tractor scraping by his equipment would suffer more damage than the plant. Colin agreed to visit Beech Row Farm once the new Atcost building was completed and I had decided on the best type of carrot market for our situation.

I looked into the possibility of growing carrots for canning on a contractual basis, which I knew would appeal to Mr Campbell. This would give more security than aiming at the prepacked supermarket approach. Canners in Kent seemed interested in a new source from Wessex and their rep showed me their requirements. It was a tight specification, grown to sizes that would fit in a tin and present nicely upon opening. Obviously small tins required all 'small' carrots rather than one or two medium-sized and made up with a few 'half' carrots. This

---

[35] machines

required meticulous detail in growing and close grading. With their buyer, John, it all seemed possible.

## Our First Harvest

In tandem with the carrots and their trial problems, I had had to switch to cereals. The first grain harvest was nearly upon us already and our new Claas combine was ready for work. As usual the grain storage arrangements had to be ready as well. I had employed another man to make sure we could cope with the growing enterprises and the building works. Tony and Linda had just married and were looking for a job with accommodation. Tony had experience of farm work but little as a tractor driver; he would be useful in aiding others as a general farm worker. His affable manner and willingness to do any job filled a gap in our team and saved others breaking off from major work.

The corn store had to be cleaned from top to bottom. I showed Tony the layout of ventilated bins and the electric control panel.

"Rule one: We have to start at the top and finish at the bottom," I instructed as a basic principle. "I want this to be your baby," I added.

Tony was a young man of few words and I wondered how much he was taking in.

"Just sweep everything down today," I instructed. We were on the top gangway with four square bins on each side. "Brush along the top conveyor, then run it with all the chutes to the bins open." I had shown him the control panel with the labelled switches.

An hour later I returned to find Tony looking like a miner except for a white mouth and nose where the mask had been.

"The next part is to open all the chutes from the bins to the bottom conveyor and sweep out each bin."

He nodded and went to work.

The next day I pointed out rule two. "When operating the store always check where you want the corn to go." I stated the obvious. It was only fair to demonstrate the importance of getting corn in the right bin; and the reverse, getting it out. I instilled walking along the desired route of the corn, opening the one chute and making sure all the others were shut.

Harvest proceeded well with no real problems. Ken looked after corn carting and baling, with Ernie and Tony in partnership on pigs and corn store. Ernie had been used to working in the corn store with the previous owners and was a good support for our new man. I did most of the combining, checking the moisture content of the grain and the priority of fields to harvest. The new combine was capable of cutting many more acres, and I advertised our services as contractors. As a result, a number of smallholders without their own combine, and some larger farms who needed extra capacity, asked for our services. It was a new experience travelling some miles and cutting 'foreign' fields, ones that I didn't know. There was always a potential for getting stuck in a wet spot that the owners themselves would have avoided, or picking up wire fencing carelessly forgotten. Even around the outside of fields, branches of trees could be substantial enough to dent or damage our new machine. Some owners complained about "leaving that bit we always cut", forgetting they took care to cut back branches in the winter when using their own equipment.

One evening I had an enquiry from a man who wanted eight acres of barley combined. I asked if it was ready; that is, dry enough. There was a pause on the phone.

"I'm not sure." The gruff voice hesitated.

"Are the heads bent over and dry?" I patiently enquired.

"I think so, sir," he replied.

"If it doesn't rain, I'll be with you in two days." I knew that I could visit the address the evening before on my way home.

I called at a council house on the outskirts of a village. The same gruff voice rode with me to the field a mile away. The field was on the roadside and seemed dry enough to cut straight away.

"What will you do with the barley when it's cut?" I asked, thinking it might need drying if being stored.

"A neighbour with pigs is buying it straight away," he said.

The next morning I reached the farm at about eleven o'clock and 'greased up'[36] in the gateway. My customer was in the road with a tractor and trailer.

"Is this your only field?" I enquired as I checked belt tensions.

"Yes, it was my uncle's," he replied.

"Is that his tractor and trailer?" It was none of my business but I made conversation.

"No, he's dead."

"I'm sorry I asked," I added, feeling I had overstepped the mark.

"I inherited the field, yer see." His gruff voice softened. "I'm Bill, by the way... I'm only a dustman." It sounded like a confession.

"I look after a farm but I'm only a farm worker," I replied. "And I'm Peter."

It seemed to level things up.

The field was combined without a hitch.

"That's one and a half trailers," I said jumping down from the combine. "So I would guess that's about twelve tons of barley. Don't let him do you." I spoke of his neighbour.

"I think he's fair but I'll remember twelve tons," Bill replied.

"I've got to give you a bill and ask for a cheque," I advised, getting a duplicate book out of the toolbox. This is a book used to record sales: the original, or top copy, is given to the customer; the carbon copy stays in the book.

---

[36] machine is fully greased for work

He already had his cheque book in hand. He looked at the invoice.

"You write it and I will sign it." His gruff voice masked a gentle spirit.

I put the cheque in the book with the duplicate, thanking him.

"Here's something for you," he proffered a five pound note.

"Thanks, but I can't take that." It sounded ungrateful.

"You're a working man," Bill was insistent. "There ain't no taste in nothing!"

"Thank you... I'm very pleased to have met you." The words seemed inadequate but he smiled, a kindred spirit. Of all the customers that harvest, he was the only one to give me a tip.

Harvest was the first time I met Mr Campbell's family. It was exciting for them that their father had bought a farm rather than another boring business. They usually phoned, saying they were coming down from London and would like to see the farm. No doubt an approach they had learned from their father.

"Dad said you are very busy so we will come in the evening," daughter Sandra announced.

I nearly always agreed to their terms as one evening followed another, requiring preparation for the next day or catching up on office work. They called at the farmhouse wanting to see the 'estate' and the extent of it. I drove them round to the notable parts like the stew ponds and the Hydram supplying our water, then through to Overley Farm and the airstrip. Such a trip was well received and a subtle opportunity for me to express mild opinions that might just get back to 'Dad'. I was sure all the family were aware of the farm and possibly planning holidays to explore it in greater depth.

A son who had qualified as a solicitor was interested in the legal position, particularly the water supply to houses. We had one private house on the system who did not pay for water or cause us any concern. They were not part of the estate nor was the access to their property. However, head office decided to 'regularise' the position. By return of post our friendly neighbour was at my door.

"Is Mr Campbell going to turn off our water?" There was distinct panic in Mr Becket's voice.

I invited him in and read the letter he had just opened. The worrying paragraph was the disclaimer, "We cannot guarantee or be responsible, in any event, for the quantity or quality of water your connection takes from our main."

"Supposing he cuts us off!" Mr Becket exclaimed.

"I don't think there is any plan for that; there is plenty of water." I tried to calm his concern.

"We have never had a letter like that before. I don't mind paying for it," Mr Becket offered.

"Leave it with me. I will see what prompted this, but there is no emergency," I assured him.

"There is if we have no water," he asserted.

"In farming we can always get by, believe me."

At last he seemed assured.

"How should I reply?" He pointed to the letter.

"Don't reply; it is only stating his position. If you write anything you may aggravate the situation," I cautioned him.

It was sometime later that Mr Campbell told me not to take any payment from the Beckets as that would endanger our position. I considered that closed the matter and told Mr Becket so. Their response was effusive but I refused any reward, except for a jar of homemade jam.

The new building was to be erected by the manufacturer's contractors and soon the frame was completed. The next stage was for the cladding team first to roof it and then to clad the sides halfway down from the concrete gutter. The skill and sheer daring of the men cladding the roof both astonished and frightened the onlooker. They mitred the corners of asbestos sheets, climbed ladders, passing sheets to a mate who walked along the foot-wide concrete gutter to fix them onto the purlin[37]. It was best not witnessed by any frail of heart. I wondered what would happen if a sudden gust of wind took man and sheet. Once the erection of the building was finished, I had to organise contractors to concrete the floor and later build concrete block walls to a height of seven feet all round, except the doorway. The walls extended a foot up the inside of the sheeting to keep all weathers out. I specified constructing a vehicle inspection pit in the front corner of the floor so that the final building could also act as a workshop although the primary use was intended to be for grading potatoes or carrots.

I had been impressed on my visits to East Anglia with the size of buildings that were necessary for vegetable grading and packaging. We were only anticipating a relatively small enterprise but it would have to be weatherproof and kept clean and tidy. It was also vital to use the latest growing techniques to produce the size specified by the processors, in our case the canners.

John, the fieldsman for the canners, put me in touch with their precision drill manufacturers and explained the best growing practice.

"Our growers use a nine-row bed system with a gap between beds that suits your tractor wheels," John explained.

"So the wheels don't run on the crop?" I asked for clarity.

"We can sort those widths when you know which drill and harvester you'll be getting."

"How do you sow nine rows in a bed? That's so precise," I asked.

---

[37] horizontal beam

John went and retrieved some seed belts from his car.

"These are belts that will be supplied with the drill." He showed me a continuous belt that had rows of minute holes. There were three lines of holes side by side across the width of belting, replicated about every inch. "Each hole holds a seed and deposits it as the belt goes over a solid pulley on its constant circular journey."

I looked in amazement.

"You will have individual seeder units on a frame that can be adjusted across the width, each unit sowing three rows of carrot seed," John pointed out. "The subtle part is the belt itself," he continued. "The middle unit has a belt with three holes side by side an inch apart along its whole length, therefore planting three lines of seed all at an inch apart. The unit on the left has a similar belt with three lines of holes except the outside row is spaced closer at say three-quarters of an inch between holes."

John drew breath before continuing.

"This means three seeder units each sowing three lines of carrots, giving you a nine-row bed. But... and it's a big 'but'... the seeds in the outside rows of the bed are closer together." There was a pause whilst I took it all in.

"Why go to all that trouble?" I asked.

"Naturally, the carrots on the outside row of the bed get more sunlight and therefore grow bigger; sowing them closer compensates for that."

"Really!" I observed rather than questioned.

"Well, that's the theory." John smiled. "Yes, it does work. We want even-sized small carrots," he finished.

"And the good news is you pay more for those," I said with a smile.

"That should have been my line; two happy parties!" We both wore broad grins.

This was the great answer to our problem. Surely we could grow what the customer required? The technology for growing only small carrots was by using nature to our advantage; no more hit and miss and relying on grading out the large ones. I ordered a precision drill with nine seeder units, explaining in my weekly report that it was not specific to carrots and would sow any small seeds depending on the size of the belt holes. This was passed without special comment and I was pleased to explain the details to Marvin when he visited in the spring.

Colin, the engineer from East Anglia, examined the new building and the surrounding area outside.

"You'll be size-grading indoors with conveyors and bagging-off points." He was stating the usual system. "Are you happy with the hopper and destoner outside?" he asked.

"Fine, it's what I've seen others, on larger farms, do up your way."

"Best to keep all the water outside," Colin urged.

"We are not washing," I pointed out

"I know, but you've got plenty of stones. I've got to separate them; you'll never do that by hand." Colin was ahead of me. I had seen Fenland farms where there were no stones at all.

Colin produced a drawing of a large hopper, big enough to take a bulk trailer-load of carrots, with a moving floor discharging into a smaller hopper. He explained that the second hopper would become a fiercely bubbling bath that would carry carrots across to the elevator and into the building, whilst stones were heavy enough to sink through the 'boiling' water onto and up another elevator. The heap of 'washed' stones would be valuable for pathways or a multitude of other uses. He went back to East Anglia to work out the cost of various items to at least give an estimate of the cost of the machinery items. The installation cost would have to be added dependent on the hours spent on site setting it up. It was an exciting prospect but an expensive one.

## New Farmhouse

In the meantime I was having to oversee the site clearance for the 'new' farmhouse. The huge saucer now contained footings and the start of walls growing upward. I could see from the plan that the house would be mostly wood and glass. The architect often visited to see how his 'baby' was growing, and pointed out main features as they appeared. Initially the building appeared modest and situated at the top of what would be the drive. This entire level was in fact the garage, big enough for several cars. On top of this and spreading around the saucer was a line of bedrooms and reception rooms forming a square; the centre would become an open atrium. The south side would enclose an indoor pool.

My involvement mainly consisted of progress reports and the hurrying of tradesmen at any pinch point. Once the building had been completed, and electricians and plumbers were busy doing their part, I only visited to issue a change of plan. One such change involved lighting. I was apprehensive whenever the phone rang at 9 am, knowing it almost certainly would be head office with another directive.

Mr Campbell, with little introduction, always got straight to the point. "Peter, my wife would like lights in the pool." He was needing his manager to take the flack for late changes.

"They finished fitting them yesterday, Mr Campbell."

There was a pause to see if Brenda, his secretary, had been involved in any conversation with the architect.

"Mrs Campbell only thought of it yesterday," he said.

"Do you mean *more* lights?" I asked.

"Yes, under the water," came the reply. "About twelve or fourteen inches below the water level," Mr Campbell directed.

"That will mean a lot of work to channel cable around the pool. The builders have finished the pool surround and the next job will be tiling," I explained.

"Talk to the men in your Christian way, Peter." The phone went dead.

He had used this phrase before. Whenever there was a problem that was difficult, even bordering on illegal, I was left to do the talking. Currently any idea was expected to be enacted without any concern for the practical implications.

I went straight to the site and found the three electricians fixing lights in the garage.

"I am afraid there is a bit of a problem." I thought it would be a good way to introduce the subject. "The governor want lights in the swimming pool."

"We're finishing here first. They haven't done the ceiling in the pool room yet," the owner of the small business, Kevin, answered.

"I mean in the pool itself," I repeated.

They stopped work and looked down at me from their steps.

"I mean underwater," I enlarged.

"That's not in the spec." The boss, Kevin, normally a mild man, squared up to me. "They'll have done the pool surround by now," he told me in no uncertain tone.

Undeterred I continued, "He wants a dozen lights about a foot under the water level, four each side and two at each end."

We strode up to the pool and I launched into the builders. "I am afraid there has just been a change of plan here. The governor wants lights under the water."

"We finished it yesterday!" the foreman said. I now had seven men prepared to throw me into the empty pool.

"Mrs Campbell only thought of it yesterday." I passed on the request again: "Mrs Campbell would like lights around the sides, under the water. I'm sorry, I'm only the messenger," I confessed.

"Well, at least it hasn't already been filled with water," the foreman growled sarcastically. "I guess we can wire it and come across the floor; there will be enough depth to cover with the final floor float," he conceded.

Just as I was trying to keep all the balls in the air on the farm, we were expecting our second baby. Hazel naturally was coping well with the preparations for the second time but missed her friend Ruth. The midwife was a marvellous support and all seemed well. Hazel's mum planned to stay for a week to look after Nichola, which was a relief for us both. The midwife arranged a nursing home birth when the baby was a little overdue, and that was a firm signal to Hazel's mum that we needed her. This time I was alerted to attend the birth before harvest started. It was great to be together before the wondrous event.

"It's a girl!" the midwife announced. We had not minded whether it was a boy or a girl, just a safe delivery. When the baby was handed to mum, we just thanked God for the miracle of new life.

"Have you given her a name?" the nurse asked.

"Caroline," Hazel answered. We had agreed on the name two weeks before.

It was good to have the centre of one's life turned back towards the family. I had been conscious that the business had been consuming all my time and effort. The family grew closer as daily living centred around the new arrival. Now Caroline was home, her needs were top of the list, with Nichola showing great interest – as did our rough collie, Lisa. Visitors had to see the baby whether sleeping or awake. Nichola expected she needed soft dolls whilst Hazel's mum insisted she wanted clean ones. The dog insisted she should be in the same room as Caroline and the family. She did not have to be in the way, her usual hearthrug was sufficient; she could raise eyelids without any movement of the head before returning to sleep on the matter.

Work on the new farmhouse continued through the autumn and winter; contractors were busy inside and out. Further landscaping was started and the farm was responsible for a 'farm-type' boundary fence. It was beginning to look as if the fields needed protection from the rapid advance of the landscaped grounds. The rough drive, laid for building purposes, was tarred and sealed with a fine bitumen coating. In the house I had to supervise the internal fittings, from cooker and fridge deliveries to carpet layers. Fortunately, the colour choices had been made by Mrs Campbell. The bedroom wing, including the master suite, was all one shade of pastel green which showed off the extent of the house. The carpet around the pool, to within six inches of the water, was a similar shade but 'waterproof'. This was not so as to repel water but to be completely undamaged by it.

I had seen to the supply of water using contractors to mole-plough in two pipes on slightly different routes from the farm to the new house. This, I trusted, would guarantee their supply even if a plough or pig discovered a pipe. One pipe we routed five yards into the field, following the track to Overley Farm and then across to the new farmhouse; the other would take a more direct line. New rolls of one-inch-diameter polythene pipe were laid, avoiding roots from the hedgerow without much trouble. I returned to the contractors the day after completing the first pipe.

"I thought you were going the more direct route today with the second connection?" I spoke to the group of three men standing by the open trench.

"We haven't got any water," the gang leader said.

"You mean, it leaks?" I enquired.

"No, just no water, not a drop," he confessed. "There is water where we started up by the road but none at the unions[38]; they are bone dry."

They undid the first union to demonstrate.

"Water starts but doesn't come through; there must be a major leak in the pipe, but there is no wet spot," he summed up.

"Have you got any welding rods?" the other man, Fred, butted in.

"Yes, but what for?" I replied.

"I may be able to find the leak," Fred said without much confidence.

I produced two copper rods from the workshop which Fred bent at right angles. He walked to the roadside and the rods spun together.

"It's here," Fred shouted. We rushed up to him.

"Is that the leak?" the leader asked. There was no reply.

"I am following the water."

Fred was criss-crossing the pipe and the two rods were responding.

"It's stopped," Fred announced, but we had all noticed there was no longer any movement of the rods. They dug around the spot enlarging the trench but there was no sign of even dampness.

"There must be something in the pipe," Fred suggested.

"It's brand new off the roll," the boss said in disbelief. "Turn off the water and cut the pipe where you are."

A few minutes later a dry pipe was bent up to show everybody. We all agreed no water had ever been down that.

Fred had started more dousing some six feet back towards the road. They enlarged the trench and started with the hacksaw again. As soon as the pipe was pierced, there was water.

"Carry on and pull that bit right out," the boss instructed. He peered down the pipe. "I can't see daylight; it is blocked by something," he confirmed.

After further work with the hacksaw, they came to it: the pipe was solid – solid polythene with no hole running through the middle of it.

"I have never seen that before; there's not even a small hole. I'll take it up with the manufacturer." The boss was less than pleased.

A length was cut off another roll and joined into the previous day's main. It solved the problem but each new length on the direct route now had to be tested before being joined with the next. The water pressure also proved sufficient as it came from the large storage tank in the stone barn. My only worry was the quantity that might be used if house guests stayed for a long period.

Once the family had moved into the new house, the dynamic changed. Mr Campbell and I were much closer, literally. I was only a phone call and five minutes away across the fields. However, I was so involved with his everyday life that I gradually learned his *modus operandi*. I was able to predict his reaction

---

[38] pipe connectors

to most things and, in doing so, avoided trouble. I became used to setting the men their tasks and freeing myself to be flexible. I could be available to my employer and thus manage the business without engaging in every practical detail. I reasoned that I must build upon the enterprises to optimise output.

I thought the large area between my house and the corn store, and across to the first field, provided good country views. On the one hand there were trees lining the edge of the road and a clean farmstead without any smells. And there was also a view of natural woods; in short, probably a good place to park a caravan for a few days' holiday. I approached the Caravan Club for permission to become a Certified Site location. They found it suitable and we expanded into the leisure business, able to accommodate up to five caravans per night.

This appealed to Mr Campbell, who was thrilled at the idea and initiative of collecting seven shillings and six pence in cash per caravan per night. It was with the small signs of potential being realised, and no doubt the chance to increase the value of the property, that he soon suggested another Atcost building. Although in farming terms it was early days, he was prepared to spend capital in order to grow the business. Often traditional farmers try to produce more from the land and only invest in buildings when absolutely necessary. The farm was its own business and I had to borrow on the overdraft at about ten per cent at the time.

I was called over to see Mr Campbell about three mornings a week. This would usually be about 9 am in his bedroom suite.

"Peter, I think you could do with an office, in the new building."

He was chatting as he shaved. He wandered unconsciously from dressing room to bedroom and back in his dressing gown using an electric razor. After a few weeks I regarded myself as an RAF batman to the Squadron Leader.

"If you make it a bay or so longer, you could have toilets and showers downstairs and an office on the first floor," he continued, as if we would be employing about fifty people, with some on night shift.

"Yes, that would be great for the caravaners," I suggested, quickly catching up with him.

"The building could be completely partitioned off at the end bay and the majority of it used for crops," Mr Campbell continued.

I encouraged the idea as I already thought one building did not make a farmyard.

On other morning visits Mr Campbell often bounced ideas off me which I was ill-equipped to answer. In the first few months that he was settling in, it seemed many outsiders thought a benevolent 'uncle' had arrived in the area.

"Peter, I have a letter asking me to be chairman of the cricket club. Do you think that would be a good idea?"

"I thought you were already chairman of a football club," I rather stupidly replied.

"They want money of course."

I accepted that as a rebuff.

"It's always money."

He continued rubbing the razor around with no stubble left.

"Do you think it will help us?"

I was reluctant to suggest anything.

"Do they have a pavilion?" The questions kept coming.

"I'm afraid I don't know," I muttered.

"Make a few discreet enquiries," he suggested.

In my next weekly report, I mentioned they had had a new pavilion built only the previous year.

It was only a week later he had another letter.

"Peter, the Parish Council have asked if I might consider standing for election." He did not wait for my comment. "I think it is far too early," he continued. "You might like to stand yourself."

"I really think I'm too busy; besides, Hazel would never forgive me," I replied firmly.

I changed the subject but had noted the inference.

"I have a request from Plant Protection (ICI's research department) to run some trials on Overley Farm," I offered. "It would be another source of income without taking up much land."

I outlined that they were looking for no more than an acre on which they were wanting to trial a weedkiller. It would be for a minimum of three years.

Mr Campbell was interested in any easy income. "I'll speak to my lawyer son."

He was pleased the plant protection firm had chosen his farm and was always glad to flag up the status of his family. The legal agreement was actually drafted by the researchers who used a standard contract. We fenced off the acre plot next to the gallop on Overley.

The work around the farmhouse continued with Mr and Mrs Campbell conducting their finishing inspections, making good the odd leaks, draughts, door hangings, intercom and phone connections, etc. Architect and tradesmen were for the most part wondering why they were called back to what to them was as an "entirely adequate finish". There was a particular complaint that was brought to my attention:

"Peter, we can't see beyond the road." Mr Campbell was referring to the view from the boardroom over the garages down the driveway. "Those trees are in the way." He was pointing out three magnificent elms on the far side of the road.

"I think they may be under a tree preservation order," I told him.

"I want you to cut them down." He had obviously been discussing the matter and had now made up his mind.

"But we can't. I'm pretty sure the previous owner had the order placed on them."

A week later I was surprised to find a gap along the lower road and all signs of the timber missing.

It was only a few more days before Mr Campbell called me to another morning meeting. As usual he was shaving and walking around.

"I have a letter saying the trees at the roadside were under a preservation order."

I refrained from saying, "I told you so."

"That is most unfortunate. As a new resident how could I have known that?" he continued. "I think we need to look at the facts. You have been very busy."

I wondered what was coming.

"You too are new, my estate manager from Sussex. How could we know about these things?"

I was beginning to realise this was a rehearsal for a convincing alibi.

"The man from the council will be coming here today; I'll tell him you are too busy to attend."

I felt a sense of relief.

"I'll tell him you and I couldn't know these things." Mr Campbell gave that annoying grimace that meant the matter was over, at least as far as the fact that the trees had disappeared, and he had more or less won.

The next day I was summoned to the house again; I guessed the reason.

"How did things go with the council man?" I asked

"He understood perfectly."

I stared in disbelief.

"Charming man. I apologised on your behalf. I insisted we replaced them."

I was speechless.

"I have got half a dozen saplings in the garage; can you plant them this afternoon?"

I knew that it was not a question but an imperative. I realised he regarded us as a duo that could achieve most things; good guy, bad guy, or the more likely inference, "My manager is not too bright."

# 24

# Proper Farming

Amongst all the building of the business, especially the new farmhouse with its attendant growing pains, was the fresh air of 'proper farming' – the farming that had drawn me into the industry, the joy of husbanding nature to achieve good crops. I wanted more of that. Indeed, crops and livestock were the core business and I was determined to pursue that.

The carrot trial had demonstrated that the soil could produce quality roots and, with the right machines, we ought to find a ready market. Colin, my contact in East Anglia, had drawn up a series of items that would grade and prepare carrots for canning. It was a veritable carrot plant (pun intended) that would be assembled on site specifically for our business. Colin and his men were in the bespoke business of making the grader, hopper and destoner to suit any customer and their particular circumstances.

Colin came with his caravan and tools, including welding equipment, expecting to stay a few days to make sure everything worked as planned. The grader and other items arrived by lorry. We set up the rotary grader in the far end of the new building under his supervision. It was a matter of siting it by the gap in the wall where the elevator would be delivering the carrots into the rotating drum. The metal frame and legs of the grader were all very substantial; more likely to bend the tractor in a collision than the machinery.

Outside the building we manoeuvred the elevator that would feed the crop into the grader, its tail-end dropping into the destoner. Naturally this all took a good deal of lifting, instruction to the forklift driver, and our huffing and puffing, not to mention 'words of encouragement'; I use 'words' advisedly. Colin, familiar with his creation, was noting and measuring critical distances between items and stopping to weld on extra brackets, or 'feet', where necessary.

During these intermissions the men were digging out the large pit with the fore-loader and bucket. This was again at Colin's careful measurements, anticipating the placing of the half-sunken hopper. This chunky receiving hopper would hold at least a trailer-load of carrots at a time, allowing the tractor driver to return straight to the field for another load. Colin was eventually satisfied and left us to concrete the sunken base for the hopper and, a week or so later, to build a retaining wall large enough but still allowing enough room to work around it. A couple of weeks later he returned to inspect our work and to finish the installation.

Mr Campbell and his son Marvin paid a visit to the site. Mercifully there was a lot of hardware for them to see.

"So this is where you have been spending my money." Mr Campbell ran his hand over the dark-green framework. "It is very sturdy," he commented.

I was pleased at the positive note.

"It will take a good few carrots to pay for this," Marvin interjected with a rather less pleasing observation.

I explained the destoner was simply a cauldron of bubbling water floating the carrots across to the grader whilst the heavier stones sank through it to the bottom of that tank from where they would be elevated to another trailer as clean stones. Inside the building the rotating grader sieved carrots to size, the small grade through the first sieve and the large ones continuing on to the second. I pointed out the two conveyor / inspection tables yet to be lifted into place.

We drove to the field of carrots; a sea of verdant tops with light brown strips of soil between the rows.

"Very neat and tidy," Mr Campbell observed. "When do you harvest them?"

"When they are big enough," I replied and then thought it worth adding a rider: "Timing is critical; any delay and the size increases almost daily. The small grade are worth more than the larger ones."

"So you will have to get the grading machinery finished quickly," Marvin observed.

I bent down and pulled up three or four carrot tops. The roots were only a couple of inches long.

"I should think another five or six weeks; I'll be keeping an eye on them," I promised.

Everything was ready in time. Colin, the engineer who had manufactured the plant, returned to commission it and make final adjustments. We had tried a dry run. We had no carrots to grade but the belts all moved and could be varied in speed; the water bubbled, driven by a 7 hp electric motor. The only untried item was the topping device he had mounted on the front of the root harvester. It was a spinning disc with braided wire fingers that he had used on another harvester. The disc was driven at speed like a flail mower and would take the carrot tops off, immediately before they were eased out of the soil and up the main web.

Ernie and Tony soon mastered the operation and, with some ladies from the village inspecting the conveyor belts for damaged or diseased carrots, the large sacks clipped onto the bagging-off shoots soon filled at speed. Unlike sacks of corn, these were not weighed, only tied up; the whole lorry going over a weighbridge at the factory or topping station. In the field we had two men from another farm with their tractors and trailers driving alongside the harvester and ferrying the crop to the large hopper. I was relieved all was well and I could give a favourable weekly report.

At the same time that the carrots could be fully considered an enterprise, the number of pigs had greatly increased. I had decided that the sows could live outside and farrow there. The combination of sandy soil and pigs would mean the dung was put where it was needed on inherently low fertility soil without us transporting and spreading it. It would also be a healthy environment for mum and piglets.

I started Ernie on building simple pig arks. These were three 'A' frames covered by five sheets of galvanised tin six feet long. The rear 'A' frame was covered in lap-larch planks cut to size. The middle frame was an inverted 'V', rather than an 'A', enabling the sow to lie flat lengthwise; the front 'A' included a doorstep to keep the young piglets in. We also strengthened it down the whole length on each side with rails of wood, ten inches up, as a farrowing rail, enabling piglets to escape as mum lay down.

Finally, there were a hundred arks in rows some distance apart. It was great to witness the porcine version of law and order as the sows were released into the field. Moving-in day was no problem as they each found their own hut, already filled with some clean straw; once occupied there was no room for a friend, or indeed an enemy. A large snout and two ears taking in the view was a 'closed' front door. The sitting tenant had every right going; the landlord only had to provide a water trough and breeding sow nuts (for good lactation) twice a day. After community feeds, they returned to the correct address without any disagreement, as did the piglets when they discovered it was possible to follow mum and return to the right hut. They were left together on mum's milk and later able to help themselves to creep pellets (supporting growth and development) from a covered feeder that barred any who were more than piglet-size.

Mr Campbell's daughter had two toddlers and liked to stop at the pigs when visiting the farm. The children were fascinated that each sow in the field had her own house. I remember her explaining to the children that they were not made of straw but strong wood and metal, so there was no chance of them being blown down. "And anyway, there are no foxes on Grandad's farm."

Once the piglets were weaned, the sows were run with the boars and the young pigs housed and yarded to pork weight. Dry sows were returned to a wood, where they were kindly clearing the undergrowth, or to similar huts in another field. The system worked with the minimum of labour and achieved two litters per sow per year. Moving the herd around gave the fields a rotational break from cereals and the pigs' manure improved the fields' fertility.

The second Atcost building was completed and really started the growth of the business. The toilets and showers were immediately used by the Caravan Club members. Mr Campbell suggested we had more sites and I had to remind him the rules stipulated a maximum of five caravans per night.

"We have two farms so we can have ten," he insisted.

I arranged for a location at Overley Farm, which satisfied both the Caravan Club and Mr Campbell. In practice all the caravanners wanted to be at the main farm where there was ample room and toilets. I also booked in 'rallies' whereby various interest groups came on a prearranged weekend and were not subject to the numbers rule. All were happy and the locals were not inconvenienced.

The Scots pine plantation was not in prime order and had been neglected. Mr Campbell thought it untidy but I was reluctant to spend time and money which was needed elsewhere.

"Peter, you could save the money on scrub-clearing under the trees by putting the pigs in there." Mr Campbell had jumped at the idea.

"They will clear it, but they'll kill the trees," I advised.

"Marvin says his friend does it," he replied.

I decided to put dry sows there and keep an eye on them, knowing that even with nose rings they would not be deterred from undermining tree roots. I was soon proved right with brambles and undergrowth cleared, but replaced by large dips and wallows. The trees were best felled and a permanent pasture established. There would be an income for the timber and a tidy field near to Mr Campbell's house.

I further improved the outlook with fencing and double gates to accommodate large machinery.

Mr Campbell warmed to the improvements and suggested field nameplates. I resisted this for as long as possible, anticipating scorn from 'real' farmers: "Don't your men know where to plough?" "I didn't know your chaps could read!" "Are you going to put postboxes on the gates?"

I anticipated the jesting in local shops and the pub, but still gave Mr Campbell a map with the fields, including the names. To my surprise he didn't like the names, insisting they were not rural enough, even though I said they were the historic names (except for 'New Meadow' where the wood had been fenced in). He, in conjunction with head office, produced a new list. In my disgust I will only tell you he wanted 'New Meadow' to become 'Strawberry Bottom'. I quietly dropped the idea of nameplates.

The serious business of farming was the first carrot crop, grown to exacting standards. Ken, with the precision drilling, produced beautiful straight beds of verdant carrot tops. Neighbours stopped to admire those beside the road. Colin from East Anglia completed the grading plant, insisting he had to be on hand to commission it and make final adjustments at harvest. I arranged for a load of sacks to take the graded carrots to a topping station. I trusted we had everything planned.

Our hopes were realised with the harvester flailing the carrot tops off like a lawn mower. It left just half an inch of 'crown' for the ladies at the topping station to trim by hand. The sacks of carrots were transported to Cambridgeshire, or Kent preferably.

Ken was charged with the harvester, and Ernie and Tony, our other workman, managed the grading operation. Carrots were tipped into the large receiving hopper with the slowly moving floor regulating the flow through the grader. Colin, seeing to the first working of the plant, set the speed and flow over the bubbling water to separate stones, then to the next elevator, through the shed wall, into the rotating grader.

"I didn't realise how many stones there were," said Colin pointing to the cleats full of stones from the bubbling water. "I'll put a larger sprocket on after this load," he said. "It will speed it up."

"The rest of it is working very well," I observed.

Inside the building the smaller grades were dropping onto the first inspection belt, one lady throwing off any debris and damaged carrots. Similarly, the medium carrots carried on to the second table and into their respective size grades. I quickly counted the sacks stacked along the wall: twenty small and six medium. "Not bad," I thought. "Big improvement on last year."

I went out to get Colin's reaction.

"About what we expect in the east," he said amongst the clatter of stones. "Probably harvest a bit earlier next time. A week makes a lot of difference."

I pointed out the same ratio to John, the fieldsman for the canners, who called the next day.

"You could try a week earlier for this crop and immediately plough and plant a second crop in the same field to be harvested before Christmas," he suggested. "The important date is to drill the second crop no later than the first week of July or it won't have time to mature." This was great advice.

The price for the small grade was nearly double the medium size; anything bigger was of no use to the canning factory. There was a very small market for the large ones for horses, sold at the farm gate; equally grateful was Ernie, for his sows.

John further encouraged me with the news that the factory was looking into using ton boxes rather than sacks, which were getting more difficult to source. I made a point of recording this in my weekly report, which would surely impress head office.

On one of his visits to Overley Farm, Marvin had taken an interest in a pair of cottages, not far from Ernie's house, that had not been occupied in my time at Beech Row and where the gardens were very overgrown. He insisted it was an asset we were not using. I pointed out we were too busy to clear the gardens so Marvin said he would arrange that, but he expected me to show any prospective tenants around when the time came. It was only a matter of a month before he told me a young lady wanted to view the property. She arrived as arranged and I drove her to the house.

We looked out over the lower fields and gallops.

"There is so much countryside; it's lovely," she enthused immediately.

I certainly agreed with the beauty but had not been struck with the quantity before, but on reflection I had not lived in London for many years, where the countryside is certainly limited. The house, some hundred and twenty years old, in similar manner was deemed "quaint". I gave a quick conducted tour of rooms, which met with approval, before returning to the kitchen.

"I love the large china sink, but do you think we could have the sort of taps you can knock on with your elbow?" she asked, noticing some surprise on my part. "My friend's hand is rather crippled and she finds taps difficult," she added in explanation.

"I'm sure that can be done; will she be viewing soon?" I asked.

"I'll be speaking to her tonight, but I am sure she will be happy with it all," she asserted.

"Please deal with Mr Campbell; he is responsible for the letting, but I am glad you like it." I drove her back to her car.

It was a week later that I was told the two ladies had accepted the property and signed the appropriate agreement. This prompted me to quickly change the taps. I returned with spanners and spade to turn off the mains. The mains supply appeared to be already turned off. After fixing the new taps and locating the stopcock to turn the supply back on, I was still met with no water. Judging by the direction of the pipe, water was fed from the farm buildings. I resigned myself to much digging to follow the galvanised pipe only to find it was only a yard long, connecting to nothing. Mr Campbell phoned the next morning asking me to turn on the water.

"I tried that yesterday," I told him, explaining there was no water supply to the house.

"I will tell Marvin and he will deal with it." In 'business mode' Mr Campbell was a man of few words but every one measured and incontrovertible.

A few days later a copy letter arrived from Brenda, her usual practice to keep all parties informed and therefore with no excuse for ignorance. The prospective tenant had signed the letting agreement and paid a deposit to secure the property, not knowing there was no water. The letter to her, signed by Mr Campbell, stated that water could be laid on, however this would incur a cost of £1,000. It further pointed out the deposit was not returnable as their tenancy had started.

Fortunately, I was not immediately privy to the language that might have been exchanged. I was later told that she had examined and accepted the property 'as seen'. The fact that she had seen taps and assumed water would come out of them would not be accepted in law. She paid the extra money and water flowed but I noted that my employer was not to be trifled with.

# 25

# The Lord Provides

Whilst starting and building the farm business, we had not neglected Sunday worship, attending the Baptist church in town. In fact, they did not have a church building but hired the Red Cross hall with its somewhat tatty canvas stacking chairs. The people were most welcoming and we quickly became active; Hazel with 'Young Wives', and me attending mid-week evening prayers. I looked after the girls so that she could attend on Tuesday evenings and I went alone to the other meeting on Thursdays. It was necessary to have fellowship with other believers and indeed a social life away from work. The Sunday working issue had not surfaced as the farm, even during harvest, had not suffered.

The church was well established and the congregation growing in number. There was a need for their own building but where was there a possible site and how could we afford it? The large Church of England building next door was no longer used and had become redundant; could that be the Lord's answer to our problem? I had now trained as a deacon and was, with others, responsible for guiding the church members who would make a final decision. I had favoured making an approach to the trustees of the church next door but recognised that taking over the old St James' building would involve a huge maintenance cost and that it had probably become untenable on that account.

A small site was offered by the town council next to the Town Hall, but there was no room for car parking. The council agreed the public car park could be used on Sundays free of charge. We had to pray for the Lord's guidance; there was still a huge amount of money needed to build a church. Our minister believed the town needed a gospel-based Baptist church, although there were other places of worship. If we were to go ahead, it would have to be with faith that this was the Lord's will for a growing town. It was decided to engage an architect to design a church to fit that site. We could finance this from church funds.

The design was circular, a stage projecting from one side wrapped around by seating. It was futuristic and practical. It was designed for maximum seating on the limited site but had the air of space and light. The reaction of all members was, "It's beautiful!" Now for the finance. A building fund was set up and great efforts made to raise money through the usual teas, coffee mornings, sales of work and personal donations. The question remained, would it be sustainable and how many years would it take?

The whole church was united in prayer and it was decided to start the work and commit to pay every bill as it was presented, on time. No funds? Then work must stop until the next stage could be afforded. The Lord's project must not owe money. We had made a start, having paid for the plans; now it would be a journey of faith. The groundwork was paid for and then a couple of subcontracted workers laid the footings. We especially thanked God when the footings were completed and paid for. We now had the confidence that the Lord was blessing the project.

It was exciting when each Sunday evening, at the end of the service, the Building Fund treasurer would come to the front and let us know the progress that week. One Sunday we knew we were very near to building the next stage. All eyes were on Bob, our treasurer, as he passed each row to the front of the Hall. He had an invoice in his hand; there was an awkwardness as he walked from the back, looking down and in silence. He stood facing us, looking up to the ceiling.

"I came up here to tell you that we can't pay this invoice. It's much more than our funds." There was no mistaking the tears starting to roll down his face. "That is… we can *just* pay it," he said slowly. There was an audible sigh of relief. "I have just been passed a cheque as I walked up here."

Somebody started to clap. Bob held up a hand to stop it.

"It is for the exact amount!"

Clapping and hallelujahs broke out. There were tears of joy and thankfulness, an overwhelming sense of the power of God. It was not only the fact that we had received a large donation that we thanked God, but that His 'signature' was on that exact cheque.

What I and most others in that meeting understood was that the Lord wanted the building of that church to be completed. It was in line with His will and we were the people privileged to do the work. Why were we so sure? Nobody knew the amount needed, yet it met, to the very pound, the total of the invoice. The person who handed the cheque to Bob had been owed the money but he thought he would give it to the building fund as his contribution. We were left to understand that God was in control; the Creator of all things can and will oversee His work.

We were all encouraged and gave as much as we could. Our faith in the Lord's provision was rewarded in monies from further afield, and the church was completed with every invoice paid on time. Many of us found our attitude to prayer had changed. We took to heart the truth of Jesus's words in the Bible: "If you believe, you will receive whatever you ask for in prayer." (Matthew 21:22)

This had actually been proven to us, but we knew that it had to be the prayers of believers in Jesus as the Son of God and we had to totally believe He would provide. There is no blanket promise that He answers every selfish whim, but we were asking for His work and glory. This confirmation was given again once the church was completed. That first year seats were full, and by year two the Sunday morning service had to be repeated to accommodate the size of the congregation.

# 26

# Fishing for Business

Back at the day job, I was not expecting another miracle nor a net full of fish. Out of the blue a salesman called who had done business with the previous owners of the farm. He asked if anyone fished the lakes where as a local boy he had ventured to try his luck. He told me the story I already knew about the monks who, years previously, had fed themselves on fish. I pointed out that the new owners were not doing anything with the ponds at the moment but were not wanting fishermen.

This chance conversation gave me an idea that there could be an added enterprise with this resource. I contacted an Angling Club whose secretary showed interest and came to view the old stew ponds. We agreed he would try a day's fishing and evaluate the possibility of our letting the water. A week later he knocked at my door with a small pike in a keep net.

"I haven't caught much but have you got time to come down there with me?" he asked.

We walked a hundred yards from the track and hydram around the field that sloped steeply to the water. It was a good vantage point for the nearest pond.

"I'm not sure what fish there may be in here but it's a wonderful site." He waved his arm around pointing out the areas of bamboo and reeds with various gaps of clear water. "I guess the monks had carp but I only caught the pike you saw."

"I thought it might suit carp," I added knowledgeably.

"It's fairly shallow but trout would make it attractive," he smiled, "if you got rid of the pike. If you were serious it would have to be electro-fished before you started." He noticed my puzzled expression. "They run a weak electric current in the water and collect the stunned fish." That prompted more questions than I had time for.

"Could you give me some costings for making this into a trout enterprise?" I ventured.

He agreed straight away and handed me a visiting card. I noticed his name was Len, and I looked on him as an important resource before mentioning anything to Mr Campbell.

I managed to put a compelling case to Mr Campbell, anticipating a rental income from letting the fishing rights, improving the water supply for the growing demand on the estate and capital growth for his investment.

Work started on electro-fishing the two ponds and was undertaken free of charge by the Angling Club as they were to have first option on fishing at Beech Row. They took our unwanted fish to a new home on one of their fishing lakes, enhancing its stock. This whole operation was done once they had let off half the water level without compromising the continuity of supply to the houses and farm.

It was clear that this was the time to deepen the ponds and secure more capacity. This would entail a contractor with a large dragline. The good news was that the spoil excavated could be 'lost' on site, hence no transport costs. It was fascinating watching the practised skill of the operator swinging the mighty jib with its bucket, attached by wire hawser, as far as possible. The work resulted in a mass of black mud on the fields on every side of the ponds. I anticipated that this would be beneficial to the future cropping, but it left an island of unreached mud in the middle. After much discussion with the contractor, it was decided to 'blow' the island.

Whilst this seemed a reasonable course of action, I couldn't help feeling the owner of the business had a 'Boy's Own' relationship with gelignite. It was not a disregard for safety but his sheer glee at the spectacle; further, it was the only way to move the muddy island within reach of the dragline and make a successful fishery. He spent all morning laying charges, warning farm staff and insisting I witnessed the explosion, standing next to him from a vantage point at the top of the sloping field.

There were two warning hooters at the forecast time, then a pregnant pause. *Whoop* – the deep-throated explosion threw mud about a hundred feet into the air with such aplomb that it dropped mostly where the original dredging had been done. The dragline returned from reasonable cover and started work again. When the work was completed, we stopped the water from running to waste down the stream and allowed the ponds to refill. After allowing time for regrowth of reeds, rainbow trout were purchased from a fishery and restocking took place. In spring the club anglers tested the new water. The agreement allowed a maximum of two brace to be taken, any others caught to be returned to the pond. The system worked well for both parties and the following year we installed a fishermen's hut between the two ponds, equipped with gas bottle and ring for making hot drinks.

We had stocked the renewed ponds with rainbow trout following the guidance of the Angling Club who were to have sole rights. They agreed the conditions and an annual rent which was a great benefit to the farm. The additional non-farming enterprises were becoming significant.

The dredging of the ponds had improved the source of water but the delivery of it needed more work. I was increasingly anxious about the storage in the loft of the big barn on the roadside. The very substantial wooden beams supporting the Victorian flooring had rusty stains. It was difficult to determine the extent of any leakage but the fact that they were wet meant rot would surely follow. The tank consisted of steel sections bolted together forming a narrow swimming pool. It seemed to have originated from an RAF tank reassembled on the floor instead of an external structure. The cover consisted of galvanised sheets laid across the eight-foot width.

I often lifted the end sheet to check that water was coming in, that as usual it was full and that the overflow was not blocked. Once, the level was up as usual but a dead rat was floating there. Whether he was drinking or swimming didn't matter, there was a foreign body in our water. I needed Mr Campbell to sanction a vermin-proof tank. I immediately drove to his house and offered to show him the completed ponds. An hour later we returned to the large barn to check on the water level. It was a good excuse to repeat my concern for the possibly rotting floor.

"I am always worried about the weight of all this on the wood flooring," I reminded him as we crossed from the top of the stairs to the long tank. "I'll just check if the water is still clear after the dredging." I took care to lift the same end of the sheet again.

"Good heavens, what's that?" Mr Campbell exclaimed. I don't think his words indicated failure to identify the rodent so much as surprise it was there. "Where does this water go?" he asked.

"It supplies all the houses here, and then yours," I replied in a matter-of-fact way.

Nothing more was said but I knew the point had been made.

A week later Mr Campbell called me over for the usual briefing. The first item was water tanks.

"You're quite right, Peter; the floor may be a hazard. Marvin has ordered two modern tanks and he will notify you about delivery. I'm sure you can plumb them in and then drain the big tank."

He covered all the information and no doubt saved the installation costs. I was grateful for new and lighter storage.

"By the way, I think we will build a bungalow; accommodation is always handy." Mr Campbell was never short of surprises.

"Where will it be?" I enquired.

"Opposite Strawberry Bottom, but we haven't got 'planning' yet. Can you see to another water pipe to the site?" He spoke with remarkable confidence for a man who had not yet received planning permission. "Call here tomorrow. I'd like you to meet the planning officer; he should be here at ten thirty."

I was anxious to get back to farming but did leave a message with the water pipe contractor that we needed another supply to the site, thinking it might be a rushed job once permission was granted.

The next morning I made sure I was in clean clothes, knowing Mr Campbell would want to use me in discussions with the planning officer.

"This is Peter, my estate manager; he runs things here." He turned to me. "Peter, this is Luke who is helping us improve the area. I want you to listen to him so we don't miss any detail he advises." Mr Campbell had coated it with sugar and I was sure he had not finished.

We walked the short distance from the farmhouse, now named 'The Beeches', to the site area just off the track joining the two farms.

Luke, map in hand, looked the area over and paced a few dimensions.

"It's a generous bungalow but I see no reason why the committee would object," he mused. "I don't think anybody is likely to object and it can't be readily seen," the planning officer added. They were all favourable comments.

"We don't need access onto the road as the new drive will come straight off the bend in the farm track." Mr Campbell was adding weight for Luke to take to the committee.

We crossed over the lane into Overley Farm.

"We want to smarten up these old buildings and perhaps make one or two stables." I was afraid he was over-egging the situation and might even frighten Luke that more development would take place. "We need unobtrusive accommodation for workers in this lovely countryside." It was the first I had heard of this, but no doubt it was the way Mr Campbell wanted to break the news to me.

"You certainly have improved things since you moved in." Luke was flattering him now.

"Luke, you know we have a fine gallop on the old airfield and Peter tells me some of our neighbours are using it." He beamed as if the local benefactor had chosen residence here.

"It would be nice if we tidied all this up and helped youngsters to ride," Luke said nodding, personally sold on the idea.

We walked back to The Beeches and Luke departed. Mr Campbell wanted me to stay.

"I think we could have a few horses; it's not good for my son Malcolm to be office-bound all day," he reasoned.

The contractor readily mole-ploughed in a short polythene pipe joining the one from my house to The Beeches, terminating with a standpipe at the site where the new bungalow was planned. Water, we hoped, was now guaranteed.

Mr Campbell was not finished. He told me to return after lunch to meet a salesman. Quite what the salesman was selling or why it was necessary for me to attend would no doubt be revealed. I followed a car up the drive.

"Oliver Swain. I've got an appointment with Mr Campbell." The man was dressed in blazer and flannels.

Mr Campbell arrived from his large garage, suitably dressed.

"Oliver!" Mr Campbell called out. "You are in good time."

"Yes, sir," came a reply and an extended hand.

Mr Campbell's handshake was usually brief and tentative, which I put down to concern in case it was construed as agreeing to something.

"Peter, my estate manager." I was always mildly embarrassed at the inflated title.

We walked round the house to uncultivated ground beyond the swimming pool windows.

"I was thinking of a tennis court here." Mr Campbell made a gesture with both hands as if it were a trench he wanted constructed.

"We could soon build one there; it seems fairly brashy and well drained," the salesman confirmed.

"Yes, we have been told it's a good site. What is your price for a standard court, nothing fancy?" Mr Campbell was direct with the salesman.

I was thinking my part was to receive a lesson in negotiating a deal.

"Peter, you had thought we could use some of our own equipment?" Before I could even stutter a reply, he continued. "We are looking for something simple; we don't play many games. Something with your nice name tag and business-like," Mr Campbell led the conversation.

The salesman was getting the message – cheap on this site but a chance of more business from friends and visitors.

"What is your price, Oliver?" Mr Campbell asked him directly.

"It depends on how long it takes and the extras, like lights..." He was stopped in his tracks.

"What was the cost of your last similar specification?"

He was getting into a tight corner.

"Oliver, this is a 'green field' site; I am asking a simple question."

"Give or take a trifle... £2,100," he replied, really imprisoned, except for a trifle.

"Oliver, we often have friends here. What would it cost for a double court?" The goalposts had moved! Mr Campbell sped on: "You will need a little more netting but all your equipment will be here." It was not intended to help, benign as it sounded.

I happened to be in the farmhouse the next morning when Mr Swain phoned, having obviously burned the midnight oil.

"Ah, Oliver! I have Peter with me; you have a costing... £3,050... plus lights." He held the phone some distance from his ear for my benefit. "Of course we will need lights. Peter works very hard and late and may want to use the court. I will do a deal now on the phone to save your time."

I fancied I heard an audible sigh.

"I agree to your quotation with the lights included. Please let Peter know when you will be starting."

I imagined Mr Swain sinking back in his chair, too exhausted to argue, wondering what deal he had been forced into.

# 27

# Stables Need Horses

Malcolm, another of Mr Campbell's sons, was anxious to live on the farm and was delighted with the positive response from the planning officer regarding the bungalow. The builders set out a flat concrete 'raft' and assembled a sectional wooden frame, complete with roof trusses, in a week. The completion of the bungalow took longer but it was evident there would be more life at the growing hamlet called Overley Farm. Ernie, who had lived there in splendid isolation, already had one neighbour and was about to get another.

"Peter, I want to talk to you about Overley Farm." Mr Campbell was planning my day with the frequent 9 am telephone call. "Pop across, shall we say, at ten?"

I agreed and duly engaged the farm staff in jobs that did not need my attention.

"I've been thinking about the stables and the young girl with her horse at Overley Farm." Mr Campbell revealed there had been discussions about horses on the lower farm. "Malcolm will soon be joining us and we have the gallop, of course; it could be another little earner for us," he concluded.

My experience with my father-in-law and his point-to-point horses had dimmed any enthusiasm. The coupling of modern commercial farming and horses are rarely a happy combination. Great were the days when draught horses were ploughing and providing the motive power on farms, but horses for leisure or sport have different requirements. As he introduced the subject, my heart sank. I had visions of horses influencing farming operations and the need for special fencing, with the ability to retain horses without them injuring themselves on barbed wire. The necessity of best quality hay and oats, even straw bedding, would be frowned upon in favour of wood shavings.

"Have you space for more stables in the yard?" Mr Campbell continued, further adding to my apprehension.

"There are no more buildings that would be suitable for horses," I informed him.

"Malcolm had in mind four or five horses, each with their own box of course."

My day was rapidly going downhill.

"What sort of horses is he talking about?" I asked.

"Race horses," Mr Campbell said, as if it were the most natural breed to have.

"Race horses?" I found myself repeating. "Who is going to look after them?"

"We will need a lad." My heart sank as I immediately thought he would be underemployed and therefore expected to work part-time on the farm.

"I don't think I would be able to use anyone part-time," I quickly interjected.

"Precisely; we would need more horses," Mr Campbell added.

This idea did little to cheer me up as more horses would likely be more trouble. I could see that their special requirements and blood stock value could swamp the farm. Their priority, in every sense of the word, could easily affect the timeliness of farm operations, including harvesting days.

"My son is interested in a racing stable."

I was stunned into silence.

"You can get some good sectional stables nowadays," Mr Campbell continued to enthuse.

I hoped he meant "*one* can" rather than including the farm.

"We could have four in a line just beyond the straw barn. Marvin and Malcolm can arrange that."

It seemed to be a *fait accompli* and I hoped they would find the required lad.

"I don't expect you to be heavily involved; we would need a lad. I'll get Malcolm to have a word with you," Mr Campbell concluded.

Fortunately, Malcolm was able to add detail to the vision the family had. It would be a 'small interest' that he would set up, with a line of four stables at the bottom end of the farmyard and a lad, independent of the farm, to run it. He stressed the lad would have to work under me so that the estate did not suffer. The farm would supply as much of the feed as possible but the accounting would be separate from the farm business. So far so good; my fears were not entirely quelled but I hoped I could remain some distance from the stables.

Contractors laid a concrete pad below the Dutch barn, generous enough to site four sectional stables in a line, and a servicing area for horses, owners and employees to attend them. Malcolm found a suitable candidate to run the establishment who was single and living in town. Frank was a son of a friend of a friend, which sounded somewhat tenuous but very convenient. I was introduced to Frank before any horses arrived. He looked the part of a jockey, being slight and wearing two T-shirts, one on top of the other but otherwise bearing no relation in terms of colours or pattern. I took them to be old racing colours for different owners. His headgear was a jockey cap whilst at work and a trilby with turned-down brim worn to and from the stables, the latter of which put me in mind of a bookie's 'runner'. He had pinched features and a prominent nose which turned out to say much about his character. In fairness I had been used to farm workers stereotypically well built, with a ruddy face and an open easy gaze. Frank appeared out of his natural environment on a farm.

The first horse to arrive belonged to a lady in town seeking full-board. Frank was able to look after the mare whilst building up various items of equipment and feed. A week later Mr Campbell told me Frank was expecting the second horse to arrive.

"I thought you might like to know I own a racehorse." He was wearing a broad smile, obviously delighted he had entered the fraternity.

"Congratulations!" I hoped it was an appropriate response.

"Quite a surprise. Malcolm suggested it, especially as we now have the facilities." Mr Campbell was still smiling. "It will be company for the other one."

Another horse arrived from a local stable which could not accommodate any more. It was the start of a small business, but hardly a racing stable. After a few months the final stable was occupied by a point-to-point mare. Frank was fully employed. The gallop was used but apparently it was not entirely satisfactory; in his opinion it was too hard in dry spells. It became a subject of friction. In a dry period I had got Ernie to irrigate it, but this was wasteful of water and depleted our meagre abstraction licence. The amount used is strictly controlled by the river authority and in dry periods can make the difference between success and crop failure. I resented horses, who were non-profit-making as far as I was concerned, endangering our carrot and potato crops.

My working relationship with Frank was not always cordial. It was a difficult management relationship which could only be likened to living with a Martian. Our worlds were totally opposed. Frank had no empathy with farming and I had little with horses, particularly highly strung racehorses. Whatever suited farm animals was apparently anathema to Frank's charges. I understood barbed wire and dusty hay were not acceptable to any horses, but nothing that the farm supplied met Frank's standards. He disliked pigs to the extent that they should not be on the same holding "because even the smell of pigs upsets my horses". Frank was in charge of the horse enterprise without reference to me, however I was held accountable for the whole estate.

Although it was never explained to me, Frank appeared to be Mr Campbell's jockey as well as the 'lad'. There was general excitement rather than expectation when we heard of Mr Campbell's horse 'Kymon' running his first race for his new owner. Although Ken, our tractor man, enquired of Frank about the betting prices, hoping to get a tip, he was evasive. The next day Frank was equally coy about the race results, saying Kymon had not finished well.

Ken relayed this to the men at bait-time.

"I don't know how well the horse ran; he only said it didn't finish well." Ken seemed disappointed.

"Maybe it didn't finish at all?" Ernie suggested.

"Well, it wasn't over jumps," Ken defended.

"No, well, there aren't any jumps here to practise on," Tony added.

"How good is Frank as a jockey?" Ernie asked.

"I reckon a good 'orse attracts a good jockey, and the governor should get one," Ken reasoned.

"I don't expect he wanted to pay enough." Ernie thought he had summed up his employer.

"Maybe cunning," Ken said. 'He's pretty canny, our boss. If you lose two or three times, the odds go up, then yer bet on him and he wins."

"If you want it to move faster yer need to put a hot potato on his arse; the horse will grip the spud tighter with its tail and go like a rocket!" Ernie lowered the tone but ended the discourse with his own brand of advice.

The attraction of the gallop increased our sales of straw and hay, particularly the lucerne hay. This was noted at our next quarterly meeting with Michael. At the same time, the results from the pigs looked considerably static. It was an embarrassment I could not account for. The next morning I phoned Brenda at head office who was responsible for accounts.

"I can't understand why the cost of pig food has increased so much?" I asked.

"I follow your coding to each enterprise," Brenda replied.

"Could you have counted anything twice?" I asked in desperation. "What is the largest cost?"

"Kymon," Brenda replied.

"That's the horse!" I exclaimed. "I didn't give you any code for the stables. That is nothing to do with the farm," I insisted.

"When you wrote that across the invoices I thought it must be pig food," she said.

"It may run like pig food but that's his name," I said hastily. "No, Brenda, I didn't mean that; he's quite a nice horse."

We both laughed.

"I'll mark everything 'stables' and then they can apportion costs how they like."

This I relayed to both Mr Campbell and Michael, and the pigs were suddenly far more profitable.

I was fortunate to have Mary as a neighbour and ally. She had a smallholding with a menagerie of livestock but principally horses. Her business was a small riding school with attendant strays to other species. These included half a dozen pigs of various ages, four Muscovy ducks, and sundry chicken, being bantams and hens 'mixed'. Mary was always cheerful and oblivious of the confusion surrounding her. Somehow she turned out pupils who were proficient and immaculately dressed for gymkhanas. She found us to be a useful source of good hay, straw and oats, together with gallops. I was delighted with her mediating presence halfway between farming and horses.

At her suggestion I compromised by making an all-weather gallop. This was a fourteen-foot strip alongside the grass, consisting of rotavated straw and grass roots. It could be freshened up whenever too compacted. Much less gallop was needed than the width required as an airstrip, so the surplus area I was able to sell to a turf company who weeded and manicured it to perfection. There were no fences or hedges, and in exchange for the all-weather gallop, Frank agreed not to run on the turf area.

At last we had a better relationship. Frank, and others, had access to an all-weather gallop a mile long. The turf company was responsible for all the maintenance, the harvesting of which took less than an inch of top soil. The turf company did all the work, weeding and preparing it to their satisfaction. Once cut and removed, there was enough root structure still in the ground to take a second cut of turf two years later when the new grass had knitted together. The company was delighted with the quality and ease such a flat area afforded. The fourteen acres of prime turf boosted farm income and my regard for horses.

Mary insisted I learned to ride and taught me free of charge. In return I set up a simple cash book system, helping her and her accountant. Her current 'system' relied on remembering which pocket she had used for each child's lesson money; even worse, which coat or overalls she might have been wearing that day.

The small enterprises and extra activities were crowding in on me. In an effort to unwind, I would retreat to my ponds. I could occasionally spend an hour down the track, only three hundred yards away from home, and reassess life. I would leave the track and walk along the edge of the field to the division between the two ponds and to a fallen tree trunk. It was too large to move, too old to be of use and too rotten except to sit on. It became a spiritual place; one where we could have a family picnic during the day or a place to restore sanity at the end of a long day.

This particular evening there was no crisis, nothing I had to chew over with God; I just needed a peaceful regathering of mind and soul. It was the perfect situation looking along the ten-yard division between the two stretches of water. The one on the left might receive the past and its problems and the pool on the right might point to the future. To anyone else they appeared very similar, on the face of it, but as one flowed into the other I imagined I could bury the past problems, wrong turns and mistakes of any sort. They would drown under the water on the left and appear on the right as a fresh, clean tablet.

There was the stillness of nature; no sound of running water, but pure therapy. The only sound, if I strained my ears, was the distant beat of the hydram pumping up water. It was a necessary heartbeat reminding me that life goes on, never stopping. It would continue when we were gone; someone else in our house, my job done by another, our girls growing up and journeying who knows where. I unloaded the activities of business, good and bad, and floated the ideas and hopes of the future.

The Lord had brought me this far. Jesus had given me peace. He explained to the disciples who followed Him that the peace He gives is not like that which the world gives (John 14:27). Calmness and confidence in Him was its secret. That was real peace. I could face the next day with confidence.

# 28

# Great Expectations

I enjoyed farming; it was always a challenge. We were exhorted to grow more and science had enabled bigger yields of crops; it had been a policy since the Second World War. There were Grow More Society clubs in parts of the country that were a sort of extension of Young Farmers Clubs; they were a mix of social and business. Farmers like nothing more than farming, and if it includes new ideas with a bit of competitive spirit, so much the better. It's quite common for farmers' wives to want and even to book a holiday, taking care not to overlap a busy work period, only to find their husbands reluctant to leave the farm, especially if missing the local Ploughing Match or Grow More Show. I have known cases where all is well and they do go on holiday, but have to attend the local market. The reason given is "just to keep in touch".

The Grow More clubs were the best antidote, where wives were welcomed and often showed the men up in the competitions. In the late sixties, mountains of food were beginning to be a problem. The old wartime mantra to 'Dig for Victory' and produce as much as possible was still in many minds. Indeed, there has always been a policy of 'the more you grow, the more you sell'. The problem was that government subsidies had encouraged production rather than it being governed by the market. There were guaranteed prices for many farm products, and government was having to store vast quantities of produce and eventually lose money by selling surpluses cheaply on the world market.

The Grow More clubs encouraged quality rather than quantity. The annual Ploughing Match not only judged the best land work but there were competitions for the best farm produce, through to cakes and flower arranging. Farmers are keen to grow better crops, much the same as small businesses seek to develop and expand their products or services. However, in the countryside there is usually another dimension – that of pride and reputation. In each locality there is often a common or predominate type of holding favouring similar enterprises: climate, soil type and elevation often being the common features. This fires competition with the added incentive to grow a good reputation. Whatever is achieved is on view to neighbours; rarely can mistakes be hidden. News travels fast in the countryside and our products are always in the shop window for all to see. Even markets are public, where livestock auctions require the vendor to stand with the auctioneer or often move their animals around the ring, closely identifying them with their charges.

Some farmers attend markets when they have no intension of buying or selling, but simply talking and observing.

"This lot looks better," he volunteers to those around him.

"Better back-ends, he always has decent stores," says a voice referring to the cattle.

"He'd do better to feed 'em than bring 'em here," comes a voice from the back row.

There is no shortage of advice, which cautions the unwary and builds the reputation of the diligent. It is a sort of self-policing which raises the standards, and is fostered in the Grow More clubs.

Apart from the Ploughing Match and Show, there are often cups for the best crop of wheat in the district, best potatoes, etc. These are judged by a respected grower from another area, so avoiding favouritism. The judge walks through the fields that are entered in the competition, making assessments of plant population, weed control[39], insect and disease control, size of ear, all pointing to potential yield. The best three entries are read out at the end of the day or, in some cases, at the Ploughing Match dinner. The reason for the competition is because farmers love their job and desire to excel. The approval of neighbours is of professional importance and a huge spur to young boys or girls hoping to follow in their parents' footsteps.

I had walked into this culture and the privilege of been treated as a farmer's son. Living and working with good farmers had been my rural education. I had learned the rigours of working in all weathers for the sake of the livestock; the endless days where hours were not reckoned, only the completion of the task. It was the satisfaction of working in nature and with nature. I worked hard for an employer, not because he insisted, but because every aspect of the job required it.

Although Mr Campbell may not have appreciated all the delights of working with nature, he was certainly acquainted with every opportunity the country estate offered. Hazel informed me I had another morning audience with Mr Campbell.

"Peter, I'm president of the cricket club, aren't I?" This was a rhetorical question, but he loved confirmation of his status.

"Yes, they asked you to consider it when you arrived here," I dutifully replied.

"I believe they invited me to make a financial contribution," he went on, still shaving as usual.

---

[39] i.e. absence of weeds

"A number of people did," I added remembering all the begging letters he had attracted.

"My daughter is engaged to get married."

I was yet to grasp its significance.

"They might let us to have her reception there."

It did not seem a great venue to me, but he went on.

"Can you imagine a marquee there, catering in the pavilion, nice short grass outside, plenty of space to park?" Mr Campbell continued.

I was seeing it in a different light, when he confirmed it for me:

"I don't think they would want to make a charge for it, do you, Peter?"

His warped smile concluded the decision.

"Are you friendly with the captain?" he asked, obviously thinking I could help in the softening process.

"Much as I enjoy cricket, I haven't had time to get to know anybody." I hoped it would exonerate me.

"I thought you might in your Christian way have a friend there. I'll get Brenda to write a nice letter to them," he determined.

Although I was not invited, it was apparently a very successful occasion.

Mr Campbell unashamedly used his new status as landowner to advantage when possible. He often invited the sports press to the estate, expecting me to host them. He acquainted me with the strategy that it was good for business, which I understood to mean share value. As chairman of a football club, his name or comments were often recorded on the sports page of the dailies. He explained that all the stockbrokers were just boys at heart and read the sports page rather than the business section, as they dealt with that all day.

"Peter, I've got some reporters coming about twelve. I want you to show them around and take them for a sandwich in the Feathers[40]." He added, as usual, that he would be too busy to do it himself. They would arrive at the farmhouse by taxi, where I would be waiting with a reasonably clean Land Rover.

"I'm sorry, Mr Campbell is busy, but he has asked me to show you around the estate."

It was all new to them and, weather permitting, would be extremely pleasant – culminating in sandwiches and drinks in the Feathers.

"Is it true that Mr Campbell is interested in another club?"

I could not help him further in his enquiries as I had no knowledge and little interest in soccer. My ignorance made sure my employer was safe.

"I'm afraid I'm only the estate manager; he doesn't inform me about football," I confessed.

"How big is the estate?"

---

[40] a hotel on the edge of the farm, known locally by this name

I had probably already answered this question but he would make a note of it. I had also informed them of the cost of some of the machinery, not least during an inspection of the carrot plant.

After a satisfactory lunch and unusual day out, I had to get the reporters back to the station by 2.30 pm. I had been assured by Mr Campbell Junior that all they would remember was that the chairman of the football club had acquired an estate in Hampshire. This, in the small print on the sports page, would indicate his industrial empire was thriving and that purchase of shares, by implication, was a reasonable security.

There was always the expectation that the farm could grow more or, more accurately, produce more money. The quarterly reviews, now mostly in the boardroom at The Beeches, were less hostile than initially. Michael was always helpful in highlighting the growth of the business, even pointing out that similar farms of similar size were less profitable.

"Mr Campbell, you know very well that not only is it paying its way but you have capital growth and indeed other savings," Michael would chide him.

"This house cost a lot of money," Mr Campbell would counter.

"May I suggest that without the farm you would not have been able to have such a house?" Michael gave a small but noticeable emphasis on the word 'such'. It was good humoured and Mr Campbell received it as he would a 'score draw' in football parlance.

Michael pointed out that we were now producing almost double the carrot tonnage by growing two crops in the same field; harvesting the first from late May to early June and the second by Christmas. Although Mr Campbell would have read my weekly reports, Michael also listed the five-acre field trial of parsnips for canning. This unfortunately was not successful, as canker was a problem, however it did show the canner's confidence in asking us to trial them.

The conversation soon turned to estate matters, as I had acquainted Michael about some of the extras that the farm staff were becoming involved in.

"I hear the stables have advanced and you now have at least one race horse," Michael introduced.

"Just a little interest that my son Malcolm has. We have a stable lad to see to that; I don't follow it too closely." Mr Campbell had leaped in, but then was dismissive.

"Yes, but it does have a bearing on the farm." Michael was more serious. "Although you cost it somewhat separately, it does incur some hidden farm labour in maintaining the gallops and building works. I'm going to embarrass Peter as I am sure he has to spread himself over the whole operation here."

There was no immediate comment from Mr Campbell, but he had to concede the business had grown and that he was mindful of my responsibilities. He waved his hand as Diana, his part-time secretary, appeared at the door, the prearranged sign that it was time for a cup of tea.

"We had a dreadful time recently." Mr Campbell seized the conversation away from the farm, asking me to tell the story. I gave them a full blow by blow account of the incident.

"It was about ten o'clock; late for my phone to ring," I started. "'There's trouble down here,' Ernie said, sounding urgent. 'A gun has gone off next door... think my neighbour...' 'I will be with you right away,' I said. I slammed the phone down, shouting I was going to Ernie's. He was waiting for me just inside his front door. 'It was definitely a shotgun,' Ernie assured me. 'I am going to check,' I replied. Ernie followed close behind. I banged on the door and shouted through the letterbox. 'He may have another cartridge; it's sure to be double barrelled,' Ernie whispered. 'We're coming in,' I bellowed. The door wasn't locked. The only light was coming from around the lounge door to the left. 'Stand to the side,' I whispered, standing by the door-handle. I kicked the door open, saying who we were. There was no sound but still the smell of a spent cartridge. One step into the room revealed all; a headless body across the settee. 'Come out,' I said, 'we mustn't touch anything.' Then I pulled the door shut. I phoned 999 on Ernie's phone: 'A man has shot himself.' I gave the stark information that they might respond quicker, then the address saying I would wait for the police."

I thought it best to stop the story there. They had heard about the incident and that was quite enough. Mr Campbell merely added he was one of our tenants; "dreadful business".

The meeting ended with a brief agreement that the farm was doing well and the date of the next quarterly meeting noted in the diaries. Michael said there was another small matter and he would bring some papers up to me in a few minutes, if I was going straight home. I agreed and left ahead of him.

Michael knocked at my door and asked if I would come and collect the papers from his car.

"Sit in the passenger seat a minute." He obviously wanted a private conversation. "I must ask you a few things but couldn't in front of the family." He seemed apologetic. "I know it's painful but there must be more than you told us back in the meeting. Please, it should be said," he insisted gently.

"Really?" I was reluctant.

Michael nodded.

"The police dealt with the undertaker and removed the body, and that was it," I said.

Michael looked straight at me and I was conscious a silent tear had run down my left cheek. "Have you seen a doctor? You've both had a terrible shock," he asked sympathetically.

I shook my head and wiped my face. Michael just put his hand on my arm.

"The worse thing was, a week after, we had to clear up." I had expressed it badly. "Mr Campbell wanted it clean for a decorator to come in before letting it again. I couldn't ask Ernie to do it alone, so we did it together." I drew breath. "I'm used to blood and dead animals... but this was a man."

Michael listened.

"He had just sat on the settee and pulled the trigger; there was more than just blood... bits of everything, everywhere. We carried everything out of the lounge, every bit of furniture and burned the lot... We even tried to sand the floorboards."

It was Michael's turn to speak. "It was important for you to tell me all that. You had bottled that up and it will get a little better now," he assured me.

I felt some relief; it was better than telling a doctor.

"Would you like me to see Ernie?" he enquired.

"No, I think I will tell him that you listened to the whole story and were very sympathetic."

A week later Mr Campbell gave Ernie and me an envelope each, thanking us for going beyond the call of duty: forty pounds each.

## Out of the Blue

I had settled down over the past seven years and learned a lot about farming the estate. I knew the thought process that drove Mr Campbell and some of his business nous. It was good to know the boundaries and what he would tolerate. He valued integrity and industry but was quick to pick up one's motive. I was called to an afternoon 'audience' on some occasions, but could rarely determine the real reason. I would be there in person; sometimes as a sounding board, other times as a foil to support a venture, and even to be instructed in the art of conducting business. Perhaps all three in the case of the car salesman.

"Peter, Basil has come to see me and I want you to meet him." I was formally introduced. "Peter is my estate manager."

I shook hands with Basil who was middle aged and no doubt the sales manager of a considerably large concern.

"He comes to see me when he has a good deal to offer me."

I recognised that Basil was being softened up with ingratiating words.

"He thinks it is a good time to buy cars, so he may be offering me a Mini for Mrs Campbell."

Basil stepped in, emphasising the overtures of his mission: "I only come when there is an offer one can't refuse." Obviously Basil could give as good as he got. "These Minis have improved out of all recognition and we are lucky enough to have had six delivered this week. Mr Campbell can choose his colour." He gave a hopeful smile to us both.

"Basil doesn't talk about price until the end," Mr Campbell addressed me, then turned back to Basil. "I think my daughter had one from you last year." He knew every detail about the purchase. "About £570, I think?"

"This is a new model altogether; it is just under £700." Basil always had an uphill encounter with Mr Campbell.

"Supposing I had two at £570?" Mr Campbell boldly launched a bid.

"These are totally advanced motors. Second-hand they are dearer than new, even if you could find one." Basil was still trying to get Mr Campbell into the real world.

"Peter might be interested in one as well."

"I am not in the market for a car, thank you," I was quick to add.

"Basil, I don't think you have ever been here without selling a car." Mr Campbell inferred there would be no sale.

"I would like at least to show you the car."

Basil encouraged us to go to the new vehicle parked just outside the garage doors. He lifted the bonnet and the boot lid. The engine was wonderfully packed into the space and so clean, being new.

"Here are the keys, Mr Campbell." Basil closed the bonnet and boot.

Mr Campbell, always an impetuous driver, went round the central flowerbed and down the drive.

Basil turned to me. "You are a family man; I've got a new Marina for only £440."

"Thanks, but I am really not in the market," I insisted.

Soon the new Mini came back up the drive at some speed.

"What do you think?" Basil opened the door for Mr Campbell.

"Handles well." Mr Campbell looked cheerful. "Make it £600."

"I can't do that, even for you, Mr Campbell." The matter rested there.

On my next visit to The Beeches, I saw a new car.

"You have new wheels!" I exclaimed.

"Mrs Campbell liked it." Mr Campbell gave one of his knowing grins. "I thought we ought to have a couple." I must have looked surprised. "The second-hand price is more than new, so I think of it is an investment." He was pleased with himself.

I thought over Basil's visit and the fact that Mr Campbell had bought the Mini at only thirty pounds more than his opening bid; even better, two of them at that price. In fairness to Basil, whatever his margin was, he had sold two vehicles out of the blue.

My 'out of the blue' experience took another form: the chance of a new job. An old friend from my time in Sussex phoned one evening. I recognised the voice immediately and, after the pleasantries of his current whereabouts and health, he came to the point.

"Are you interested in moving? I mean to a new job?" Gerald was a farm manager himself.

"I could be, I suppose." I was guarded as the thought had not entered my head. In spite of all the hard work and pressures of dealing with a thrusting industrialist, I was content and enjoying the challenge.

"I thought you were always ahead and looking for more, old boy." Gerald went to a better public school than me.

"Well, what are the details?" I asked.

"My governor has been asked to look out for a farm manager for a large estate and asked me if I knew anyone." Gerald was awakening my interest.

I had lost none of my ambition to farm a thousand acres but would need to hear more details to move from our pleasant situation and friends. Gerald continued to fill me in.

"It's a big estate in Shropshire, not far from here, but I don't know the owner personally. My man has just been asked to put out feelers and I thought you might be interested."

"I'll tell you what, Gerald, give him my address and say I would like more details."

Hazel was not quite so impressed with the possibility of moving but we agreed to wait for more information. It sounded like a distinct promotion; I was interested in having a greater emphasis on farming rather than so many small enterprises, but every aspect of my work was in the detail.

A week later a letter arrived with more information about the position and a view of the further growth that was envisaged. I was invited to send my CV if interested. It was the possibility of further expansion that encouraged my interest. I wondered how many others were being considered for interview and why the approach had been by word of mouth.

"Gerald, I want to let you know I've got an interview for the job you mentioned."

"Great, old fruit, come over and see us; we're only four miles away." He was excited, which encouraged me.

"I don't think I will be able to look in as I will be staying all weekend with the owner."

"Wow, they must like your CV," Gerald concluded.

"Is there anything funny about the set-up?" I adopted a serious tone.

"Don't think so." There was a pause as if quickly thinking. "You will know more than me once you've been there... especially for a weekend," he ventured.

"Maybe there are three or four staying there and they will be assessing us, one against another. Have they got a manager at the moment?"

"No, I don't think so; the farms are mostly let," Gerald concluded.

Hazel said she would have found it a handful with the girls for the weekend, even if invited.

"You'll never answer the questions without going. Anyway, it will be good for you to get away and you will be interested in seeing another farm." Hazel was always full of good sense.

I would have preferred to go together, but no doubt if the interview were successful there would be a chance to visit before accepting the job, assuming I ever got that far.

North Shropshire was largely new to me. Although I had visited the notable tourist spots, I had no picture of the predominantly farming scene. It now seemed to have endless variety, both of dwellings and countryside. It was a beautiful morning travelling through ancient villages surrounded by small fields suddenly opening to large landscapes of well-farmed crops. At the next turn there was water and reeds and a hamlet forgotten for four hundred years.

The village had a mix of houses; black and white cottages, some thatched, a few modern, even two bungalows. It seemed a history of occupation; a house built 'where and when', conforming to current needs or fashion. The farm drive was a quarter of a mile further on with large arable fields each side viewed through an avenue of oaks. The Georgian house stood in gravel to the left and the business sheds and barns on tarmac to the right. I noticed 'Office' written over the nearest barn door; once inside it seemed the old tithe barn had enveloped a modern bungalow.

I introduced myself to the receptionist.

"Ah! You have an appointment with Mr Prince; please follow me." She led me to the next office and knocked on the door.

Mr Prince had the appearance of a country gentleman from top to toe, poorly disguised in corduroy trousers and open-necked shirt. We shook hands and he indicated a chair opposite his, the other side of the ample desk.

"Will you have tea or coffee?" It was his first question; my answer he relayed to Shirley. Coffee and biscuits arrived in elegant fashion. There was no sign of any other applicants. Mr Prince turned straight to business.

"I'd like you to tell me about your farming thus far."

"Well, sir, I started from the Town Boys' Training Scheme; I worked every day on an arable farm." I went on to recount an expansion of my CV.

"I've studied your CV but am particularly interested in what you've done at your present job."

I did my best to itemise the start of enterprises at Beeches Row Farm and their growth. I fielded the occasional question without missing much of my journey.

I glanced at my watch; I had been talking for more than half an hour.

"I'm sorry, sir, I have been talking too much."

"Don't worry. I asked you to expand; that was fine. By the way, not so much of the 'sir'; we hope to work together. I'm Robert Prince and my wife, who you will be meeting later, is Elizabeth. We prefer not to shorten names; no doubt you prefer Peter?"

He put me at ease with his explanation.

"The best thing we can do now is to show you the estate."

We went out of the rear of the barn to a less-than-new Land Rover. We drove through some trees and up a private road to a large farmhouse and some traditional buildings.

"My mother used to run the estate from here when Dad died."

We continued up the track, arable fields and a few pastures on either side. We stopped where the track ended and got out.

"You can see the fields finish here but the woods go all around the high ground." He waved his hand. "I could drive you through the woods but you've seen trees before. I look after the foresters and two gamekeepers. The farm manager will look after the farm." Robert smiled for the first time.

After a light lunch I was driven around the other farms, six in all; it was difficult to get my bearings. Robert explained that the farms had been traditionally let to tenants but now it was important to farm it himself, hence the need of an experienced manager. As tenancies ended, they would not be renewed and the farm would be taken back 'in-hand'.

In the afternoon I was taken to the farm where the first tenant was leaving. This house too had a Georgian façade and was just outside of the farmyard. Inside, the hall led straight to a majestic wooden staircase, and four ample bedrooms and a bathroom that needed furniture to fill it. Downstairs were a lounge, dining room and large kitchen-diner. Each room was about eighteen-foot square and eleven-foot high. If I secured this job I would certainly live in a 'residence'.

The afternoon was spent walking the land and examining the estate map. I noted the field names and growing crops, as there seemed no current cropping plan. Robert told me that on the Sunday he would want my suggestions on how the farming could start after the tenant left.

We started straight after breakfast.

"What needs to be done in preparation for 'D-Day'?" Robert asked.

"I would need an accurate history of each field, what it has grown in the last two years and preferably details of any problems," I ventured.

"What do you mean 'any problems'?" Robert had admitted he was a forester rather than farmer.

"Any boggy or rocky patches to be avoided and possibly making it impracticable for arable or root crops to be grown," I replied. "Also, any significant weed problems."

"The tenant is rather unhappy about leaving; I will get my agent to press him."

"If I had that, the next thing would be to prepare a cropping plan for the year based on a planned rotation."

Robert grunted; obviously this was new to him. "I could do a rough rotation now, knowing some of the crops he has grown," Robert brightened.

"I would need to budget, on perhaps two or three cropping plans," I added.

"Could you do that?" he asked.

"It's the job of a manager," I smiled. "I would also have to calculate what labour would be necessary and the minimum amount of machinery required in year one. Also, where a contractor could be used to save capital in the first year or two needs to be included in the costing and an approximate surplus arrived at," I added.

"If you will do all you've mentioned, I think you have qualified for the position; I'll look no further." His announcement came out of the blue.

"Thank you, sir. May I show my wife the house before I formally accept?"

"Of course. I didn't mean to rush you," he added.

The weekend was over and there was so much to consider.

# 29

# All Change

It was difficult leaving Wessex; we had settled into the area, job, church and friendships. The family had grown and all was well. Although we were satisfied where we were, I had the chance of advancement and that call was too great to refuse. Hazel was less sure but understood my motivation. We had to say goodbye to friends at church without ever having worshipped in the just-completed building. We valued our local friends and neighbours, but at heart we knew we were unlikely to see them again.

Finally, the work and establishment of the farm had been satisfying, although hard won. The same process was about to start in a different county, but hopefully there would be more time to spend together as a family. The excitement was the expectation of more farming content and less 'agribusiness'. Although I had enjoyed the money-making enterprises appended to the farm, they seemed to carry more management effort and more stress. Perhaps it was due to their association with people more than with nature? Working with the seasons and variable weather has its challenges, but experience and tradition has grafted man to farming in much the same way as animals are hefted to the hills and moors.

We had 'inherited' the carpets and curtains from the outgoing tenant, which was a great start as the dimension of the rooms were more than double that of Beech Row. The Georgian windows had shutters but also curtains with a ten-foot drop. The beautiful sweep of stairs were polished oak which we soon had to cover partially. The girls did not understand "go up and down quietly"; the resulting noise, amplified by the ample air space and bare walls (I refer to our lack of tapestries), was verging on deafening. Our compromise was a standard central stair-carpet revealing generous oak on either side. The girls could cope with the instruction "walk on the carpet".

My first requirement was to find a head tractor driver / foreman who could conduct the farming operations in my absence. This was not difficult as Gerald, who had alerted me to the position of manager, had just such a person in mind. Sam came with excellent recommendations and was wanting to relocate to the area. Gerald had built up a network of distant relatives and acquaintances that made him a fount of all knowledge. I had always known of such networks from the time of starting in the countryside. It immediately impressed me that everybody knew everyone else; more fearsomely, they all appeared to be related, however tenuously! This had been something of an obstacle to my social life as it stopped me offering an opinion about anything. If I talked of a person in whatever light, it could brand me an enemy or ally by association. In the most extreme cases I would find out that their family never talked to the other because of some dispute one or two generations previously.

I could appreciate that ill feeling could result when one had purchased a field that had always been promised as 'first offer', only to find it was snatched from under one's nose by an offer that "could not be refused". This would trickle through the extended family as real hatred, even to the extent of their crossing the road to avoid each other. Similar things arise in auctions where one party outbids another just to spite them – childish and sometimes costly, but somehow achieving a certain satisfaction by 'getting your own back'. In short I had to know what hidden histories and reputations existed locally, and I knew Gerald could be relied upon to advise me of impending 'foot in mouth' situations.

In addition to Gerald, local tradesmen and auctioneers helped me out in a guarded way by suggesting certain business traits to help my settling in. My immediate concern was to set the farm off on the right foot. I had to implement the cropping plan by buying necessary equipment on a just-in-time basis. The first necessity was two tractors and trailers. I approached the local machinery dealer for a quotation, emphasising that this was the start of an expanding business. The trailers were to be identical, with wooden drop-sides and metal extensions for bulk grain. The sales manager, Max, took me into his office to ensure our conversation was private.

"Are you sure you want two brand-new trailers and two tractors?" he enquired in a hushed voice.

"Yes, is it difficult to have two the same?" I wondered if there was a temporary shortage.

"I can't remember your estate ever buying anything new," he confided.

"Well, I wouldn't want to start a business of this scale with second-hand," I asserted.

"I didn't mean to offend." Max was trying to retrieve the initiative. "I'll give you the very best discount."

"Leave the tractors for now and make the trailers an order," I said.

I decided to clarify the purchasing policy with Robert but couldn't forget Max's reaction.

"I've ordered two trailers from Max who you suggested was our most local dealer for spares and sundries," I announced the next morning in the office.

"Two!" Robert exclaimed.

"Yes, we're starting with nothing at all and they are identical for grain harvest or roots."

"I usually have second-hand in the woods; I guess it is different on the farm." Robert was taken aback, no doubt realising he was now a farmer rather than a landlord.

"I will go to the main agent for tractors. Fords are the other side of town, aren't they?" I think we ought to have a new 70 hp one for ploughing and main cultivations and a good second-hand one for lesser work." I hoped the slight compromise would lessen the shock. "It is all budgeted for but there will be a little give or take on the items," I added, to help the situation.

I talked to the gamekeeper and head forester to get their reactions. I was not encouraged. I had come from an environment where the best was first choice but a good financial return expected. I knew that a 'make do and continually mend' policy was bad business. I would have to tread carefully and show as much early profit as possible.

I had to find another worker; an able shepherd as well as being conversant with general farm work. I did not anticipate a huge sheep enterprise but would need to utilise the unploughable fields and meadows as effectively as possible. Currently I had a neighbour renting grass for some of his flock until we were up and running. Steven and Sally had only been married a year but proved ideal for our situation. He had come from farm worker stock and a smallholder business but was keen to advance. He had done a year at farm college, which gave a good foundation of the science behind modern methods. Steven also had a dog that was half-useful. Sally worked as a hairdresser but was prepared to help out as casual labour if called upon; it all boded well. My main concern for the young married couple had been the tied house, which I regarded as below standard. The estate had two maintenance staff and I needed them to improve it. The cottage had not been used for some time and needed damp-proofing. The walls were solid stone with no damp course; the only remedy was to remove the whitewash and coat the walls with bitumen. Appropriate plastering gave a tolerable seal and smoother finish. The end result met with the couple's approval and Steven started working with us.

The previous tenant of the farm was taking his last harvest and releasing fields for us to prepare and plant with winter corn. There was just time to buy some ewes and a ram to make a start on the sheep enterprise. I arranged for a trusted dealer to find a hundred ewes, all good in mouth and udder, plus possibly including a pen of ewe lambs ready for the tup, if he could. The race for early profit meant ploughing up fields that could produce reasonable arable crops. This would help the cash flow, which at the beginning was like a bucket with no bottom. Even the fencing repairs and a few new subdivisions of fields was an outlay in materials and sundry tools.

I was able to introduce the 'Sussex gate' to cheapen the fencing, which hopefully would only be a fairly short-term measure until we could invest in more livestock and revert to full-sized fields. This type of gate was simply a continuation of the wire netting fence, terminating in a stake dropped into a wire loop at the base and held upright by a similar loop at the top. Three or four stakes were stapled to the netting to stiffen it but were not banged into the soil, the whole assembly being pulled tight to meet the end-post of the adjacent wire fence. I soon found that this was referred to as a 'Wessex gate'; a testament to practical farmers wherever they lived.

With the previous farmer's cattle gone, we ploughed up two large, flat pastures that were suitable for potatoes. The soil was medium-heavy clay and virtually stone-free, a real contrast to the sandy land I had become used to. The ploughing was done in autumn with the expectation of frost aiding a fine tilth and the potential to grow potatoes with clean skins.

Autumn ploughing and cultivations were in full swing and it felt as if farming had really started. I had purchased equipment as necessary and chosen good second-hand where prudent. The plough was foundational and new, guaranteeing a true frame with nothing bent or welded. Sam would have no excuse for poor work. In practice Sam was meticulous in achieving good work. As so often with ploughmen, he took pride in straight, even furrows as a foundation for the cultivations to follow. This aided later cultivations to be straight with no ground missed. Although still a young man, he had been schooled to do a quality job.

I too had had this indoctrinated in me by the foreman, Mark, on my first farm in Essex. As a man who had walked behind horses and steered the plough, he and the horse understood 'straight'. Mark told me of the strength and struggle involved in ploughing with a new horse. There could be no conflict between the horse and the plough; and the relationship had to be easy for horse and man. There can be no contest in strength or the horse wins. Mark explained that the horse has to settle into a steady gait that they can maintain all day. The ploughman then concentrates on depth and width of furrow. The relationship is such that the horse feels any excess pressure and keeps to the easiest rhythm. The first cultivation normally follows the direction of the furrows and subsequent ones can be at right angles. The old workers took pride in getting things straight, particularly the sowing of crops. The old saying was, "If it looks right, it probably is."

Our first year, the weather was seasonal and produced fair crops. We purchased both second-hand combine and potato harvesters. This was necessary as the number of acres of each crop was relatively small and the precise markets not yet identified, especially in the case of potatoes. The first cereal harvest was fairly dry and trouble-free. It was stored in bulk on a ventilated floor rather than in storage bins. A powerful fan blew air through a central tunnel with flaps and into underfloor ducts at yard-long intervals. The air, often heated, could filter up through the grain, gently drying it, hopefully, to sixteen per cent moisture content. Some was sold soon after combining, with the rest marketed as prices hardened through the year.

The potatoes were largely sold in 25 kg paper bags for the wholesale greengrocery trade. This gave an immediate return and avoided storage; a happy arrangement because there was no satisfactory building for the purpose. Keeping potatoes through the winter required specialised safe storage and would have to wait. The whole marketing operation would be fine-tuned once we knew more about what the farm was capable of producing and the appropriate markets. This would be reviewed in conjunction with Robert and his accountant, Stuart, who took on a similar role as Michael, our consultant in Wessex. It was a great help to have a third party between owner and manager in the running of a large farm or estate. They had valuable knowledge of farm businesses because of their several clients and were independent. Their interest was to achieve the best result for the owner consistent with the vagaries of practical agriculture.

Stuart, a senior partner in Bradshaws, had followed in the footsteps of his father who had started the accountancy firm and was well known and respected for his knowledge of farming and rural affairs. He seemed comfortable in any situation, talking to farm employees as easily as to owners of considerable land. One could see him as a diplomat or even a counsellor. He had an overview of most financial situations which focused clients' attention. This, coupled with a disarming charm, often elicited details which some might have wished kept private. Our financial review was conducted in the conservatory rather than in the office, which was cramped with three desks: mine, the estate secretary's and a spare. The latter was in effect a depositary for files being worked on and all items in transit: those coming into, or being collected from, the premises. Such items could range from mail, soil samples, small containers of chemicals, outdoor clothing, dog leads, to a few brace of pheasants when in season. It was not conducive for having important and private meetings in the office.

The conservatory added a certain status to proceedings and an unspoken privacy that business discussed never leaked to the office in the barn. After brief pleasantries, Robert, being the owner of the estate, led the discussion.

"We seem to have spent an awful amount of money," he started the meeting.

This could not be contested and I noted that I was included in the 'we'.

"You have been establishing a farm business which doesn't come cheap," Stuart agreed but with caution. "Tenants do have considerable costs."

"I'm the landlord," Robert asserted.

"Precisely," Stuart continued. "You are both landlord and tenant now. In effect, you have the surplus from both businesses. Peter has spent rather more than budgeted, but it seems necessary and of course the cash outflow has come early."

"I have purchased good second-hand items where possible," I added.

"Robert, don't regard this money as lost; it is merely locked up at the moment," Stuart pointed out.

"I expected to be better off." Robert was almost childlike in his disappointment.

I could hear tenant farmers everywhere glad that a landlord was experiencing the reality of the world they lived in. Farming is not only a tough life physically but also financially. They do it because they love it; a way of life, indeed a way of being. It is a privilege to be guardian of God's creation and to leave it, hopefully, better than you received it. Their financial reward is often smaller than others in the chain to the consumer, which seems unjust. However the major reward is their relationship with nature, an essential cog between seed-time and harvest.

In the second year, the weather played a major part in the fortunes of the business. A farmer always plants in hope. His investment is huge in money and energy, but he has no control over the seasons and markets. The crops generally were planted in good conditions, and with favourable over-wintering the seed-beds were good. However, it remained dry for Easter and dry again. A little irrigation was possible in some fields, but the summer continued without rain. We thought it must rain soon... but no! Cereals were dying off rather than ripening. Harvest was still dry; the early grain was mean and pinched in ear. Yields were disastrously low; grain and straw withered. *No rain.* We started harvesting the potatoes, which were similarly small in size and tonnage. I wondered if we would be able to sow next year's wheat in the rock-hard soil and, even if were possible, would it be unlikely to germinate? We listened to the forecast, hoping for rain.

On 12th September I was inspecting the potatoes in the furthest field with Richard, our Advisory Officer from ADAS (Agricultural Development Advisory Service), when there were the first spots of rain. It came on heavier; we danced around like five-year-olds, lifting our faces and opening our mouths wide to actually taste it. I think the soil sighed with relief. We had worked together and become friends; it was a joy to be soaked to the skin. Back at the house, I gave Richard a pair of trousers and a pullover so he could at least drive home without soaking the driving seat. The rain did not stop; after a few days brooks were full and cart tracks saturated. It was the year I bought our first four-wheel drive tractor and that was necessary simply to reach the fields.

The autumn was wet, as if catching up for the deficit of the drought. I recorded the rainfall daily as a useful guide to farm management. The amount per twenty-four hours was recorded and told me the likely soil conditions in the fields. I knew that if 15 mm had rained on heavy soil, it couldn't be cultivated that morning. The men would be put to those small but vital tasks that it was difficult to find time for. I could leave at least half a day before making a detailed inspection of ground conditions, depending on the anticipated job. The annual rainfall was remarkably constant at about 650-700 mm (26-28 inches). However, the distribution within the year was totally random. June or December could be the wettest or driest; in fact, any month could be. This makes arable farming a real challenge; in practice one should be ready for the season and be ready for rapid action when ideal conditions prevail. In other words we had to be guided by ground or crop conditions rather than dates on the calendar. Although area forecasts are very valuable, many farmers become experienced at fine tuning them for their particular holding.

The top potato field had water standing in the rows through most of the winter; nothing could be done. Any attempt to get a tractor up the rows would be futile as it would soon get bogged down, as well as ruining the soil structure for any following crop. Eventually, dry weather and a March wind had allowed the surface water to disappear but the soil in the potato ridges was still too wet to use the harvester. If we ploughed the crop in, suffering a total loss, the soil would be smeared clay, only fit for a potter's wheel. We had to be patient, reminding ourselves one can't work against nature.

In April we harvested some muddy tubers and several clods. Many potatoes had rotted but we somehow graded out about a third of the normal tonnage. The good news was that the market was so short of potatoes that the price was high; almost anything resembling a potato was accepted. Quality did not matter as the dry weather had greatly diminished the output nationwide. On top of this, those potatoes put into stores had not wintered well. What had seemed a disastrous year turned out to be the most profitable and 1976 would go down in farming history as the 'Potato Year'. It is perverse that a poor crop can be very profitable, with the important proviso that all farmers have similar yields. Of course, we never set out to grow a poor crop; that would ruin a business.

Our experience highlighted the need for field drainage and I set about checking what had been drained in the past. This coincided with government grants to defray the cost of under-field tile drainage. Plans were drawn up for four of the wettest fields to be drained with clay pipes at about a chain apart (twenty-two yards) to a connecting 'main' drain and into a boundary ditch. The work would done by a specialist drainage contractor. He would carefully sight levels across the field, and the gigantic cutting wheel (not unlike a chainsaw) would cut a six-inch-wide trench through the field some thirty inches deep. As it crept across the field, it would lay foot-long clay pipes in the bottom, the dug soil left in a neat ridge on the top to one side. The lateral 'runs' usually had four-inch-diameter pipes and the main joining them up was six inches in diameter. About six inches of washed stone would be run on top of the pipes and the soil ridge bulldozed back on top. It was gratifying to see water very quickly trickling into the ditch.

# 30

# Too Much Change

Another farm business had been set in motion, but the cost had been great. Change is always difficult to manage and rarely welcomed by all. Setting the farm up from scratch took concentrated effort by all concerned; finance by the owner, embedding by employees, and time and deadlines by the manager. I had neglected my family.

Hazel had not been entirely happy about moving from Wessex and her friends there to be planted into a new area fourteen miles from significant shops; psychologically I think she felt more adrift. Most farmers are attached to their motor vehicles like a prosthetic limb. This is due to scarcity of public transport in the countryside which naturally runs between centres of population. Farmers mostly want to travel from farm to farm, even field to field, however far apart they may be. Even to get the girls to school, about three miles away, necessitated a car.

Our relationship had been strained to breaking point. The girls had settled in well and found new excitement with fields and woodland tracks to explore and imagined friendly ghosts and tea parties. They also had a large rough collie to take along and explain things to. In practice the dog said nothing but seemed to know more than they did. The collie had been a surrogate mother to our youngest, standing over her and offering up her long fur as handles to get upright and take her first tentative steps. Their real mother had not had such a happy transition. Friendship and company were lacking as I had selfishly married the farm. We found life together untenable and felt we had to separate. Hazel returned to her family with the girls, and I stayed with the job and its challenges. Later we both rebuilt our lives, but inevitably scar tissue remains.

I put my back further into the work but it was a lonely time. Activity masked the gap but it was there in the shadows. There was a sense of failure and success which can never go together. The failure would be affecting the whole family in one way or another and for me seemed to be a foundation of hardcore rather than tarmac. Success was in the past and the new job was a struggle that held little joy. On the farm there was always a tension between capital expense and vision. There was a reluctance to venture out in case it weakened the estate which had been handed down through the generations. This can easily happen with prized herds or flocks, built up by careful breeding by grandfather but for yesterday's markets.

Some estates had been built up from trading with the colonies and acquired the status of a manor, with the owner often being seen as the squire. They owned large areas and had influence over several hamlets. However, the world was changing and money had to be earned; investments were less certain. The value of the estate lay in the land and what it could yield. If the land was only producing food, which was increasingly a smaller percentage of the consumers' personal budget, then profits dropped. Agriculture was also subjected to the whims of the supermarkets and their purchasing power; this was governing both landlords and tenants. A mind reset was needed to see land as an asset rather than restricted to crop production.

I had moved from farming with huge vision and unlimited capital, to locked up capital and limited vision. In Wessex I had been building up an estate but now I was trying to hold one together. In my quieter moments I was musing over the importance of vision as the vital element in all ventures. It was at this time that my old employer asked if I would consider returning to manage Beech Row again. The manager who had taken my place had not been successful and Mr Campbell had lost money. I was offered a significant increase in salary but was expected to spend only about two days a week farming, the rest being involved in other ventures. This offer had arisen whilst Hazel was still with me, but going back would not have helped our marriage.

I had always felt one could only go forward; to return is rarely the same. I had a lot of doubt about what the other aspects of working for Mr Campbell would entail. I imagined the pressure to achieve in fields outside my training and experience. Also the probability of chasing all over the country on business; in short becoming much more urban than rural. Gone would be the synergy with nature. I thought money was less important than quality of life, so I turned the chance down. I had turned my back on success in most people's eyes and had not achieved satisfaction in my present post. Where would my present job lead? The promise was still that as each tenancy expired, my responsibilities would increase. I still had my vision of managing a thousand acres. Whatever choice I made, there were uncertainties. Farming was my dream and I had to pursue it. The whole family had seen massive changes and I had to give more time to my venture in north Shropshire. Managing the farm consumed me; I had to make it a success, building on my experiences in Wessex, knowing it would be challenging.

## Water Everywhere

We had experienced the drought and now there was water everywhere. It focused my attention. Water became an obsession; it was vital, it was needed in the right place at the right time. Others were thinking the same; water was more vital globally than oil. Turning to my local patch, we had improved several fields that needed under-drainage, but we needed to store water for irrigation. There was an ideal boggy patch covering a third of a field not far from the farm buildings; could this be a good place for water storage and fishing along the lines seen at Beech Row Farm?

The site of the ponds was at the lowest point of the home farm, and water from the fields naturally drained that way. The contractors began by bulldozing the topsoil to one side and then pushing deeper, making sure not to pierce the clay subsoil. Eventually we found that the clay continued down to at least ten feet below surface level. They created a pond at the bottom of each 'home' field and interconnected them. This immediately made use of the bog, and future land drainpipes would drain into them. Springs bubbled up through the clay and the ponds soon filled, with an overflow returning the water to a ditch. The topsoil was returned, sown with grass seed and a few trees planted. It was not as natural or picturesque as the monks' stew ponds, but they had benefitted from years of maturity, allowing nature to beautify them.

We now had impounded water, but had to seek a greater abstraction licence. We had obtained approval from the Water Authority for impounding water but not to use it for irrigation. This prompted jovial discussion with their local officer. He had visited the farm when we were planning the ponds. First appearances can be deceptive for both parties; him turning up in a mud-free car, green wellies and collar and tie, to be met by (I should say *accosted* by) our new mechanic, Gary. He was a real country boy, dedicated to machinery and tractors but not tuned to the niceties of welcoming salesmen or officials.

"Is the boss about?" the smart young Severn Trent Water officer enquired.

Gary, who was rather overweight and never buttoned up his shirt or boiler suit, apparently had one hand on the car roof as he leaned down to the driver's window, a large spanner in the other.

"Which one: the owner or the manager?" he asked.

The officer studied a piece of paper. "The manager, I think."

I was coming across the yard towards the workshop.

"He's here." Gary pointed his spanner towards me.

"Morning! You've come to see the ponds?" I assumed. "Leave your car over there. We'll go down in the pick-up."

He seemed grateful that it was some distance from Gary's workshop.

I was in my usual practical mode; dressed in old clothes with cloth cap and work boots which I always thought of as 'army boots'. This had arisen in the early years when the girls, anxious to 'help' Daddy, would carry one boot each to the outside door. If I just referred to "boots" they might bring wellies or work boots. On the farm I was usually dressed to lend a hand with any task as the necessity arose, such as help lifting a rear tractor wheel, field gate or, of course, guiding stock through a gateway. Consequently, being indistinguishable from my men was the most practical apparel.

The field was no longer boggy and I drove to the pipe joining the two ponds.

"You see we have control over water coming in from the stream or exiting back to it," I pointed out.

"Yes and the stream still flows well," David, the officer, observed. I had noted his name from his card.

"We hope to stock them with trout but also irrigate from here when necessary."

"You'll have to apply for an abstraction licence," David insisted.

"I know, but it seems odd, having done all the work and natural springs having filled it, that we have to pay to use it." I knew I was being provocative but couldn't resist a little dig.

"We own all the water and have to control it." David quickly held the river board's line.

"We own the land and the good Lord provides the rain. Anyway, the stream is flowing past as ever it has," I provoked further.

He looked at me wondering how serious I was.

"Do you know, *we* should be charging *you* for supplying water to your stream." I was on a roll now.

"Are you serious?" He was somewhat concerned.

"I just wanted to point out the injustices of life." I raised a wane smile. "The serious point is, we need a reasonable abstraction licence for second early potatoes. It's vital for getting a good skin finish and scab-free skins," I insisted.

In due course we were granted a licence, but hardly as much as I felt was needed. Water seemed to be a recurring feature of my responsibilities. Although the home farm's water was supplied by Severn Trent Water, much of the estate had its own private supply dating back to Queen Victoria. The pipework was rusting away and often leaked. The maps of the network were difficult to follow, as buildings had been demolished and roadways altered, not to mention hedges and field boundaries changing over time. The maintenance team could remember a lot of the alterations, but accuracy was always a point of heated discussion.

Any problem was usually noticed by a tenant in one of the many houses, complaining of low water pressure. This would call for immediate action on my part, and I would assure the tenant that the problem was probably a simple leak that would soon be mended. In my own mind, a dark shadow would descend as experience told me that simple leaks could be the start of long searches and imperfect answers. As it was, the estate's private water supply was not a case of a simple phone call to the public water company and leaving the problem to them. We had two maintenance men, Alfie and Adrian, whom I could immediately redirect to the task. They were often referred to as "the AA" but were rarely as quick at finding the problem.

The AA would be somewhere on the estate but engaged on a job that they could not quickly leave, such as building a wall, concreting a driveway or plastering a ceiling. Invariably they would be in the midst of wet cement or half-erected scaffolding that would cause half a day's delay. To compound this, they were steady in their work, which some might call slow. I found them 'country', which resulted in a thorough job and excellent local knowledge but without urgency. Alfie knew all the local gossip and every family relationship going back years. He would inform me that the previous occupants of the house were related to so-and-so, where they worked and what their cousins did. Adrian, who was some years younger, was soaking up this information and able to add some colour to it. I feared that on Alfie's retirement we would be left with needing an identical replacement. In the case of water supply, their combined knowledge was invaluable. Whilst waiting for them to arrive at the complainant's house, I would phone other tenants enquiring about the state of their supply. This defined the extent of any problem. The AA would start at the property concerned and walk towards the first stopcock, looking for any wet patches and shutting off various stopcocks, tracing the route back to a particular reservoir. This I endeavoured to learn, as it would be useful in their absence.

Back at our present problem, it seemed other houses were not experiencing low pressure.

"If we shut this one off, it will cut off Mrs Smith," Adrian suggested.

"Nay, there's a tee," Alfie argued.

He had the habit of catching hold of his peaked cap and twisting it two inches towards his ear and back again. I had noticed this whenever deep thought was needed, as if to engage his memory.

"What tee?" Adrian enquired.

"When they first went to polythene water pipes." Another twist of the cap. "When Mr Street was going to start a market garden."

"Where's that tee?" Adrian called

"About the end of Mrs Smith's garden," Alfie answered as he walked to him.

"Nothing here," Adrian said.

"Well, don't expect a manhole; it was only a tee." At that, Alfie kicked about and moved a large stone by the fence-line.

"It's a bit wet," Adrian observed.

They went back to their van and returned with a couple of spades. It was indeed wet. They continued carefully, then *clunk*.

"Could it be the pipe?" Alfie suggested. They opened up the hole.

"The polythene pipe tee'd off this."

Digging along the galvanised pipe they found the tee piece. There was a significant spurt coming from the union.

"Turn off the first stopcock," Adrian instructed Alfie whilst enlarging the hole.

A simple half turn on the spanner stopped the water. I told them to leave the tee uncovered for a couple of days and check again, but in any case to fit a single stopcock for Mrs Smith's house as soon as time permitted.

Water problems recurred frequently. It wasn't long before I was flagged down by another resident of the hamlet who had seen me drive through to the fields beyond. On my return journey I found the lady beside the road, somewhat distressed, and waving a glass of water at the car window.

"Look! Look!" she yelled.

I got out and peered at the glass.

"It's a worm!" she informed me in some agitation. "It's out of the tap."

I didn't think she wanted me to identify it so much as to explain its presence in her water. There it was, about two inches long and appearing quite healthy. I knew I must choose my words carefully; it certainly looked like a worm. I followed her back into the house. She demonstrated what had happened by turning the tap on; and suddenly there was another worm in the glass. More accurately, it was the other half of the first one, but I thought it best not to mention that.

"Ahhh!... Do something!" She was too stunned to faint.

She flopped onto the kitchen chair, breathless and silent. I threw the contents out through the doorway and turned the tap on again. The water was a little cloudy. I let the tap run. Fortunately, there were no more of the Annelida family. I apologised profusely and could only suggest it was a unique occurrence due to the reservoir being empty and then refilled. I explained that normally any sediment lay undisturbed at the bottom of the tank and clean water was drawn from the top. I returned in the afternoon with a bouquet of flowers on behalf of the estate, which she graciously accepted.

Our water system was of such interest that the next spring I conducted a youth group from our church on a countryside awareness evening. The purpose was to demonstrate the differences between town and countryside and to sharpen observation. We stopped and listened to various sounds and tried to identify the source; we also identified trees and their various names and uses. As we came across a disused railway line, I explained that Mr Beeching had closed about a third of the nation's stations to make the industry more efficient.

We also came across a very low brick structure by the side of the lane with a flat concrete roof.

"What do you think that is?" I asked

"I think it's a bomb shelter," a willowy boy with glasses answered. There is usually one in a group who is top of the class and likes to show they are. By this time a couple of the boys were walking on the roof of the structure that was only two feet above ground. These were the adventurous who even jumped up and down, unable to crack the six-inch-thick concrete roof.

"Why *can't* it be an air-raid shelter?" I asked.

A girl put her hand up. "Because there are no people living here?" she offered.

"There's no door," another girl suggested.

The boys were still jumping up and down.

"Well done, but I'll tell you the secret: it's a water reservoir."

I explained that rainwater seeped into pipes with holes in them on the forest floor and drained a long way into the top of the reservoir.

"How does it get out?" another inquisitive boy asked.

"It drains in through the pipe in the top just under the concrete and goes out underground the other side. There is a pipe with a filter, well above the floor, so clean water comes out of the taps." I also explained that it kept cool buried in the soil and the hatch on top was for men to check the level and take samples. Being on high ground the water gravitated to taps for all the village's use. After the youth group had returned home, I wondered whether they had had rather too much information and how much they had related to their parents.

# 31

# Potatoes Galore

The potato crop had proved profitable, even in the year of drought. The result was a huge acreage planted the next two years as farmers tried to get in on the act. I decided the only way forward was to become more efficient by improving quality and with focused marketing. Supermarkets were increasingly demanding clean, washed potatoes with blemish-free skins. There was some market for potatoes that had been dry brushed which generally kept longer and were less prone to going green. The disadvantage was that minor damage could be missed in grading and disappoint the final customer. At the same time, high street greengrocers were being squeezed by the supermarkets. This resulted in fewer wholesale markets and the growth of specialist graders and packers.

As farmers we had to pay very special attention to detail, from soil preparation to harvesting and storage. The introduction of destoners meant the potato ridges were free of stones and clods which were lightly buried under the soil in the 'valley' between the ridges. This was the gardener's equivalent of sieving all the soil in a potato ridge before planting the seed potato. The purpose was to end up at harvest with fine soil that would fall through the digging web and be free of stones that would bruise or damage the potato on its journey from soil to bulk trailer.

Research had shown that common scab, which causes unsightly damage to the potato's skin, could be greatly minimised by irrigation precisely at tuber initiation. In practice it means trying to achieve damp or moist soil conditions during the very start of the root tip swelling. If a farmer is on his knees scrapping around potato plants only a foot high, he is not looking to see if there are any tubers yet but checking whether the soil is moist at root depth. The art of potato irrigation is to keep the crop growing steadily through dry spells and avoid growth cracks and distorted shapes. An even-sized sample with clean skin is the aim, rather than the large tubers in a gardener's competition, where the largest potato, onion or marrow wins. Having grown the right thing, I was keen to keep it in the best condition until marketing it. This would necessitate storage in a frost-free shed but at a controlled temperature, without which the respiring potatoes would gain heat, causing condensation and rotting. The only sheds available were Dutch barns with corrugated iron sheeting as walls, which would require a concrete floor and insulation. The good news was they had a sound roof and sturdy frame. In order to keep capital expense to a minimum, we decided do as much work as possible with farm labour. The downside was the timescale to complete the sizeable alterations before potato harvest.

The start was to get Sam on the forklift with a big bucket to level up the whole site. It had been erected on the natural slope of the yard and dropped three feet from back to front. Most of the soil included an element of hardcore and was used to make up the lower front elevation. I had drawn up plans with a concrete floor throughout, with a main air duct each side of the large front doors. These main ducts had side branches, a foot square, running at right angles across each bay. We hired shuttering to form the ducts and bought ready-mixed concrete in 6 yd³ loads. This was laid by Steven and Sam with instruction and help from the AA team when free from maintenance jobs. They had to construct a concrete ramp from the double doors to match the higher internal floor but it worked well. The tin walls were lined with bales stacked to about nine feet high as insulation and which formed a useful walkway once the store was filled. We used loose straw to cover the levelled off potatoes, to allow moist air to condense in it, so keeping the crop dry. A large coaxial fan was used to control temperature and moved from one main duct to the other as necessary. We were now able to market the crop through the winter and early spring and to catch favourable markets.

The farm business had grown, with more fields coming into the arable rotation and an increase in the potato acreage. We were growing oilseed rape and moving to cereal seed production where possible. It was good to have Gary as mechanic on the staff but he could not solve all our problems. The increasing complexity of machines, and often the inaccessibility of the part that needed replacing, meant we had to resort to specialists.

The new potato harvester caused the first headache. It had performed perfectly well for a couple of weeks, but after a night's rest in the shed, still connected to the largest tractor, it was reluctant to start work. I relate this in personal terms because one depends on vital machines, and their welfare affects the farms profitability. This harvester required a tractor driver and four people, usually women, on the sorting table to discard cuts, clods and diseased potatoes as they passed along the inspection table to the bulk trailer travelling alongside.

I had collected the casual workers from the village and taken them to the field. Sam pulled into the potato baulks and tried to drop the digging web to work. Nothing happened. The hydraulics which should lift the digging web in and out of work, didn't. Sam worked the lever time and time again with no result. He was no longer on friendly terms with our essential machine, and using less-than-encouraging language had made no difference. The ladies on top were anxious to get moving but nothing could be done. I listened to the electric control box click as Sam worked the lever, but the digging web refused to drop into working position.

"Sam, I've got an electrician working at one of the houses; I'll get him along." I drove off in haste.

The electrician heard my explanation of the problem but said he couldn't help.

"It's not mechanical, it's the electric box," I insisted.

"You said you heard the clicks so the connection is live."

"Yes," I confirmed.

"It's not electric, it's electronic; you want an electronic engineer." He was resolute.

I glumly accepted his opinion and went to the office to appeal to the main agent who had supplied the machine. They said all they could do was send for a new box and they had never had to stock one previously.

I thumbed through the business directory for an electronic engineer and explained the problem.

"We don't normally do that sort of job but I can send a man out next week."

"Next week!" I exclaimed. "I need you *now*!" I tried to calm myself. "I don't wish to be rude. I've got four women ready to work and a lorry to fill." The call ended.

I called at the workshop and took Gary to the field for another look at the job.

Sam had a sledgehammer in his hand.

"Don't use that, much as I would like to," I called out, pacing up to the machine.

"I already have; it just needed a smack." Sam even smiled. "It is what she wanted."

I noticed the digging web had dropped to the ground.

I turned to Gary who looked puzzled. "It could be dust," he suggested.

"A sledgehammer is not a duster," I added.

"I must have dislodged something," Sam confessed, but we all grinned; the day was saved.

The new storage was a great improvement, with less damage to tubers and some temperature control, but we had to go further. The building needed insulating to eliminate the condensation running down the corrugated sheet walls. We decided on polyurethane sprayed over the inside of both the walls and roof by specialist contractors. The sprayed product hardened to form a skin two to three inches thick that had every appearance of scrambled egg. It was another expense but much cheaper than building a state-of-the-art environment-controlled store. It also marked the introduction of growing potatoes for chipping (French fries). These would be a special variety called Russet Burbank, grown on contract for a planned market. The contract specified the price per ton and the month of delivery, enabling us to budget with some assurance.

The potatoes grown for the ware[41] market needed to be planned in a similar way with a major pre-packer who, via their representative, would monitor both crop and grower to achieve the best quality. I found this link, even better described as a 'relationship', most helpful and enlightening. Mike, a fresh-faced young graduate, phoned in the evening saying he was in the area and could call at my convenience, preferably the following day. He knew when it was coffee time and somehow always seemed to make that deadline. He was a trained agronomist and in close touch with the requirements of crops throughout the area. Visiting the other growers, he was quick to disseminate potential problems and say how other farmers were dealing with them.

There was a knock on the office door, although it was open.

"I thought I heard a high-powered machine come into the yard," I quipped.

"Not yet!" Mike knew I was referring to the new car the firm had promised him. "And I am not sure it will be very high-powered."

"Not with all the cut price potatoes we are sending you?" I chided him.

We had a happy relationship, literally needing each other and because it was light relief for both of us; for him from the monotony of many miles driving and for me from too much paperwork, our common concern being a healthy potato crop.

"I guess you have got time for coffee?"

"Just hot water, thanks." Mike was serious, but I never remembered until he reminded me.

"I never remember: not tea, coffee, chocolate…"

He stopped me. "Hot water in the morning, whisky and cold water in the evening." We both laughed.

"What are other crops doing?" I got down to work.

"Most emerged well but some 'earlies' are showing scab on the sand."

"You're not worried about scab on Russets, are you?" I enquired, thinking chipping potatoes have their skin removed.

"Slight scab we can cope with, but do all you can to avoid it," Mike cautioned. "If it is too deep we can't peel them satisfactorily."

"What are the cereal crops like?" I was always interested in what he had noticed on other farms.

"Not special on the light land but reasonable on heavier soils. Most better crops seem to have black-grass bug infestations," Mike elaborated.

We drove to each potato field in his car. The crop was a foot tall. He took a spade from the back of the estate car and we walked twenty yards up the rows.

"You are dry here," Mike observed as he dug up a plant.

"Tubers are forming," I added.

"There is a touch of scab but that is all." We were both pleased.

---

[41] eating potatoes, not seed potatoes

"Have you ordered your blight spray?" Mike asked.

"You are not selling that now?" I teased.

"I understand it may be scarce; don't know why," Mike informed me.

It was the throwaway comment that was useful. I made a mental note to enquire locally that day.

I realised we needed more storage space and looked in detail at the single Dutch barn adjoining the refurbished one. The earth floor was sloping more than the one we had completed; also, the tin walls were in poorer condition. Making it level might expose the telegraph poles at the higher end completely, rendering the shed fit for nothing. The only possibility seemed to be to take out about two feet of soil at the high end, leaving a fall of about one in thirty, and concreting it. This would secure all of the frame and provide short-term storage for potatoes or grain. The walls would be lined with small bales and the bottom end closed off with large straw bales. It would not be worth contemplating any ducting to ventilate crops but it would be an invaluable reserve for any enterprise; even lambing, if free.

I was always conscious of my meetings with Robert and the accountant, Mr Bradshaw. These assessments seemed somewhat random, about half yearly, and I assume were called when my employer thought necessary. Whether it was concern for the farm or estate finances, it probably amounted to the same thing. Undoubtedly the growth of the farm business had sucked up capital, but the bank manager mentioned no concern; more to the point was Stuart Bradshaw's assessment. We met as usual in the conservatory and I was required to bring Stuart up to date with practicalities. I started with the potato enterprise and its growth, including more secure marketing with the chipping contract, which was well received. I also talked about the storage and how essential that was to catch the best market opportunities. Looking to the future, I mentioned a trial crop of both cabbage and onions pending further research; also a trial wholesaling potatoes to greengrocers, caterers, etc.

Robert was somewhat reserved, wondering if I had time to do anything more. Stuart suggested more growth was possible, even desirable, but not at my expense in terms of labour.

"You have grown from nothing and we are well within the expectation of other farm businesses," Stuart continued. "The recommendation is not to employ any extra labour but call in contractors at peaks. This would also avoid excessive purchase of machinery which seems to depreciate, or become effectively obsolete for modern practice, in a few years."

I was entirely in agreement. "I had to be very 'hands on' to start things off, but I am happy to delegate wherever possible," I responded.

"You certainly work hard and long hours," Robert intervened, to my embarrassment.

"Any business needs a bit of driving on," I said defensively

"I think it is a matter of balance, or perhaps priorities. Manage first, then work practically if time permits," Stuart said with satisfaction.

He was the consummate accountant, but I knew the value of figures in controlling a business. It is all too easy to concentrate on doing a good job without asking if the task is going to improve the profitability. There was a growing move on many farms, especially the larger holdings, to plough less and to cultivate with spring tines. These were frames with tines of spring steel, shaped like large question marks, pulled through the soil vibrating and levelling it, often achieving a tilth to sow seed without the cost of ploughing.

To avoid suggestions that we might think of dispensing with the plough, I added a caution.

"I have tried not ploughing land after cereals when oilseed rape would follow and used just a pass or two of the spring tines, and it worked well. We drilled the seed and rolled it in. Mind you, if there is a lot of debris to bury, we would have to plough that under."

Robert turned to Stuart.

"There we are, Stuart; that's what's called management."

Stuart answered by running through the performance figures with evident satisfaction and the meeting ended.

Oilseed rape became a regular crop in the rotation. It fitted in well as a break crop from cereals, was sown in September before winter wheat or barley, and harvested the following August between barley and wheat. We could manage the oilseed rape with our own labour and combine harvester. The potato acreage had increased but we used contractors to avoid much greater expense on modern equipment. The growing, storing and marketing of the crop was becoming much more specialised and exacting. The specialist contractors came with several tractors to plant a field in optimum conditions and at harvest time supplied their machines and trailers for transporting from field to farmyard. This enabled our staff to grade the crop into store or, for immediate dispatch, up an elevator into a bulk lorry.

In spring, friends and acquaintances were amazed to see up to five tractors in the same field turning a ploughed field into a completely planted and ridged field in a single day. We would do the deep ploughing, and possibly the first rudimentary cultivation of breaking the ploughed ground to dry it, then broadcast fertiliser over the area. The contractor's team would start their circus with another cultivation and then form rough but straight ridges, so that a shower of rain would not hinder the work. The first tractor would deep cultivate and the second, twenty to thirty minutes behind, would form straight ridges. The next machine would destone a pair of ridges, effectively lifting them like a roll of carpet; the stones and clods carried up the fast-moving web and the fine soil dropping through to the ground. The stones returned to where the valley of the ridge would ultimately be, enabling the later tractor operations to run on firm ground. The next tractor would form a new pair of fine soil ridges twenty minutes later. This operation was followed by the actual planter opening up the ridges, dropping a seed potato into it and closing the soil back over as if it had never been disturbed. Job done. Our part of the job was to maintain a steady supply of seed potatoes to the field in ton boxes to be lifted off by forklift and tipped into the planter hopper.

# 32

# Shepherding and Trials

Just as the arable enterprises were growing in size and maturing, so were the sheep. Steven was having to deal with increasing numbers of ewes and needed to improve the quality of the livestock. I had originally bought ewes sound in mouth and udder but of somewhat second quality; in other words, somebody else's cast-offs. I had also purchased a few yearlings that were more expensive but had a productive life ahead of them. Now, with a flock of nearly two hundred, it was the time to cull the poorest and start rearing our own ewe lambs. Whenever we had the flock in the 'sheep shed' for routine treatment, Steven would set aside those with completely worn down teeth or several missing teeth (broken-mouthed), plus any other defect (such as the bacterial infection known as black quarter). These he would batch up and take to market. In the autumn we would look to the market for replacement ewe lambs ready to go to the ram for the first time. Sometimes I asked a local dealer to look out for a bunch of lambs or ewes for us.

Henry was knowledgeable and totally honest and, as such, an asset one would be foolish to ignore. He was not an old man nor would he easily fit into any stereotype. His head and shoulder appeared to be everybody's idea of a country man, with a ruddy complexion and cloth cap, but below he became a tradesman, with a pullover and casual trousers and elastic-sided boots designed to be pulled on quickly. The defining note was that this seemingly 'normal' attire was spotted with stains. It seemed that whatever came close to Henry stuck to him. I cannot say he smelt unpleasant, that would be unfair and unkind, but he did give an impression of being a hard worker. Indeed, he always looked as if he were in the middle of it. The only variation was the occasional blue boiler suit over the top of this attire; but that too had the same stains, looking as if purchased from the same shop.

Henry was the first 'go to' man for livestock; his knowledge of what bunch of animals would fit a given customer or location was legendary. He would know the holding and the financial outlook of the farmer. Most enquirers would want nothing but the best stock, but the critical difference was what they would pay. Henry seemed to know what the true priority was: quality, price or value for money. He knew my constraints without discussion. Although never articulated, he knew I was managing a farm for the landlord and that money was tight. On the other hand, quality had to be good but not outstanding. Any livestock I purchased had to have the potential to turn a profit. He was so experienced that he knew where to find the right stock before the farmer had decided he wanted to sell them. A few words to the somewhat reticent vendor that he had a customer for his animals, and that he could replace them with some ideal 'growers' at a favourable price, nearly always clinched the deal with both parties. I only had to ask Henry for eighty to a hundred ewe lambs and they would be with me within a week, no more discussion.

Steven needed occasional help to drench[42] the ewes and at the same time check hooves that may be overgrown or have foot rot. I would have to send two men and possibly help out myself in order to get the sheep safely into the yard and the sheep-handling area. This was a disused poultry house set up with gates and portable interlocking hurdles to funnel sheep around to a dip and draining pen. If they were only to be drenched or pregnancy-tested, the dip would be covered over with floorboards.

The sheep often had to cross or journey along a main road to reach the yard. Steven would set off with 'Trigger', closing any gates on the way to the field. It is worth mentioning that he had trained Trigger himself and made a half-useful dog of him. Half-useful equates to being in good control half of the time. In fairness Trigger was not pure bred, nor did he have quite the look of a Border collie; he was slightly larger and with a carefree tendency. His independent mind meant he was both guard dog and sheepdog, able to nip both sheep and unwelcome visitors in equal proportions. Nevertheless it was good to have his services, which achieved useful if not show trial excellence.

The gathering routine was for Steven to go to the field where the sheep were grazing and send Trigger around the back of the flock to bring them to him. The sheep, on seeing Trigger and knowing his insistence on a quick gather, would get to the gate at the gallop. Steven, satisfied that none were left, would open the gate and keep ahead of them. I usually got a man to walk with him as two could better keep the tide back along the main road. It was also necessary to place someone at the top of the farm drive to halt traffic and make sure the sheep came down the road into the yard. With all exits closed, and only the sheep shed doors open, they usually went straight in. Trigger, at this point, was content for the shepherd to tie him up outside his kennel. He had enjoyed his exercise and would resume guard duty with evident satisfaction.

The sheep would then flow through the penned area to be examined in the 'race'. By this time they were in single file facing the drafting[43] gate, where Steven or an assistant could administer an oral shot of wormer or another injection into the loose neck skin. Having treated the six or seven confined in the race, they could be released into the left- or right-hand drafting pen. The drafting gate was

[42] oral medicine for worms
[43] selection

operated by a long handle, swinging left or right, so simultaneously opening and shutting the entrance to either pen. Once in a pen, they could be examined for lameness and be turned to sit on their tails, leaning backwards between the shepherd's legs. With four feet in the air, their overgrown hooves could be paired down, much like cutting human nails.

Once the flock had been treated, it was time for another circus – returning them to the field. I likened it to a circus because all performers know what should happen and have practised all the movements; when the live performance takes place, the public are involved.

As well as sheep, we had purchased some beef stores – cattle that we were 'growing-on' and would be marketed as 'forward stores' or even 'fat', meaning prime for the butchers. Henry had found a bunch of eighteen Charolais-cross stores that "would suit us nicely". He spoke as if they were wandering about and he was lucky enough to have his lorry empty at the time. We had grazed them for about three months and were needing to move them to a pasture that was too long for sheep (who do best on short grass). This entailed them walking about six hundred yards along the main road. We had chosen the best time of day, about 9.30 am, between rush hour and the shoppers at 10.30 am. It was a bright midsummer morning and I mustered all the staff together for the job.

Sam and Gary were armed with stout sticks to deter front runners of the group from overtaking them and splitting the bunch. Steven and I were at the rear encouraging those who fancied the roadside grass more than the field they had left to keep up with the others. All was well until a car came from behind. The cattle took no notice of the impatient driver revving his engine with his foot on the clutch, but Steven turned angrily and waved him down. Soon after, the driver tried another tactic of running up closely behind and applying his brakes. I stepped to the car and tapped the driver's window insisting, "Keep back – you are scaring the cattle." The driver would not be deterred and did it all the more.

The sound of his horn was noticed by the stock, who quickened their pace to a slow trot. It also parted Steven and me as we were nearly run over. The cattle had started to part and the motorist took his chance. I bellowed to Sam and Gary (my actual words don't need recording) who turned round to see a car in the midst of trotting beef. This was the height of disobedience to the country code and a recipe for disaster. The men quickened their pace; so did the cattle. By this time everything was moving at 10 mph. As cattle moved to and fro against the car's paintwork, the driver lent on his horn. Both men and beef were near their limits. For this infringement, Sam rapped the bonnet of the smart Volvo as it parted him from Gary. By this time we were all running flat out trying to keep pace with the cattle and slow them to a jog.

We never saw the car nor the dent in its bonnet again. Fortunately, two cars came from ahead and saw running beef and waving arms. They stopped and waved their arms as well. This had the desired effect and the advancing army slowed to a walk and turned into the open gateway. Between puffing and panting, we thanked the drivers and shut the gate. The cattle? They were oblivious and chewing fresh grass, unaware that they had broken the sprint record for the furlong[44].

## Trials

The beef and sheep enterprises were conventional but never going to be major contributors to farm profit. It was time to investigate alternative crops that might increase output, much as the carrots which were so important at Beech Row. There they were nature's answer to cropping on sandy soil. I thought a limited trial on our heavier soils might reveal another crop well-suited to our conditions. A small trial area would be a prudent experiment before launching into expensive equipment. I thought savoy cabbages could be the answer as they should grow well, and if marketing were too problematic, the livestock could at least eat them.

Gary helped with a borrowed precision drill and together we cut off two acres of a field with an electric fence that was sloping down to a ditch. It was a medium loam and reasonably free-draining soil, which we thought would be important at harvesting time. The seeds germinated well and needed some hand hoeing to thin them and produce good-sized heads. We soon discovered pigeons thought they were tasty as young plants and began picking out the growing shoots. Our immediate response was to buy 'string bangers' that were essentially fireworks stapled every six inches along a yard of loosely woven string. They were hung on sticks or canes and a match ignited the lower end. As the string slowly smouldered upwards, the banger was ignited about every fifteen minutes. We could only attend to replacing the strings twice a day and the pigeons soon learned this. A cat and mouse, or rather the banger and pigeon, routine meant that the banger exploded and all the birds flew to the nearest tree. After a few minutes the bolder birds would flap down to the crop followed at small intervals by the others joining them.

Gary set up a gas gun which caused a great bang and slowly recharged itself to ignite again. This was an improvement provided it was shut off through the night so that we could all sleep. We tried an assortment of spinning silver discs, mirrors on strings that turned in the breeze, and even a scarecrow. Remarkably, in November there were nice heads forming on the cabbages ready for early cutting. These we trimmed and put into green nets for marketing. I tried some with greengrocers in town, which were well received but uneconomic to deliver in such small quantities. The marketing had to be on a commercial basis and would need to go through a wholesale market in the next town. I decided to fill my large trailer, and the Land Rover, and take the cabbages to the weekly

---

[44] 220 yards

auction. This worked well but was still small scale. It was a lot of effort and not without its trials.

One such trial occurred along a nice stretch of fast road some three miles from the market town. It was a sunny morning and I had a sense of relief to be free of the farm for a couple of hours. I glanced in the rearview mirror and the road was clear. I could see the trailer wheel and the cabbages firmly strapped down. I looked again; surely I could see rather more of the cabbages than usual? I was looking in the mirror more than at the straight road ahead. I could hardly believe my eyes; the trailer was moving further out of line; soon it would be alongside. My mind raced; I was going at forty miles an hour and the cabbages at least forty-two! The trailer had a jockey wheel on the jack and, although slightly nose-down, was doing very well. If I stopped, it would simply pass me, and there would be nothing I could do to halt its progress.

As the trailer was coming alongside, I accelerated hard. There was no traffic coming in either direction, but I had lost sight of the cabbages altogether; there was sure to be a dreadful mess. I stopped and did a panicked three-point turn. Amazingly, the road was still totally clear. The trailer was on the opposite grass verge, facing home; even more remarkable, all the nets of cabbages were still neatly tied and strapped on tight. I walked around it and could find nothing wrong. It was if it had been parked on the verge for later collection. I inspected the rear of the Land Rover; there was no damage but the dropper pin was missing from the clevis hitch. I had lost the pin. I walked back down the road, leaving the trailer there as it was not in anyone's way. I needed the pin to continue the journey and eventually found it where it must have dropped off. Surprisingly, the safety pin was still in place. Returning to the trailer, the ball head of the dropper pin was locked into the hitch. The pin had sheared off cleanly at the ball joint. I took the two pieces to the tractor dealers in town and purchased a replacement pin. The storeman was as incredulous as I was. Returning to the trailer, I hitched up with the new pin and cautiously pulled off the verge. The cabbages were delivered to the market and I returned to the farm with the empty trailer as if nothing had happened.

We also experimented with a variety of Japanese onion which was harvested in August. They too grew well and were not affected by pigeons, but proved difficult to market. My experience with carrots was that they grow on a contract for an assured market. It was obvious that the marketing needed to be assured before venturing into anything in business. I was still keen to try other crops in the search for better returns than those received from standard cereals. We were encouraged to try linseed by a corn merchant. It was new and somewhat experimental in husbandry techniques. The attraction was its multi-use in nutrition and industry. Linseed is similar to flax but is grown for its seed, whereas flax is grown for its stem[45]. Surely it would have an assured market through the corn merchant?

The first year, it was pleasing to see the blue flowers as a change from the bright yellow of oilseed rape. At harvest it was shorter than most cereals and tough to cut. Although the huge combine does the cutting of the standing crop, the driver is able to feel the cutter bar working under pressure. Repeatedly one had to slow the forward speed in order to cut rather than pull the plant up. The next feature was the slippery nature of the seed and the need to store it no more than five feet deep. Whereas we could walk over the top of wheat stored in a heap or silo, linseed was very dangerous as there was no foothold. Trying to walk in the seed, it disappeared from underfoot and it was possible to drown in it. It was necessary to have separate storage from other cereals and we gave up the crop after two harvests. The other problem was that the 'straw' from linseed was of little value and it seemed best to be spread and ploughed in.

---

[45] hemp

# 33

# A Bed of Straw

Straw is valuable to livestock producers and for generations has been used for bedding. In East Anglia the straw used to be burned as it was expensive to bale and transport to livestock farmers in the west of the country. The burning used to be a cheap way to clear the fields, cleanse them of weeds and, as a bonus, trigger germination of wild oat seeds that would otherwise be a major weed problem in the next cereal crop. The burning is now banned for environmental reasons but modern machinery and demand in the west have made it financially viable to transport straw over long distances. In corn-growing areas it can now be sold by auction just as it is coming up to harvest. We had more straw than we could use so it was a useful income to sell the surplus with little effort. I informed the local auctioneers that we had several fields available; they set a date and advertised the auction date for an evening some three weeks before harvest. Interested farmers came to view the crop of growing corn to assess how much straw it was likely to yield and therefore how much it would be worth for them.

I met Ieuan the first year we sold straw by auction. A week before the sale there was knock at the office door and a short man in bib-and-brace overalls introduced himself in a foreign language. At least, that is what it sounded like. He had a pipe in his mouth which, although unlit, didn't help his dialect. I had to ask him to repeat whatever he had said and discovered it was a sort of Welsh-English.

"I have come to see the straw, you see." This is what I gathered without his pipe interfering.

"You are welcome but I can't show you around at the moment," I said.

"I have seen 'em by the road." He adjusted his cap displaying limited strands of greying hair.

"May I ask your name?"

"Ieuan," he mumbled; at least that's what I thought he said. I tried repeating it without success. He offered the same sound, but I failed again. In the end we agreed on 'Ian'.

He had viewed the roadside fields because he had seen the auction lot numbers on posts or tied onto gates.

"Have you any more?"

I decided to show him three fields up a lane leading to another part of the estate.

He walked into the crop along a tramline, sweeping the wheat with his hand. I stayed at the gate. Ian seemed satisfied and I thought I'd found a potential customer.

"Will a big lorry get in?" He was looking at the width of the gateway and the turning circle.

"No problem," I assured him. "We'll make it bigger if necessary."

I took him back to the yard and his ex-GPO van, now a khaki colour. As he drove off, he called out that he would see me at the sale.

The sale started from the farmyard at 5 pm. Sam, my foreman, had provided a large four-wheeled trailer with straw bales down the middle serving as seats. Most potential customers rode on the trailer whilst the rest followed in cars. At the first gateway several went into the field to quantify, if possible, the likely yield. The auctioneer, Michael, stood in the gateway more or less addressing those still on the trailer but conscious of others around him. I was always fascinated by his ability to have eyes everywhere and even take the odd bid that was a secretive nudge on his back. The size of field was announced but the bidding was for the lot; the price per acre was for the customer to calculate. The bidding was brisk and by 8 pm we were back in the yard. Michael stood collecting cheque payments using the trailer floor as a desk. He knew all the purchasers except Ieuan and his brother, who had to give their address details as well as a cheque.

"That new Welshman comes from Lampeter," Michael mentioned, surprised.

"Yes, came a week or so ago to view and see the crops," I added.

"There were three buyers from that direction. It's some way but they know what they are doing." Michael had taken note.

Michael told me his firm would be sending purchasers' contact details within a week together with our cheque for all the sales. It would be my responsibility to inform them the day before combining took place.

Ieuan arrived the day after I phoned him, on an old International tractor towing a baler.

"Have you driven all the way from Lampeter?" I saw him pull into the yard.

"It's taken me about six hours," Ieuan said.

I looked at my watch. "You must have started about 4 am."

"I wanted to avoid the traffic in Brecon," he justified.

"But Brecon's got a bypass the width of a motorway! Never mind. Well done, you are here," I encouraged him.

I realised it was no business of mine what time he wanted to travel. I had an enthusiastic customer and he needed to be encouraged. However, it impressed me that straw was so important to livestock farmers where none is home-grown.

"Can I leave this in the yard until you cut the first field?" He motioned to the tractor and baler. "You see, Haydn is collecting me to go home."

"Oh, your brother. Yes, of course," I agreed.

The day before combining Ieuan's field I phoned him. He arrived the next morning in his khaki GPO van. Its origin had not been completely disguised, as the crown motive on the sides shone through the hand painting. It came stacked with supplies for at least a fortnight. There were enough packs of baler twine to tie several fields of bales. Added to this was a large tool box and a substantial hydraulic jack hiding several jerry cans of diesel fuel, some of which had leaked, plus a wicker hamper.

Ieuan lifted the hamper onto the ground.

"What have you got in there?" I enquired.

"My food." He smiled, exposing the gap where an incisor had made way for his pipe to reside. "My food, man."

Ieuan opened the hasp to reveal about two pounds of cooked sausages. There was a large cheese and two cut loaves which I think were covering a home-made fruit cake. Any spare space had been filled with Welsh cakes baked by his dutiful wife.

"She looks after me," he explained.

I felt I had intruded on his private larder and only commented on the diesel cans.

"Whyever did you bring fuel? You could use ours from the bulk tank."

"I like to be independent, then there's no problems." He looked up to the potato shed. "Can I sleep in there?"

I was hesitant; we had cleaned it out ready for the potatoes after the corn harvest.

"I sleep in the van itself." Ieuan opened the passenger door revealing what was probably a sleeping bag. "I like to drive into the shed and sleep in the van" – I detected a note of concern – "so it's dark."

"Yes, that's fine," I assured him, wondering if he had a ground sheet to at least separate the sleeping bag from the spilled diesel.

Later Ieuan's brother, Haydn, arrived in his pick-up with horse-box. He had a small farm like Ieuan and supplemented his income with contracting. Once Ieuan had baled the outer rows of straw in the field, they assembled a tubular-framed bale sledge from the horsebox. Also out of the box came a bale grab which would fit on the front-end loader of the tractor to lift a stack of bales up onto a lorry.

"I see you are well equipped." I was passing the field as they were unloading.

Haydn was the younger of the two brothers but appeared a generation apart. There were few country airs about him and a less open face. His features were sharper and cheeks quite hollow; it was hard to believe they were related except that they were of similar height. They apparently went to different tailors or perhaps Ieuan's had died. Haydn was brisk and business-like whilst Ieuan was country with no flies on him. Ieuan told me they had jointly inherited the bale grab from their uncle and would be sharing the straw.

It was a busy time for me, keeping our own harvesting team going and half an eye on the three separate buyers of straw. I needed to monitor buyers who were clearing bales from fields and inform others of the combine movements. We also offered loading facilities for those who were using haulage firms to transport their straw home. That meant one of our team and forklift needed to be available when the lorries arrived. It was almost dark when, passing Ieuan's field, I saw work had stopped for the night. I noticed the horse-box and pick-up were in the field but blocking the gateway. As I entered the yard, Ieuan was preparing for the night and I went over to check up on him.

"You seem to have made a good start; is there anything you need?"

He was rubbing his hands with an old towel to get off the worst of the grime.

"You are welcome to use my bathroom," I offered.

"I would appreciate the kitchen tap," he hesitated, fearing it was an imposition.

I led him to the office and through to the kitchen. He was equipped with a towel and large bar of soap.

"You are welcome to come in here each night and you know where the toilet is in the yard." Then I added, "By the way, it looks as if Haydn is still in the field."

"He's sleeping there." He seemed unconcerned.

"Wouldn't he like to come back with you?" I asked.

"He's got to sleep there," Ieuan replied.

I must have appeared puzzled.

"In case anybody pinches our bales," he explained.

"Will he sleep in the cab?" I asked.

"No, he will have some bales in the horse-box."

Passing through the kitchen, there was a powerful aroma of carbolic. I became aware of our different cultures and the great importance of straw to the point of sacrifice.

Harvest proceeded and the weather was conducive to us all. Ieuan was on his third field.

"Nice morning!"

He didn't reply. "A lorry is coming again this morning," he scowled.

"That's good," I thought.

"He's dipped the tank." Ieuan was not happy.

"What do you mean?" I asked.

"I loaded my lorry and 'e says I never put enough fuel in," Ieuan replied.

It transpired that they shared the bale grab but the tractor and fuel belonged to Haydn exclusively. I could hardly credit it. Two brothers, one more prosperous than the other, falling out about a gallon of fuel! Of course, I didn't know the family history, nor should I.

Several harvests passed and Ieuan had straw from us annually. Our business and friendship continued on the basis of absolute trust. I loaded his transport with the remaining field of bales because he needed to get back to his holding. The lorries were somewhat erratic as Ieuan tried to find one that had made deliveries to the Midlands and was returning back to Lampeter empty, so almost halving the cost. Unfortunately, he was always hoping they would squeeze on more than the legal limit. He would give me "a tip for the driver" asking him for an extra top layer. The height restriction was eight bales high, but I was expected to seek nine, particularly if it would clear the field. I was nearly always refused; whether it was because of low bridges or the fear of the law, I never resolved.

Some buyers would have their own lorry, with a demountable livestock container that they could use for straw. One such farmer came with his sheepdog who rode in the cab. After an hour and a half the otherwise obedient dog had vanished. The owner called and whistled in vain and had to leave without the dog. He asked us to pass word around that such a dog was lost on the estate. Time passed but there was no sight of the dog. The owner was totally distressed and even put word on local radio in the hope of finding him. I made enquiries with two local vets and the woodland staff and gamekeepers to no avail. I knew how indispensable a sheepdog was and hoped he would be found. About three months elapsed when the phone rang. The farmer gasped with shock; the sheepdog had turned up at the back door.

It will always be a mystery how he found his way back and how he survived for food. Apart from being thinner, he was in good health and ready to resume where he had left off. I have often wondered about animal navigation but recognised a little in our family pet. She was a rough collie that rode everywhere in the back of our estate whatever the crowded cargo. On holiday that was her night quarters, indeed her 'kennel'. However long the journey, she would lie down at rest, appearing to doze the time away in peace. On every return journey she would sit up ten miles from home without fail and in silence. We noticed this as we turned a corner, one of several hundred both left- and right-handed. However, that lost sheepdog's navigation over three months was not only a mystery, but a miracle.

# 34

# Buckets of Porridge

Life has always had its ups and downs, and Christians and church attenders are not exempt. In fact, the late David Pawson, a renown international preacher and Bible teacher, when asked what it meant to become a Christian, started with one word: trouble. Throughout our separation and divorce, I clung to my Christian faith; it was so essential to seek the Lord; without Him I had no stability. I was still regularly attending church and asked to continue as a lay preacher. It seemed the various events of life were like the tenacity of porridge to a saucepan; and yet porridge is the epitome of nutrition. The struggles in life strengthen us.

Family life had totally changed and I missed the girls, now aged nine and seven. They had settled into their new situation and seemed to be cheerful in our regular phone conversations. We met up about once a month, at a halfway place between north Shropshire and Essex. It was a long and emotional journey for all of us. The girls were as excited as I was to see them, but we were always conscious of the time. It hung over me as we tried to be normal, as if it were just a half day out. But it was not normal. It was not normal for any of us; it was contrived.

Although Hazel had the children to care for, these rare reunions were a reminder of the split. No doubt they were costly for her but it was never talked about. I imagined she would enthuse the girls about the visit but cautioned them not to mention this or that, not to get upset. "Daddy is alright and we are too." A lot of "count your blessings" and "enjoy the lovely time". Many a time we had a picnic together as there was not much opportunity to do much else. The food eaten, we could walk in the leisure area or 'there and back' down a lane we had not done recently. I always had an hour to myself with them as Hazel disappeared, sometimes to a café if open. Perhaps we lacked imagination but the girls didn't show it. The time elapsed, sort of ran out; so did the conversation. We were all trying hard, but the new normal was only 'OK' and we knew in an hour we would be back in 'real time'. During school half-term holidays there were sometimes longer stays; they would come to the farm again for perhaps three days. That would be like old times; they were getting new responsibilities like looking after Dad. I'm sure for Mum it was a lonely time and a reminder that the new normal was not normal.

The farming occupied me fully, and that was no doubt some of the reason 'normal' had changed. The business was intensifying but it didn't have the buzz of Beech Row. I felt other farms were growing a little faster. Technology was advancing and promising to accelerate further, and I felt it was losing touch with nature. In short, I was experiencing a 'porridge' moment. Things were becoming turgid and more effort was needed to escape its gravitational pull. That is the enigma about porridge; it slows one down and yet it provides, sooner or later, the grit to advance.

Sam was on the combine cutting a very good field of wheat and I was congratulating him on the progress.

"When you finish, get straight on with Lapwings. Tell Tony to take a trailer there but leave room for you to start the first round," I instructed. Then I pointed to a wisp of smoke by the engine. "What is happening there?"

Sam stood up. "Looks like a wire alight... Not sure," he said.

He stopped the engine and looked in his toolbox for a spanner to disconnect the battery. In no time it was worse; I could see a small flame. He took the sack he had been sitting on and tried to smother it.

There was no time to disconnect anything.

"Leave it; use the extinguisher," I shouted.

Sam banged the top of the extinguisher and powder spewed out briefly. It was no use; the flames grew. He tried smothering the fire again.

"Leave it! I'll call the fire brigade."

Sam had jumped down, but now he was foot on ladder going up again.

"What you doing?" I shouted.

"My toolbox!" He carried the heavy box down to the ground and ran smartly twenty yards away.

I turned and ran a couple of hundred yards to the house just along the road and hammered on the door. It seemed to take ages and I was just about to knock again when the door opened. I think the woman was just about to greet me.

"Fire! 999!" That was sufficient.

She turned and I followed her into the hall where there was a small chair and desk at the bottom of the stairs. She passed the telephone receiver to me. I dialled the digits.

"Fire, combine fire!" I said without introduction.

"Address?" Her voice was calm and measured. I had just run a furlong in about forty seconds, but managed a reply.

I walked back to Sam who was watching from a safe distance as if expecting fireworks. The fire engine covered the nine miles much quicker than I had ever achieved, but then cars never gave way for me. Small flames were licking around the engine bay. They were soon reduced to smouldering and blue smoke from any oil they could find.

"You were lucky there wasn't any more debris about," the leading fireman announced. "The lads will make sure it is all out."

"I think it has taken out all the electrics," Sam said despondently.

"We won't be able to empty the tank or move it," I added to the woe.

The last two fields had to be cut by a contractor.

The despondency didn't last long; the harvest and autumn workload filled both my mind and the days. Drying the corn to a safe moisture content and the dispatch of some varieties was necessary and urgent. The wheat that had been grown for seed had to be cleaned and moved as soon as possible for the merchant to sell in time for the autumn planting. I had purchased a mobile corn drier to supplement the underfloor system in the corn store which mostly conditioned the bulk of the harvest. There were no storage bins that could hold small tonnages or keep different varieties separate. Some segregation of crops destined for animal feed could be held in the cattle yards until needed for winter housing of livestock.

This busy period coincided with seed merchants buying grain and taking samples, and was my introduction to Tom. He breezed into the yard and wound down his car window.

"I just want to tell you, feed barley is seventy-four pounds today." He wound up the window and drove out.

I thought some would regard such an initial visit as rude or even impertinent, but the incident stuck in my mind; it was so comic, it was memorable. About a week later he called again but this time got out of his car to hand me his phone number, saying he was in the grain market and had dealt with the estate next door for years; with that he got in the car and drove off.

I had to confess I was intrigued, and made a point of speaking to Brian, the manager of the adjoining estate. After a few comments on the weather, state of the potato market, sheep's feet and the wool price, I asked who Tom was.

"Oh, he calls on you too?" Brian chuckled.

"'Calls' is about the word," I said.

"I've done quite a bit of business with him over the years," Brian admitted. "He always offers about the market price, usually a pound better. One thing, he is always honest; his bond is as good as his word, as they say."

"I was intrigued with his style, in and out, without getting out of the car."

"The men call him the 'Flying Dragon'!" Brian chuckled.

"Dragon?"

"Welsh emblem! You're slow today."

I took the chide, noting I would have to get my own back.

Tom's next visit was on an afternoon when he must have had a little more time – or were his previous occasions carefully choreographed?

"Call me Tom."

"I'm Peter; it's better than Boss," I suggested. "Who do you work for?"

"Myself; it's to keep the bailiffs out," Tom replied.

I had to listen carefully to catch the words; his voice was deep and rather Welsh.

"We could do with moving a couple of loads of barley."

"Lead me on; I'll take a sample," Tom responded.

After taking two small samples in packets, I managed to drag him to the office for a cup of tea.

"I'm only offering you tea to hold you down for a few minutes," I joked.

"I don't want to take up your time or make appointments. That's the way I operate, not to be a nuisance." His explanation made sense.

"How does your business operate?"

"You give me grain and I pay you."

I liked his sense of humour and didn't take offence.

"I'm really your market man; I find the best market," he added. "I deal with a number of merchants, seeing you get the best price and they get the most appropriate quality."

"And they pay you?" I added.

"They throw a few crumbs my way," Tom conceded.

I warmed to his simple analysis and openness. Brian, my neighbour, had a good track record of business with him which helped my confidence.

As we both had time, I asked Tom how he had got into the corn merchant business.

"My parents only had a smallholding in Montgomeryshire. There was no chance of my working there; it could hardly keep them alive. I left school and was a boy in a merchant's," Tom recalled.

There was no sense of disappointment; he seemed to welcome the chance to tell his story.

"I didn't want to work on the land anyway; it was cold and wet most of the time and sort of endless."

Sadness crept into his voice and he looked out of the window as if drifting back. I had the sense of 'endless' not only being the hours of toil but lack of progress or advancement.

"I had to sweep up, put orders together, and eventually buy and sell. A sort of delivery boy."

"How did you get about? I asked.

"I had a motorbike and sidecar."

"I can't imagine that." I had to laugh at the thought.

"I never spoke English until I was seventeen," Tom added.

Suddenly I had been transported into an other's life; rural and harsh. The 'endlessness' made me reflect, but at least Tom had broken free. My own experience touched his in various ways. I had had a good education but moved from town to country, with little thought of huge financial reward but hopefully a good quality of life. My breaking free was from the perceived routine of office life, Tom's from toil and lack of reward. We both recognised that farming depended so much on scale to provide a reasonable return. In Tom's case, breaking out to another job seemed to be the only exit, but for those who were left, his parents, how could they escape? Perhaps many would say they were content with their lot; it was their 'normal'. What else could they do? In town they would be like a fish out of water. In their small house and few fields they would count proximity to nature as a blessing.

My thoughts were drawn back to 'buckets of porridge'; the rough with the smooth, the good times and the less good. There was no opting out but a journeying through. I had reached a point of slow progress in the job and, whilst agreeable, it was lacking vitality. Perhaps I needed another break or change of direction.

Just when I could do with a nurse, one arrived. She had made her own break. Rosalind had decided it was time for her to move out of London but had not really thought much about where to go. She packed two cases and was off to a more rural setting to start a new life. She had left Kings College London as one of the first nurse specialists in diabetes after the break-up of her marriage. It was going to be a totally fresh start and Shropshire seemed as good a place as any. She had taken to country life as soon as she had alighted from the train. She quickly found accommodation and registered as a patient with Dr Frank Field at the local doctor's surgery.

It was not surprising by way of introduction to mention medicine and their separate career paths. Both had left medical care in London and landed in the countryside.

"It's a bit different here close to the Welsh border," Dr Field confessed, having come from London himself.

"It seems so small to me and so few people," Rosalind observed.

"There are plenty of people tucked away and with all the usual complaints. I have a jolly full surgery."

"Are you on your own?" she enquired.

"This isn't one of your group practices; I'm head cook and bottle washer!" There was a tone of resignation in his statement.

"Only you and the receptionist? Don't you have any relief?"

"Not at the moment."

"You need at least a practice nurse," she asserted.

"You'd better be one then," Dr Field said out of the blue.

It was the shortest interview Rosalind had ever had. It was also the culmination of Frank's months of concern. He had agonised about the need for some professional help and been unable to define exactly the job description. His wife was always suggesting a locum but he doubted anybody would do all the necessary tasks, and then of course it was the expense involved. The suggestion of a practice nurse had suddenly answered the question. In the course of a week, it shook down to Frank becoming the resident doctor and Rosalind taking the strictly female cases. It also transpired that Rosalind took on the practical necessities where a lot of blood and other issues were concerned. It quickly became a more streamlined and congenial practice. Frank was soon to admit to other professionals that the new practice nurse had a better bedside manner and neater stitches than he.

On a rare trip to the surgery I noticed the new nurse and her stitches were indeed very neat. I immediately preferred her bedside manner to Dr Frank's. Our paths had crossed. It was the start of something great, both timely and necessary, that would develop in time (but more of that later). The old saying is that 'accidents, problems, disasters come in threes'. I am not superstitious but seemed to be static. My journey, like porridge, had cooled off; neither hot nor cold, edible but becoming a sticky mess.

The farms were not doing badly and our accountant, Stuart Bradshaw, was upbeat. However, one morning I was requested to join a meeting that was not in our usual schedule. We met with the usual pleasantries in the conservatory, but I detected a strained atmosphere. There was no mistake about the sombre air; I wondered where I might have transgressed. Robert was first to speak:

"We have suffered one or two reversals." It was like the commanding officer announcing a retreat.

"We need to make some changes," Stuart added to the gloom. I seriously wondered if I was being softened up for the big goodbye.

"It is all about economics, Peter. I have been offered very high rents for arable land, but Stuart will explain the position." Robert was formal.

"I am afraid farming is changing and there are some big rents being offered, particularly for arable land which landlords can take advantage of without farming the land themselves. This works for the new tenants on the basis of low overheads and the use of contractors," Stuart outlined.

"I see." My expression was terse but I held back from saying anything more.

Stuart continued, "They can simply pay a high rent because they have minimal or no labour, and often use big capacity machines to be contractors themselves."

I was aware of this shift in farming but had thought the nature of a resident estate owner enjoying shooting, managing his own forestry and fishing would not succumb to any loss of control. I had imagined that with no farm labour, the loss of a number of perks such as the farm workshop and ready hands to assist both forestry and maintenance staff, the estate as an entity was safe from break-up. My mind rushed to the fact that the usefulness of the farm forklift, moving timber that very week, would be lost.

"I thought I came here on the basis of more farms coming in-hand?" I tried to keep my composure and a measured tone. "Although we are farming more land than when I started, we are geared up to expand now rather than rent land out,' I said.

"Ah, your work has been very much appreciated," Stuart rushed in. "Robert meant..." He was cut short.

"I can speak for myself, thank you, Stuart. Peter, you have done very well." He cleared his throat as if to make a declaration. "Things have to change but that is no reflection on you. This is all confidential and you must say nothing about any changes outside this room," he warned.

"We need your help and expertise in making changes," Stuart added. "We are thinking of a new tenant taking on your arable land, starting with the autumn planting."

"The business won't be viable with just a few pastures left," I asserted.

"We need your help in letting those separately and running down the farming operation."

"So I will be running myself out of a job?" I concluded.

"No, it won't be quite like that; there is a lot more to plan, with your help." Robert sat back.

It seemed plain I would have to find another job.

Stuart and I left together and let ourselves out of the rear entrance to where the cars were parked.

"Come with me; sit in the passenger seat a minute." Stuart obviously had something to say. "I must tell you in confidence that Robert needs some money."

I said nothing; it seemed I would be the one needing money, not him.

"His investments have taken a plunge; that is all I can say."

"So it means stopping farming?" I enquired.

"If you sell up all the machinery and stock, it will avoid selling any land. Plus, of course, there will be a guaranteed income for the estate," Stuart suggested.

I left, having been given that detail but told to phone him if I needed.

I drove back to the farm. Going down the drive, I wondered what the timescale would be. I made a cup of tea and, instead of returning to office work, I went and sat in the lounge. I sat and seriously pondered my future. I would be a fool if I thought I had any future here. Surely it was just a matter of time? It was now June; harvest would soon be upon us and then we would be selling up the crops, vacating the fields one by one. Then what? I'd have to look for another job. The evening was consumed with the new reality. If I looked for another manager position, I had no idea when I would be able to take it up. How could I apply for a position and say I'd move when all the men had left and I had sold all live and dead stock? "And why are you leaving your present job?" I could hear the question.

The awful truth hit me; I would soon be fifty – too old! Employers would be looking for thrusting young bloods in their thirties for the senior management jobs. It would be hardly worth replying to adverts, coupled with my selling up what appeared to be a significant farm business. I would be redundant, quite literally. Depression stopped me sleeping. I even considered my private life and hope of remarrying; surely I had nothing to offer, not even a house or a job. The only brightness was Rosalind; I had a lady friend and our relationship was blossoming to the point of talking of engagement. How would she react to my looming status? What had I got to offer her? I had to break the news to her regardless of confidences.

She was due to come the next evening and cook dinner; I would have to tell her then. My work on the farm was a blur; everything was tainted with the thought of finishing. I felt for the men and yet could not mention a thing. The problem with farming is that employment very often involves a tied house. The tradition had been because a worker needed to be near to his job, particularly stockmen. Historically, wages had been lower than for urban employment, but somewhat compensated by the renting of tied accommodation being of minimal price, even free. The obvious downside is that losing a job means losing your home.

Rosalind turned up as expected with a stew, which just needed reheating, and a kiwi-decorated cheesecake.

"I saw your face light up; was that for me or my cooking?" she quipped.

"Always for you, my darling." I kissed her before she could put the things down.

I was cheered up and we enjoyed a lovely feast. I was sure if we were married I would put on weight.

The recent news could not wait; I had to tell her as we settled down, well satisfied.

"There is something I must tell you," I started.

"Is it something serious? It looks as if it may be." My face had betrayed me.

"I've had a worrying meeting with Robert and the accountant." I hesitated. "I have been told that the farming here is going to run down and a tenant will take over."

"Why is that?" She frowned, not understanding.

"Apparently, Robert needs serious money; the machinery and animals will have to be sold and I will be redundant." I sighed; at least it was all out.

"My darling!" Rosalind exclaimed without comment. We sat holding hands whilst the news sunk in. "You will have to get another job," she said after a moment's silence.

"That's hardly possible. Mind you, I thought you might say another partner."

"Why? You are not going to get rid of me that easily." She sounded indignant.

"I was afraid…"

She grabbed my neck and we kissed as if locked together. I came up for air.

"You are an absolute treasure." We kissed and caressed.

"We'll manage somehow." She seemed to relish the challenge. "I've got a job and I know you will never be idle even if another job is hard to find."

What had promised to be a disaster had become a bonding. We were both smiling, eyes bright.

"Does that mean we will carry on together?" I asked.

"Of course," she replied confidently.

"Will you marry me?" I got no immediate answer... We were stuck in an embrace.

Then she replied. "The answer is yes."

"I promise we'll get the ring together... I had not planned the evening like this." I was apologetic, feeling I should have made it more of an occasion.

Everything had changed; depression had become joy. I had the full confidence that together we could achieve anything. The work on the farm became normal, just like approaching any harvest. There was a job to do, and the future, at least for Rosalind and me, was assured.

I had a further private meeting with Robert to discuss the details of the rundown and notice to give to all the staff. It was agreed that they should be told before cutting the first corn as it would be disingenuous to gather all the harvest and then dismiss them. I suggested a softer approach.

"I realise they have an official notice of one month, but open-ended in as much as whilst there is work they may continue on a casual basis."

Robert let me continue.

"If that were the arrangement, they could be actively looking for a job, and still continue with our essential harvesting, corn and later potatoes; it would give them flexibility and a little less pressure. It gives us labour for longer than a month and a gradual reduction of manpower, which I could cope with. I could find casual labour or contractors to fill any deficiency," I finished.

This brought a smile to his face. "I think that is a great idea," he enthused. "I was bothered about giving notice, especially to the long servers."

Just before we were due to start harvest, I arranged for Robert to come to the workshop, which doubled as the mess room and meeting point, the men leaving together at five o'clock.

"I want to speak to you all together because we have been through some difficult times. I have a few problems at the moment, causing real upheaval." He had an involuntary clearing of his throat. "I am having to give the farm over to tenants, which means we won't be farming ourselves." Another pause. "I am giving you formal notice in these envelopes, but want you to continue at your convenience in finding other employment. I want to thank each and every one of you for your service, indeed hard work. I appreciate on the land you have gone beyond the normal to get things done. I thank you very much." He handed the envelopes around. "I understand that your holiday pay has been included up to a month ahead. Peter will field any questions." With that he shook each hand and walked out.

I assured the men that this was the best result, inasmuch as we could do nothing to alter our employer's business intentions. The small consolation was that we had time to sort ourselves out with a new job. We had time to do that starting from now, and the cushion of casual work through the potato harvest; in effect three to four months' grace. I further assured them of seeing their rights respected and that I would willingly give them references for future employers.

## Redundancy

I too had an envelope and carried it into the house. I opened it with trepidation knowing that it would be similar to the staff's. I read the short letter twice, taking in the stark facts. It formally terminated my employment and tenure of the farmhouse; it was fixed for September 30th. The enormity of the situation hit me; I was redundant. I had known it was coming – but to see it in print!

I wandered into the garden, still with letter in hand. All this would go, in fact *had* gone. The garden and fields beyond that I had looked after, husbanded; it was floating away. It was like a ferry leaving and I didn't know when the next one would come... if ever! I turned back and saw the grand farmhouse; that too was going. Redundancy was real and personal; I had never experienced it previously. I reasoned that these were silly thoughts and I had much to be grateful for. I tried to reason afresh; it would be just as bad if not worse for the men. They had families and homes; they were facing an uncertain future and probably a new location. This self-pity had to stop.

It didn't stop. I remembered the euphoria of Rosalind's can-do reaction to the news. Yet I was feeling this so personally; I was redundant. What did it mean? Superfluous, no longer necessary, my training and experience were of no value. Like old machinery rusting in the farmyard, I might be useful as a spare part or perhaps a short-term answer whilst someone was on holiday.

We worked through the harvest whilst I also made arrangements for a farm sale of both sheep and machinery. The auctioneer came out and together we chose a couple of dry fields adjacent to the road. Access was important for livestock lorries and low loaders. There needed to be a one-way system and some security to prevent items being stolen. The auctioneers would see to the advertising and signage. I would have to provide most of the pens and copious straw bales. There needed to be room for a makeshift office for the purchasers to pay for items and of course a refreshment tent.

# 35

# The Sun Appears Again

Rosalind was an inspiration. Amid all the negative thoughts she remained upbeat.

"I have a lovely engagement ring, but we haven't talked about a wedding day."

"I thought it was a little premature at the moment," I replied.

"What do you mean, premature?" she rounded on my comment.

"Well, with all the uncertainty…" I wasn't allowed to finish.

"Why are we getting married? Because we love each other!" She answered her own question. "It's got nothing to do with circumstances and we are not youngsters."

I agreed about our ages; now I had hit fifty I had a different outlook on life. However, I still had energy and ambition.

"I want to get married; of course I do," I assured her.

"Let's just do it; we have to promise 'for better or worse'." Her whole face lit up, lifting me to the same height. "We want to be in it together."

I forgot current doubts and we looked at dates.

The sun was shining again. Whatever happened, Rosalind had a cottage in a nearby village so we would have a roof over our heads. We could get married on almost any date as I was looking after a small chapel on the other side of town. We would just need a minister to run the service and a registrar to attend. Rosalind had no trouble exciting her best friend in the hunt for a dress. It was not to be white in the traditional way of young brides but less formal, and that was all I knew.

The invitations went out to friends and family, including the girls, and the day was perfect. Rosalind was stunning in a knee-length blue floral creation and perfect large-brimmed matching hat. As a couple we would have looked the part in the enclosure at Ascot. The reception was in the most capable hands of friends who wanted to give of themselves. They knew we did not need any more electric toasters, having both been married before. Their expertise centred around wonderful cooking (some were professionals) and the premises I was about to vacate. The dining room in the farmhouse even had a central glass chandelier, hanging from its eleven-foot-high ceiling. We spilled out onto the lawns surrounded by fields, making it a country idyll. The sun was indeed shining and any future gloom could only be short-lived before it appeared again. We were blissfully happy.

A month after the redundancy letter I was called to another formal meeting with my employer.

"Naturally you have been in my thoughts regarding the future. Have you made any plans yourself?" he asked.

"I have not applied for any post," I answered truthfully but without revealing any direction of thought.

"Well, Simon Sanders has given notice and is retiring. I will need a new tenant for Woodhead Farm. Would you be interested in taking it on?"

"I have never given any thought to a tenancy." I hesitated out of real surprise.

"I don't expect an answer now; it needs a lot of thought. I just thought it might suit you." He was brisk and to the point as usual.

"I'll need a little time to work out some figures." I struggled not to close any doors.

"The rent will be £13,000 a year, and of course you know the farm and house."

"Thank you, sir," I replied, unintentionally slipping into a tenant-landlord relationship. "I'll let you know as soon as possible; it's been a real surprise," I added.

"I see, but give me a reply in a week, or at least an indication." He shook my hand as if it was all done.

It was far from done; I had very little money to start a farm. I had already been praying very much for God's guidance; now it became intense. Throughout life, from the time of my eleven-plus exam, I had talked (i.e. prayed) to God. He had proven Himself to me. He is real and now was the time to ask Him for very special help. I noted the mounting problems to be surmounted. God had cared for me and answered my calls in the past; surely He would do so again. The Bible tells us, "'For I know the plans I have for you,' declares the LORD, 'plans to prosper you and not to harm you, plans to give you hope and a future.'" (Jeremiah 29:11)

I had shouted at God, "Why am I redundant? I have trusted you all the way. I am not a saint but I believed you had plans for me..." I didn't doubt; at saner times I simply asked for His guidance. "What can I do, Lord? I want to be in your hands." I prayed in this vein; there was nothing else I could do. I knew there was no chance of a senior management job at my age. But now I had suddenly been offered something I had never contemplated. Right from my boyhood ambition I had not considered being a farmer; that was impossible. I had wanted to be a farm manager, one who has all the joy and responsibility of farming with nature but not the money to achieve it. The Lord had brought me this far with plenty of ups and downs, but He never promises a smooth path.

"Lord, how can I be a tenant... but what else can I do?" I didn't expect a booming voice of reply, but I do believe He puts things in place. I thought of laying a fleece before Him, like Gideon when he wanted guidance, but that didn't seem appropriate. A day or so later He 'nudged' me to put my trust in Him. After all, He had provided for me in every way; I simply had to trust (i.e. really believe He would make it possible to be a tenant). I responded with this prayer:

"Lord, you seem to have given me this chance as a way forward, impossible as it seems, but I totally need your help. I will take the tenancy if you will guarantee to enable me to get to the age of sixty-five. I must not fail because I must not disgrace Your name. Amen."

Now came the money. I had to commit all my resources and then God would have to provide; I had made a covenant with Him. I managed the £13,000 rent up front but had no idea where the first year's finance would come from. I phoned Robert telling him I would like to accept the tenancy of Woodhead Farm. He was pleased and asked me to meet with him and his land agents the following week.

I had met Bill Cooke previously when tenant matters and other business were necessary. He was a large and cheerful character with a ruddy complexion which I had attributed to whisky as much as fresh country air. He was the picture of a country gentleman, complete with tweed suit and cut-glass accent. I knocked and joined Robert in his office; it was where he met people when paperwork was involved, rather than a 'conservatory meeting' which usually meant less paper and more confidentiality.

"Come in, Peter, we've finished our business; this is just about you now." He seemed relaxed. "You don't mind Bill being in on the discussions?" It was more of a statement than a question. "I thought it would be helpful for us all to be together on this."

"I'm happy," I returned, not knowing what I might be happy about, but certainly I trusted Bill, who had been a support at times.

"Bill knows about the redundancy notices of course, and indeed your acceptance of the tenancy. There are a few loose ends to tying up the farm business and I would like you to continue as farm manager here for a year or so whilst you are starting Woodhead Farm and getting that going. Although the staff will be leaving, I'd like you to oversee the dispatch of crops and facilitate the changeover to the new tenant. Now, I propose you work on half salary, and have the use of your pick-up, whilst you field phone calls and manage the rundown." He sat back to receive comments.

"I would be pleased to carry on," I readily agreed.

"Good, good!" He seemed as relieved as I was.

"That is good," Bill added. "It would be a very satisfactory way of continuing trading, both practically and for tax purposes. I'm sure it's much better for you to continue handling everything rather than us getting involved in the nitty-gritty. Are you sure you can manage both that and starting Woodhead?"

"Yes, I'll have to use a contractor for major work, but I'm sure it will be fine." I tried not to look too euphoric.

It was the answer to my prayer. I had never conceived such an arrangement; my abiding concern had been how to survive until the first harvest. Now I had an income and an overdraft, I could start equipping the farm and gradually take over from employing contractors as finances permitted. I reported everything to Rosalind and we thanked God for providing a new job, even a farm; a progression from redundancy to renewal beyond our wildest dreams. We could only wonder how it would be financially possible, yet I knew He had answered my prayers so remarkably at other times. Each time I had understood a little more of God's love towards those who put their full trust in Him. I also knew that the path is never easy, never without apparent reversals. I was learning that the testing times were to strengthen us to trust further, and to remember to give Him the glory.

I produced farm budgets but nothing could realistically show a profit in the first year. We needed to get through to the second harvest and that would be touch and go. Rosalind brought some practical encouragement.

"You are working out sundry expenses," she noted as she glanced over my shoulder. "Is that for us to live on?"

"No, my dear, they are hopefully small items difficult to quantify," I replied.

"I'll still be working at the surgery; we can live on that," she reminded me.

"That's great, darling, but there are always items that are needed, like another wheelbarrow and a new chain for the saw, workshop sundries. I know from experience the list goes on and on, and it's not the boss paying for it now, it will be us." I then brightened up. "But we are trusting the Lord. It will be tough but He's said yes to us taking the tenancy."

# 36

# Moving – Our Own Farm

We had to vacate the home farm farmhouse by September 30th, which was before the sale of equipment and the end of potato harvest. Some of the fields the new tenant had already taken over. He had access to the corn stubbles as soon as we removed the straw. It was all a rush but at least I knew those fields were no longer my concern. I left the men busy and spent time moving our furniture and belongings to our new farmhouse. It was much smaller than the grand place we were leaving and we had done a lot of downsizing of items that we did not need or simply would not fit in. Rosalind had spent all her spare time cleaning and preparing for the major move, which I was hoping to achieve without a removal firm. This we regarded as an essential cost-saving as we embarked on our frugal new budgeting. The carpets were the first to move, obviously making it easy for furniture to be placed on top and in the right room.

The only method of moving was using my pick-up and trailer which had served to transport sheep to market, amongst other cargoes of dubious cleanliness. It was essentially a strong two-ton capacity car trailer that I had reconstructed from scratch. I had alighted on an old broken-down pony box in a field when farming at Beech Row. I had often passed this field noting that the box itself could never be used, but perhaps the floor and wheels might be serviceable. Eventually I plucked up courage to call and ask if it might be for sale. The lady immediately said, "Take it." It was an eyesore she had not known how to be rid of. I could see the chassis was strong, but the rest rotting and falling to bits; and there was no sign of a roof. It certainly could not be towed away, so with help from my staff and a flatbed trailer we collected it and returned to the workshop at Beech Row. After much welding and galvanised sheeting, I remade a trailer eight foot by four foot and sixteen inches high, with a removable top made of metal hoops and plastic sheeting. It was now to be our removal vehicle.

Remarkably, Rosalind's only concern about moving was for her cat, Thistle. He had moved in, as she did, the day we were married as if the estate was his birthright. How could he now abandon the estate for a new abode with possibly less tasty 'livestock' than he was so partial to? Surely he would wander back the two miles as the crow flies and rule the farmyard that he had become accustomed to? Coupled to this was his aversion to a cat cage, that only spelt a journey to the vets.

The new tenants wanted to totally renew our farmhouse and therefore the oil-fired Rayburn was surplus to requirements, which I readily moved to Woodhead on the farm's forklift before it was lost in the sale. My first load of furniture consisted of beds and two wardrobes. It would be our first night at the new farm. Rosalind opened up the house and was making a cup of tea before we even started on the furniture.

"I am still worried about Thistle. Do you think the vet will have something to keep him from going back there?" Rosalind asked.

"I don't know anything about cats," I replied. "I suppose you could ask him."

I arrived at Woodhead with a very full load. Unroping it, I went to pull out the mattress which doubled as a rear door. I stared at the wardrobe standing upright behind it. Thistle was sitting on top of the wardrobe. As I watched he coolly jumped down via the mattress I was holding and followed me into the kitchen.

"Don't worry about Thistle," I called up the stairs.

"Why not?" Rosalind called down.

"Thistle's arrived," I shouted.

"I was going to bring him up in the car at the end," she shouted back.

"He was sitting on top of the wardrobe and here he is."

She bent down to make a fuss of the cat but he never welcomed that, even from his owner.

"Well, the cat's got attitude. He had seen what was going on and decided to be on the first load," I added.

Thistle never went back to his old territory. He considered the new farmyard, particularly the top of the straw bales in the Dutch barn, suitable for privacy and surveying the area. The rest of our furniture followed the cat to Woodhead Farm.

The next day, a Sunday, we took time to relax in the afternoon, having stowed away the everyday items and made space to live. Although there were still a few cardboard boxes of sundry kitchen utensils and ornaments, we decided they could wait to be unpacked. It seemed important to acquaint ourselves with our new surroundings. We walked through the farmyard empty of implements and livestock and looking stark. I had made no plans, being so busy in vacating the home farm. My only priority was to get the fields that would be cereals cultivated and sown; the rest could wait.

We headed down the slope of permanent pasture and into the first real field, currently a reasonable ley but potentially ploughable. The view was glorious, with Scots pines bordering the fence and dropping away in the distance. We walked through a gateway into the woods and took a path skirting the field. The autumn colours still decked most of the trees but had thinned to allow the sun's rays to pierce horizontally, making us blink. The path was strewn with leaves and edged with brambles. Their fruit had gone, but we were about to start. It was exciting to tread new paths not knowing what was round the bends. We came to a plantation of Christmas trees, only about three years old, struggling to compete with the tall grass. The last field had just been ploughed and I had earmarked it for winter barley. We walked over the ridges and back along another forest track.

Thistle had followed us, like a dog, but at least five yards behind. As Rosalind cast a watchful eye back, he would occasionally be seen to leap into the undergrowth and return with a small mouse or shrew. I referred to this as his Mars bar; a small treat until supper time.

"I have never known a cat more like a dog," I commented.

"He's always done it but wouldn't put up with a lead."

"And I don't suppose he would gather sheep?" I smiled.

I had known we would need sheep as soon as Woodhead was mentioned but we certainly could not afford them yet.

The track continued through a larch plantation and we walked along a small public footpath to the right framing two sides of a stubble field. We crossed our long farm drive to our fields eastward. These had been used for both cereals and as sheep pasture but were eminently ploughable. I was hoping to grow as many cash crops as possible, which should be more profitable than sheep. The previous tenant had had an established flock and only grew barley on the flatter fields, as a cash crop and for their own winter feed. I had noted the state of the fencing which was showing its age and would need a good deal of patching before being sheep-proof. It was another future expense before we could make best use of the rougher fields. For the first year I intended to let some of these pastures to neighbours who were always looking for extra keep. It looked as if I would have to raid the 'sundries' even to get some pastures fenced for letting. Nonetheless we reached our new home refreshed and quite excited at the prospect of making our own way in farming.

I now had to travel to work, about two miles, until the major part of the home farm was handed over to the new tenant. The men cleaned down each item of equipment we thought would not be needed again. Contractors harvested the potatoes and our equipment was used to extract soil and elevate them into the stores. The date of the sale was fast approaching and the men worked overtime to power wash and get tractors and machinery clean. Finally, it took nearly a week to make neat rows of all the items for the great day.

In the auction the cheaper items were in the first lots, building up to selling the large machinery and tractors. I was always surprised that any and everything is put in a clearance sale and even the most trivial items seemed to find a buyer, including wood offcuts and scrap metal. I was not only agent for the vendor but an interested buyer for my own farming venture. I spent most of the day before the sale answering questions from unannounced callers roaming the lines of lots before the auction. Most enquiries were about the condition of tractors and the age of harvesting equipment. They wanted to know about servicing and how long a purchase could remain in the field. One enquiry was the chance of leaving a purchased machine in the buildings for safety, rather than the vulnerability of it remaining in the field.

The great day started with the usual ringing of an old school bell. It called prospective purchasers from under, and on top of, machines as well as any in the refreshment stall. The start had the usual introduction; the chief auctioneer standing in the back of a pick-up or farm trailer welcoming the prospective buyers. In this case I had asked Steven to drive my pick-up, which was not part of the sale, along the line of lots, stopping at each one for the auctioneer to do his work.

"We are honoured today to auction, on behalf of Mr and Mrs Robert Prince, their valuable collection of modern machinery, subject to the usual conditions of sale. Copies of these can be had from our office on site." The slight anticlimax after such a grand opening was the offering of the first few lots. Adrian, the 'son' part of 'Broadbent and Son', stood at a wooden desk they had strapped securely on the back of the pick-up. He was dressed in a white coat over a tweed jacket and topped off with a jaunty trilby which looked as if it had originated in the Austrian Tyrol.

"Let me start – Lot one: 'assorted wood offcuts'." Adrian started at twenty pounds and soon reduced it to five pounds in order to get a real bid.

A call of "two pounds" came from the crowd. The initial lot was the usual sparing ground between auctioneer and reluctant buyers to establish who was going to value the items: the auctioneer reaching for the high ground and the crowd, mostly farmers, wanting something as cheap as possible. Invariably the true value was the price paid on the day.

The hammer smacked the block of wood tied to the top of the desk. Lot two was a heap of scrap metal which soon met forty pounds, to my relief. The third lot was a rough but very solid wooden workbench which received no bids at all, at which point I made a slight nod and secured it for the giveaway bid of two pounds. I had purchased it at a farm sale for about the same price when I joined Robert and had considerably strengthened it. The sale progressed quickly through the small cultivation equipment of harrows and rollers, and I found I could afford some of these items for my tenure at Woodhead. I had not made a list of equipment but at these prices could not fail to secure the basics. The old four-wheeled trailers had been useful when I started on the estate and would perform the same use at Woodhead. They were useful for carting bales or even a couple of pallets of seed corn. They could be left on a field headland, serving as a platform for the tractor driver to refill the drill.

Steven drove the auctioneer and pick-up along the row of implements; the reversible plough and assorted cultivators, including power harrows, had been well examined by prospective bidders before the sale started. It had been interesting to watch their casual first inspection and then passing on, feigning disinterest. This was often repeated a few minutes later to assess the wearing parts or the welding where breaks had occurred. In fact, with three or four expressing the same 'disinterest', one might be forgiven for thinking there would be no bids at all.

The sale processed up the next row, where the lots were more substantial. The irrigation pump and aluminium pipes interested several farmers. The bids rose to near new prices as many wanted extra pipes to reach a further field or needed ten replacements for their ones damaged over the years. It has surprised me how pipes, left in the potato rows ready for the next watering, get forgotten when another tractor driver arrives to spray for blight control. The spray man only has to enter the row to flatten a pipe with the front wheels of his tractor, turning a four-inch main into an aluminium ribbon incapable of any repair. The other sale attraction was our purpose-made pipe trailer to transport the thirty-foot long pipes. The sprinkler, with its four-inch bore pipes, was equally sought after.

The substantial potato equipment, conveyors and an oscillating elevator were keenly contested by smaller-scale farmers with modest acreages of potatoes wishing to modernise but unwilling to purchase the latest machines. The harvester similarly sold well.

"We now come to the tractors, which have been well maintained and are ready for work." Adrian was warming to the brisk bidding and on a roll with the well-presented tractors, starting with the older ones and ending with the four-wheeled drives and the portable corn dryer.

As the sale ended, Adrian and his staff were busy with a queue of purchasers, chequebook in hand, wanting to settle up and retrieve their purchases. I had long been used to farmers handing their chequebooks to the clerk to fill in the details using a rubber stamp for the payee line; my urban upbringing had been never to part with such a valuable book.

The sale over, the crowd thinned, and trailers and loaders filled the gangways. In two hours the car park and sale field were virtually empty. They had drained away down to the main road and scores of byways to new 'homes' as if my work had simply been spread like butter over several counties. A week later Robert informed me it was a "very good" sale and seemed satisfied at the realisation of capital. I was pleased that, for all the concerns over purchases, he realised the farm account was in the black rather than in the red.

All that remained was the dispatch of the last of the cereals and then the farm handover to the new tenant would be complete. The remaining hundred tons of barley I had sold forward on contract. It had been a deal with the 'Welsh

Dragon' who had secured a favourable offer that I was pleased to accept. I had to use what was now *my* forklift and big bucket. I expected to load four lorries one after another to go straight on a ship for export. It was satisfying that the price I had secured on contract was some five pounds per ton higher than the spot market price on that dispatch day. It was great that the forward marketing had paid off. Too often it goes the other way, the merchant knowing more than a farmer. The farmyard was now at the disposal of the new tenant; everything had been completed except the dispatch of the final hundred tons of our barley. Later that day I received a call from the port giving weight and moisture content of the first two loads.

"I can't understand 'eighteen per cent' moisture. It was just under sixteen per cent here." I was far from happy and asked the girl to check it again.

"I'm sorry, sir, it's all done by a sampling machine as it stands on the weighbridge."

"I loaded it myself; there was no problem here. Can you take another sample and test again?"

"It has gone; the lorries tip and go off for the next loads. It's in the ship's hold straight away," she explained.

There was nothing more I could say or do, except to feel aggrieved. By teatime she phoned back with the details of the next two loads. The barley was accepted but with a similar deduction. Although we had checked all samples leaving the farm, their sampling ruled. When the paperwork arrived for all the loads and I checked weights and deductions, the price per ton was precisely equivalent to the spot price on that day, negating any advantage in forward marketing.

It was a sour note to end on but I was relieved that the rundown was finished. I would now be a full-time tenant farmer. The reality was that I was given the pick-up as a parting gift but my half-salary would cease. I handed in various papers the next morning at the estate office.

"Thank you for all you've done." Robert, smiling, shook my hand. "I wish you well. We'll see you about, of course; you're a tenant now."

## Another New Start

It was an exciting time. Everything had changed. We had changed house, which was smaller and less grand but promised to become home very soon. The views had changed; the home pasture ran down to a strip of trees but the track bisected them to the lower fields. Walking through them there was a panoramic view of the valley and our pastures to the south. Our house was on the corner of the cluster of old farm buildings; quaint but built for yesterday's farming. As soon as we left our front gate, there they were, a few paces away and yet unseen from inside the house. Bill Cooke, the land agent, had referred to it as "cosy" and only a "smell" away from work. From the gate the track ran upwards to the horizon and eventually a road. We were half a mile from tarmac and nearly a mile from a public road. It was a benign isolation.

The new situation was a total change from being in the centre of all activity. The large home farm was in another person's hands and totally out of view. We felt self-contained and masters of our own environment. I had shed most of my responsibilities and was master of my own destiny. The limiting factor would be lack of finance, but it had already been limited in my previous job. It was a long way from the days at Beech Row with unlimited capital borrowed at ten to thirteen per cent provided I could return about fifteen per cent.

I had only a pick-up and a forklift; the first job needed to be an opening up of the farmyard. There was very little room for a large vehicle to turn around. I levelled off a couple of feet of bank coming into the yard and similarly by the back of the single-storey calf shed. This would enable the bigger lorries to manoeuvre and get up the rise back to the main road. As the whole yard was on a slope, several parts needed soil pushed or carried to make level areas for future equipment and standing places. I anticipated areas for baled and plastic-wrapped silage and implements to be unhooked and stored in the open. Covered space was at a premium.

My contractor soon ploughed, cultivated and drilled the winter barley crop, also ploughing old pastures that were level enough to become arable fields. Without livestock I needed as many acres of cash cropping as possible. A neighbour raised his eyebrows when he saw us planting wheat.

"I see you will be trying wheat up here." Basil had casually drawn level with the trailer of seed wheat. "Too high for wheat up here."

"I think it will be OK; it'll just come a week or two later than down the valley," I returned cheerfully.

"My old man used to say, 'Never come to much at nearly eight hundred feet.'"

"Did he try it?" I enquired.

"No, stuck to barley t' feed the stock."

"Well, I haven't got the livestock," I tried to justify.

"Well, this is sheep land and a few beasts." Having dispensed this advice he drove off.

I felt sure new varieties of wheat and maybe even oilseed rape would give better returns than livestock that I couldn't afford. Anyway, I intended to try cash crops. The first thing I needed was a cheap tractor to do all the small jobs like top dressing the corn and later spraying, rather than employing a contractor for all the husbandry. I mentioned this to Robert's secretary at the estate office. To my surprise she said her husband had just purchased one in a sale.

"Has he got some land?" I realised it was a silly question as soon as I uttered it.

"No, I think it was cheap and he just wanted to tinker with it." She was obviously thinking it was an unnecessary toy.

"What did it cost?"

"Oh, about six hundred pounds, I think."

I couldn't believe it. I had no idea what it was like but was sure it was my sort of price.

"Do you think…" I hesitated. "I mean, could I come and see it?"

She looked at me as if I was in the same boring category as her husband.

"Any time after seven, I guess. I'll tell him you may look in." She continued typing.

I wondered if by any chance he would be prepared to take a profit selling it on to me. After all, he had only bought it to tinker with. I phoned to make sure he was in and visited his workshop two days later.

"Hello, Eric. Sue told me you had an interesting tractor."

"Yer, bit unusual." Eric looked up.

It *was* unusual; an old red tractor that I couldn't place.

"What make is it?"

"Belarus," he replied.

I must have looked vacant.

"Russian," Eric added.

We both walked around it; levers and handles seemed everywhere.

"Does it go?" I asked.

"Well, I drove it back here," he replied. "And the power take-off works."

"I badly need something like that myself." I summoned up courage. "Would you take a bit of profit and sell it to me?" It felt as if I were taking a toy from a child.

Eric didn't answer.

"I'll give you a hundred for it," I offered.

"OK, that will be £700 then." He didn't seem too enthusiastic, but admitted Sue had told him of my disappointment at missing the auction.

I was thrilled to bits, thinking that it must be a 'runner' and at a fraction of the price of any well-known make.

"I'll deliver it to you when you have the cash available," he offered.

"It will be nice to try the old girl out."

"Thanks. When you deliver the money, I'll run you back."

Two days later I examined it with him in detail. It was a high step up to the ample platform.

"What's this lever?" I had my hand on a long steel lever with a rod down through the floor.

"That's the handbrake and the other side it engages the power take-off." He pointed to two levers that would be more at home in a signal box. We looked at each other. "Big wenches in Russia." Eric broke into laughter.

"On the collective you probably had two sitting up here," I added.

Everything was large, strong and functional. Even the clutch peddle was of similar build and no doubt requiring a wrestler's limb to operate it. However, it had all that I needed: a draw bar to tow a trailer, hydraulic arms and top-link for mounted implements, and a power take-off to power equipment like a fertiliser spreader or rotavator.

I soon got used to this strange tractor and used it to top dress some grass fields with nitrogen using the Vicon hopper to broadcast the granular fertiliser. It was a bit ungainly compared to the compact controls of British tractors and required rather more strength on levers and steering wheel. I wondered if it had been designed for two Russian women to operate on the 'bridge', one to navigate and the other to weigh down on the long-handled controls. Alternatively, it may be the designer anticipated regular shots of vodka during the working day.

The first field was fairly flat and square, giving me time to get familiarised. The second field was sloping and cut in two by a rough track like a belt across it. I decided to fertilise the top half driving up and down, being the safest, rather than across the slope. It was steeper than I first thought so I slowed down approaching the track, ready to turn upwards. This proved successful and I had competed half the field, but coming down on the next run a gentle braking locked the rear wheels rather than slowing the tractor; it continued apace. I immediately released my foot and gently tried the brakes again with the same result. I was now piloting a sledge, or more likely a bobsleigh. There was no way to turn across the slope without rolling the tractor over; it had to continue downward. I knew there was nothing I could do except hold on tight. I had throttled down but dared not knock it out of gear. We met the grassy track at right angles with a shudder and went over the other side with a thud as we dropped a foot down to the second sloping field. I released and reapplied the brakes, to no avail. I was gripping the wheel harder than two women; just trying to steer slightly to the right and maybe to a gentler gradient. In a second I had taken in the looming prospect. We were heading for the lower hedge and sheep netting. All scenarios flashed through my mind... depending on impact. At full speed on the damp grass, would the tractor maybe turn a somersault? Hitting the wire fence, would we bounce off or roll it down and be stuck in the hedge? I kept pumping the brakes. We began to slow. I steered further to the right as the headland flattened out. We stopped almost parallel to the netting. I was in nervous exhaustion; the hopper was empty, but that didn't matter; everything was in one piece.

The lesson of caution was as necessary as the notice on a field gate saying 'Beware of the Bull'. I knew that damp grass, particularly ryegrasses with their large, shiny leaves, could be slippery. The care I had taken had not been sufficient. Just as the bull might be appear amiable, he might be less so if he was having 'one of those days'. I was certainly having one.

## Bed and Breakfast (B&B)

Rosalind had agreed we were in this together; that was certainly true both mentally and practically. In addition to her job at the surgery, she was now planning to take on becoming a farmer's wife and even starting a B&B in the farmhouse. I agreed to help her in every aspect and she was prepared to help with the sundry farm emergencies. I had in mind the lack of staff on the farm and the need for extra hands on the occasions when even four would be hardly enough.

In order to diversify into a B&B, the accommodation needed altering. It would involve substantial alterations and some expense. I had the landlord's permission, but at my cost. We decided we had to offer en suite accommodation or at least a private bathroom. There was one bathroom upstairs and four bedrooms. The problem was that the two large bedrooms led through to the two smaller ones. This was, no doubt, a cosy arrangement for a family with small children who could occupy the smaller linked bedroom, but not so suitable for strangers as paying guests. I planned to subdivide the smaller end bedroom into an en suite with a children's recess. It would end up being billed as a large double with a family recess and its own internal bathroom.

Without these alterations the possible scenarios were too dreadful to contemplate. Supposing the couple in room one retired early and a younger second couple returned from a restaurant or nightclub later. Should they knock on the door, waking the first couple to apologise for their late arrival home, or should they enter as quietly as possible and crawl on hands and knees hoping they would not be noticed. Even more shocking was the possibility of retiring at more or less the same time and passing through the first room just as they were changing into their pyjamas.

"Supposing they don't wear pyjamas?" Rosalind asked.

"It's possible that a man leaving the bathroom knowing his wife was already in bed could climb into the wrong one," I added.

"Supposing the couple in the far room wanted the toilet in the night…?" Rosalind's voice tailed off.

"We can't ask guests to schedule their retirement. Even if we managed to start yawning at, say, the ten o'clock news and suggest how tiring the countryside makes us, I doubt many guests would take the hint," I ventured.

At the other end of the house, the small end room would be blocked off and a new doorway made off the landing. The guests would have a double bedroom with their own private bathroom immediately across the landing. All this restructuring involved bricking up and cutting down access points and creating two new bathrooms. Downstairs a similar walk-through lounge to a smaller one was knocked into one. The lounge had a huge chimney-stack providing back-to-back fireplaces in each room. I knocked out the back of the fires so that they shared the same large grate, enabling the single fire to heat both rooms at once.

This provided a great feature which always intrigued children, enabling them to walk around the chimney-breast spying on parents by bending down and looking through the fireplace.

The alterations and redecorations took up most of our first year at Woodhead. I was able to make the time to do the work as the main farming was done by my contractor, Barry, and his men. I started by making a bathroom in the corner of the largest bedroom. The plumbing took some planning to connect a toilet to the septic tank. In the end it was easier to run the waste water to a new soil pipe and prepare fresh groundwork around the house to connect to the septic tank. Internally I had to install a cold water supply from the spring and a tank in the loft. The hot water came from a new copper cylinder and immersion heater. The final touches of boxing-in the bath, tiling and decorating made the new bathroom very appealing. There was no window to the outside so the electric light was needed at all times, in common with many hotels.

The large job downstairs was to make the lounge bigger by knocking down the wall and incorporating the end room of the house. A steel beam was installed from the internal wall to the central fireplace and similarly from the fireplace to the external wall on the other side of the house. The chimney-piece was a massive structural construction holding much of the house up. There was a good deal of stone and bricks to remove, not to mention dust. The end result was a much bigger room with a central fireplace which guests could literally sit around, whichever part of the room they were in. The few guests we entertained at the end of the season seemed very satisfied with their stay. The comments in the visitors' book mentioned the informality and the general willingness to please, which encouraged us. There was also a genuine interest in practical farming, as they were so close to our daily routine.

# 37

# Building a Business Again

Apart from completing the farmhouse alterations, I started improving the farm buildings in preparation for more intensive farming. A Dutch barn, previously used for some bales and general storage, could be the basis of a modern store for grain or potatoes. It needed a concrete floor and the southern aspect closed in with corrugated sheeting. The main frame was second-hand but the telegraph poles were sound. This made it easy to fix wooden purlins and complete the sheeting of the whole shed. I was able to use the forklift bucket for levelling the floor area and hire shuttering before concreting the floor in sections.

It was costing more precious money but was so necessary if I was ever going to farm successfully. I could see my current account sliding into overdraft. This had a salutary effect on me; I was going into debt, from which only profitable farming could rescue me. I had been used to handling large amounts of money and justifying its necessity to the business but it had been somebody else's money. I had only to make a convincing case, supported by a budget, and the project had usually been agreed. I had no reserve capital or indeed a financially comfortable relative. I didn't own the land and thereby the facility of selling off a small corner to continue trading. Rosalind owned, apart from a small mortgage, a cottage and had let it when we married; that was her nest egg. I was putting everything into the farm, which, as a tenant, would never be mine. I had used my redundancy money to pay for the alterations, not to mention my labour. The overdraft was becoming a deeply personal matter. I had to continue, in faith, believing the Lord had given His assurance and He would enable us to continue.

I had to have some casual labour on the farm and prevailed on a neighbour's son to help me when I really needed it. David was a jack of all trades and ran his own business which relied mostly on his own labour and expertise. He knew everything rural and had a can-do outlook; what he had not experienced before, he worked out from first principles and common sense. We shuttered the length of the shed starting at the tin sheeting. The ready-mix concrete came in about six to seven cubic yard loads. These needed a little rough levelling and tamping with an eleven-foot piece of timber with handles at each end. It was hard work but we could manage three loads a day. We also had to make a pair of doors sixteen-foot high for the end that faced the yard. This was to allow access to lorries, but unfortunately the bulk lorries still could not tip a load of potatoes if rejected and returned to the farm. The finished store had electric lights and power points and was insulated with solid bales placed around the walls. It was not perfect but a distinct improvement, albeit on a small budget.

My tenancy had been established, and at the end of the first trading year, the income from crops paid off the bills. However, there was little left for repeating the exercise, the annual cycle of sowing and harvesting. I could not go on planting and harvesting crops using a contractor and subletting the grass keep. I was now faced with gradually mechanising, doing all the cultivations and expanding the sheep to farm all the two hundred and fifty acres by myself. Although Rosalind was managing our housekeeping, I had no external income.

Although the financial position was a concern, we had much to thank the Lord for, enabling us this far. Looking back, I had been lifted out of redundancy. There were no uncertainties about new areas or difficult employment situations, the sort that only develop as you try to mix with new personalities. Our move of only two miles was hassle-free and our friends were where they had always been. In short, I was morphing from the management of a farm business to a farming life derived from the countryside.

Quality of life was beginning to assert itself. I was working harder physically but with a lower burden of paperwork, less justification for actions, fewer deadlines, and no hindrance from tenants needing the 'AA'. Life seemed freer. The hours of the day were filled, but were at my disposal.

I was enjoying the building work and seeing it materialise day by day. It was a visible sign of progress and of labour rewarded. The nineteen ewes further enriched my day; not by directly being part of the future, but pointing to a larger flock when finances permitted. They had only been an opportunist purchase that my dealer friend had found "well worth the money". In a way, they were a deposit on a future flock of yearling ewes. It was in my daily walk to the old girls, who were at the end of their productive life, that I encountered the vibrancy of nature.

I could drive my pick-up to most pastures but walking was much more fulfilling. I walked up two steep fields that would never be arable and were nature's gym for the unfit. On the way the pasture was fresh with dew, soaking my boots. I often stopped to take in the view and gasp the fresh air; how gracious of God to refresh His creation! It was all living and breathing. I noticed young growth around a group of sheep droppings; nearby thistles had flowered and scattered most of their downy seeds, weeds that are a nuisance to the perfectionist but a larder to the insects and birds. I had missed this closeness as a manager hurrying from one task to the next. I knew and appreciated nature, so vital to farming, but the rush of worldly business had kept it at arm's length. Now I was almost eye to eye with it.

I could afford time to lean on the gate and take in the sheep. A few ewes noticed I had arrived, but in seconds were grazing again. I was not feeding or threatening them; their interest was smelling the next tasty growth. I was aware that sheep have good long sight and very poor short vision which is why they see danger a long way off but easily lie on their young in a small lambing pen. I watched a few close to me, head down and nibbling at the short grass. They were all the same; frenetic nibblers and giving a slight pull of the head to tear off the tougher blades. This was repeated time and again; a grazing practice learned from the first days of life. There were none on their backs unable to get up. That would be more of a problem nearer to lambing when rotund and lying down, inadvertently passing the point of no return. Stuck, backbone to the ground and feet in the air, they would have no way to purchase against *terra firma*. If they are not helped to turn over they suffocate in a few hours. The other observation was to see if any were holding a rear leg in the air showing how painful it was to bear weight. Any with a painful front leg tend to hop forward on three legs, indicating they need urgent treatment.

I had mentioned this shepherd's routine observation to a B&B guest who had enquired. The ewes had been grazing the pasture immediately below the farmhouse which almost touched the dining-room window. The next morning she drew my attention to one that was "very lame".

"Ah! Well spotted. Did it have a blue spot on its foot?" I asked.

"I don't think so," she replied.

"Actually, I sorted it yesterday," I added.

"What did you do to it?" she persisted.

"I cut its hoof back and any foul out," I said without thinking.

"That is why it is still hurting," she said.

I thought quickly to end the discussion. "We always treat the feet with antibiotic spray."

"But it must still be painful," she continued.

"But it is getting better. We are not better immediately once we have visited the doctor," I insisted.

I don't think anything would have entirely convinced her, and resolved that too much information was dangerous to town and countryside relations.

Rosalind, who had become a thorough farmer's wife, suggested she would deal with the next enquirer.

"We need to be truthful. What would you tell them?" I asked.

"Sheep are either very stupid or possibly as clever as brain surgeons. That ewe obviously wanted a bit of sympathy and held her leg up just as she passed the window. In fact, she was probably wanting a guest to see she had been successful treated; that's the reason for blue on her foot. It's a bit like signing your name on the plaster of a broken bone." I congratulated Rosalind and promoted her to farm host and responder to guest enquiries.

"Mind you, it may be best to omit the signing on plaster bit for fear of being patronising," I laughed.

In this new life I was determined to have Sundays off again, allowing time with my wife and certainly to get to our church. Although we had been attending a big church in town, I had been asked to head up a small chapel of which they had oversight. I had done some services for them but felt quite unqualified to be responsible for running the little chapel; besides, I didn't have the time. The church member presently overseeing the work was retiring and moving to Scotland, so I was asked again to take over. I said I could only do it if I had the help of a couple of others to share the work. I soon had one who could act as secretary and a builder who would see to the maintenance of the property. It seemed a good team.

The chapel was on its knees in terms of numbers. The first job was to reach out to the local village, which would mean radical changes. We insisted they needed to change to a modern hymn book and to have their Sunday service in the morning rather than at 3 pm, when non-churchgoers were doing other things. The regular congregation of four received the changes with open arms. Often in churches, change takes endless discussion and even years of resistance; this was agreed instantly. There was an air of optimism and faithful prayer was soon answered. The congregation started to increase.

Back home we had the opportunity to treat Sunday as the Lord's day, making a day free from work. It was Sunday afternoon and I was devouring the *Farmers Weekly* when I spotted a competition. I had for years made it a priority to attend the Smithfield Show which exhibited most aspects of farming and was held in December, a time of year when most farmers were free. In fact, it was the only occasion some country folk would venture to London. When I was buying a lot of machinery in Wessex, I became well acquainted with my machinery salesman who liked to go but was nervous about driving to Smithfield. I offered to take him or meet him there.

"I don't mind driving in traffic but it's London. There is traffic everywhere and I am nervous trying to find my way," he confessed.

"I could take you," I offered.

"I have to take other customers, thanks all the same. I manage it but the customers always know a different way... or they think they do," he sighed.

"How do you manage then?"

"I get them to bring thermos flasks and we all have coffee before we get to Smithfield."

I imagined that would suit farmers who wanted to save on the cost of London prices and yet possibly think nothing of ordering a tractor at the show.

"I wait by Putney bridge and look for cars that have a bit of straw hanging out or real mud up the side. I follow them to a car park and Earls Court," he confessed.

The competition in the *Farmers Weekly* was very straightforward, asking, 'Why do you attend the Smithfield Show?'

"What is the prize?" Rosalind asked over my shoulder. "It's two thousand pounds," she answered her own question.

"Yes, we don't need a 'Holiday in Barbados for Two' and definitely don't need the first prize of a Land Rover; I've got a farm pick-up. But we do need the third prize, two thousand pounds!" I exclaimed.

"Do it and mark it third prize only," she jested. "No, I'm serious; if you don't try, you can't win."

"OK, I'll think about it now." I considered it briefly and penned it in a moment. "I go to the Smithfield Show because... it germinates ideas, fertilises plans and harvests the state of the art," I answered.

It seemed simple enough and I gave it to the postman the next morning. The wonderful postmen and women were always happy to collect our post as well as deliver, and we showed our appreciation with a bag of potatoes when they needed one.

The autumn was closing in and I spent more time in the buildings preparing for the nineteen ewes due to lamb indoors. The only suitable shed was the yard where my predecessor had stored his barley in circular bins. He had sold the bins before I arrived and the concrete-covered yard was ideal for livestock. I set about borrowing fertiliser pallets from my neighbour as I had not accrued many. They were five by four feet in size and ideal for making personal pens for the ewes once they had lambed. It was a simple job to tie four together, stood upright, forming a self-standing pen. A line of these made the whole structure more stable and saved a pallet or two as the dividing 'wall' served both yards. In good farming tradition, string from bales held everything together. It would be straightforward when a ewe lambed in the strawed yard just to lead her to the row of pens and splendid isolation from jealous mothers-to-be. In like manner, it prevented lambs straying from mum and the essential milk bar.

It was always a delight to be on duty at lambing time, and with only nineteen ewes that duty was solely mine. Although we had a shepherd on the estate, it had always been good to assist him and be a relief when needed. I had usually monitored the night shift as I lived on the edge of the farmyard. Now only nineteen ewes in number, I would be the only shepherd, night or day; these were *my* ewes.

The evenings were drawing in and I was using the evenings to catch up with paperwork whilst Rosalind was cooking the dinner. I now experienced complete days without seeing anybody except perhaps the postman, so although we were both working, at least we were together in the evenings.

"I've got a letter from the Smithfield Show," I called out to the kitchen.

Rosalind came in an instant.

I continued, reading aloud, "We've won a prize!"

"It's not the money," she was reading with me. "It's the Land Rover!"

We looked at each other. I had never won anything like it: a Land Rover!

"Amazing... Well done, darling. You haven't won the money but first prize!"

I was stunned. "We haven't won the holiday; that's the good thing." I was trying to take it all in. "We haven't won the cash, but something much more valuable." I was speaking my thoughts aloud. "Who can grumble at first prize?"

We jumped up, hugged and, hands on each other's shoulders, examined what was happening in the kitchen.

"I can sell the Land Rover; turn it into money."

"But it's a prize for you," Rosalind said.

"But we need the money."

We had a wonderful dinner but I can't recall what we ate. I could do no more paperwork. We sat together on the settee.

"I wonder how long before I can sell it?" I mused.

"Don't worry about that; just enjoy it," she said.

"No, this is an answer to prayer. I believe God has provided it." I was thoughtful.

"You didn't pray for a Land Rover," Rosalind observed.

"Don't you see? We prayed for guidance, indeed *assurance*, not to take the tenancy unless He made it possible. I simply wrote out that advertising ditty as if it just flowed from the pen."

We sat there stunned.

"It really wasn't me... I just wrote it down," I asserted.

I told Rosalind the experience of God answering our prayer to build the church when I was in Wessex; how we couldn't pay the builder's invoice for completion of the groundwork. We had covenanted with the Lord that we would only continue with the project if we didn't have to borrow money. At the moment, literally, that we couldn't pay, a cheque for the exact amount was handed to the treasurer who was on his way to the front to announce that we had no funds. The church member had no idea what was needed; if anything, he was only handing over the commission he had pledged to give to the Lord.

"This win must be His way of keeping us here, because I pledged not to take the tenancy if it meant failing and disgracing His name. This seems to be the wonderful way He operates."

We just thanked God straight away.

That year we were both going to Smithfield. I couldn't think; my mind was only on the presentation of the prize. We stayed overnight in London with Rosalind's parents in order to be certain of a timely arrival at Earls Court. It would also enable us to drive the new vehicle home. We reported to the Land Rover stand and were told to come back at 11.30 am, in readiness for the presentation by no less than the Minister of Agriculture, Fisheries and Food at 12 noon. I walked around the maroon vehicle, tilted to one side as if it were going over a boulder, hoping to appear an interested enquirer. Somewhat embarrassingly my ploy worked.

"Can I help you, sir?" came a voice from a very smart suit.

"I'm just interested, thank you," I replied.

"They are ideal for town and of course country; good in all conditions." The suit had a label, I noticed: "Sales Manager – Land Rover".

"Yes," I agreed.

"You are a farmer, sir?" he continued.

I wanted to explain my interest but was concerned not to mention I had often had one supplied by my employer. I had to curtail further sales talk.

"Actually, I think it is mine," I smiled.

"That's good you know how useful it is," he continued.

"What I mean is, I won it in the competition," I confirmed.

"Ah!" He stood back a pace and took a paper from his jacket pocket. "Are you Mr Jennings?"

I beamed a nodding agreement.

He led us through the tented backcloth to an office. "We have our winner, Alice. Can you give him all the details?" With that he disappeared to the front of the exhibit.

Alice filled us in on the details of the procedure and the strict timing. It really was going to be mine, but there was no triumphal gesture or pose. My thoughts, even apprehension, were what words of response to make at the presentation. Surely I must thank the *Farmers Weekly* and perhaps the show organisers? It would not be correct, I thought, to mention Land Rover; or should I? I guessed they had discounted the cost of the vehicle to the sponsors and it was a good advertisement anyway. There seemed nobody to answer such questions. We toured around the stands somewhat aimlessly; not least because I was in no position to purchase machinery. On previous occasions I had been looking for the latest advances and questioning company staff about the merits of their machinery. Now I had stepped down from high farming to a modest mode of making sufficient money to continue in the industry.

At 11.30 am we met the other prize winners and politely exchanged where and what we were doing. It was just past noon when Mr John Gummer, Minister for Agriculture, Fisheries and Food, arrived with a couple of important-looking 'suits'. The local public address system announced the special event, but it certainly didn't penetrate the whole of the Earls Court hubbub. Nonetheless this was the moment. A fitting word of thanks to the minister "in his busy schedule and earnest endeavours on behalf of the industry" and we were on. The third prize winner was announced and handed an envelope, then the second prize their envelope.

There was a little more fanfare and we were called across to the stand together. The minister shook our hands and mentioned how useful such a vehicle was to farmers; he paused, about to drop the keys into my hand, and everything froze whilst we were quickly arranged for the press. There were a number of camera flashes. We were manipulated into various poses, culminating in being in the driving seat. This was by no means easy as the vehicle was still on the boulder at some 60°. The door was pushed shut, mercifully preventing me from sliding out in a crumpled mess at the minister's feet.

"Slide the window fully open and put your hand out," the photographer insisted.

It felt like I was doing hand signals. I had no wish to turn right, particularly at this angle.

"Further out, like a cup."

It was becoming more comical. Alice had not mentioned this.

"Minister, can you dangle the keys please?" came a voice from behind the camera.

I was focusing on the keys, some six inches above my 'cup'.

"All smile!" came the general instruction and many flashes of light.

There was a round of applause. I beamed as I received the keys. It was all over and the minister was off, no doubt to another appointment. My very few words of thanks could not be heard, which no doubt was a mercy as the important thing was the photograph. We were taken into the small office behind the staging.

"Thank you for coming and we will let you know when the vehicle is ready," the managing director said.

I looked aghast and then at the keys.

"Ah, yes, they are no good to you." He was smiling, holding his hand out for them. "You'll get your Land Rover from your nearest dealer. Where are you now?" He scanned a directory.

It was an anticlimax; not only was I not driving my prize home but I would have to get a train. It was a couple of weeks before the pre-delivery checks and collection could be arranged. Joy was restored in the week before Christmas when I took possession of a very distinctive maroon, short-wheeled base, hardtop vehicle

I was delighted and most careful not to get it dirty. I still used the pick-up for getting about the farm, which in fact was much more useful in terms of what it would carry. My first long journey was back to London to spend Christmas with Rosalind's parents. It was a dream to drive compared to the older models as it had a very responsive diesel engine and the acceleration to beat most cars. I was delighted in being the first away from lights in the sparse Christmas traffic. I confessed to boyish pride in that the urban drivers might not recognise a true Land Rover.

"Do they make them that colour now?" I imagined the queries from other drivers.

"Not with an engine like that," would surely come the reply.

It was a good Christmas, uncluttered with work or responsibilities, My neighbour kept an eye on our small flock that was in the yard but not yet lambing. We had a freedom of mind, being truly our own boss, coupled with the relief that we were driving in the God-given vehicle that would secure the business financially.

## Seeds Sown

After Christmas the seeds of the new farming venture were sown. It started with the few ewes we already possessed and their lambing in March. Compared with the previous flock on the estate, it felt like looking after pets. Of course, I fed and lambed them as any shepherd would, but being in such small numbers there was time to enjoy them. There was little likelihood of two ewes needing assistance at the same time. I was able to casually observe their state of health and nearness to lambing as I leaned on the gate. After they had realised my presence was no promise of feeding, I became a piece of wallpaper as far as they were concerned. Some would mooch around in the straw hoping a sheep nut might just have been missed from the morning feeding; others would be pulling at the hayrack. The remainder would be lying down ruminating. I wondered as they chewed and chewed whether they were thinking of pastures green or contemplating their previous pregnancy. On balance I had come to the probability that nothing was going through their minds at all. This was because they had very little brain and had to rely on my services. On the other hand, maybe they were supremely clever as they had all their needs met with no effort.

I reflected they coped with life very well. Having given birth, they gave ten minutes to licking the newborn dry and stimulating it to stand and that was it. The 'milk bar' was at the right height and only her offspring could use it. The penalty for stealing from another ewe was a near-fatal butt as a deterrent. The next lesson was that the milk bar moves and it is best to follow it. So much for education; it is over in the first day. Then there is endless time to skip and jump about or ruminate. This put doubt into my mind, having spent several years in education and little time to skip or ruminate. Perhaps they are as wise as Solomon.

The next 'seed' sown was literally the first potato crop. I had decided to plant two of the well-worked arable fields to potatoes. This would give them a rest from barley and break up any hardpan[46] by ploughing deeper than had been done previously. The marketing would be via a chipping contract much as I had done for the estate. I engaged my usual potato contractor who did all the major tasks leaving me the light jobs of fertilising and spraying. I was able to broadcast

---

[46] dense layer of subsoil impervious to water

half a ton of granular nitrogen, phosphate and potash (NPK) with my second-hand Vicon hopper, leaving the way clear for his team to do the cultivations.

It was a real joy to see the tidy finished rows stretching across the land, brown and weed-free. My next job was to spray the ridges just before crop emergence to kill any seedlings and form a chemical 'skin' preventing late germinating weeds emerging. I had managed to purchase the old estate sprayer cheaply in the auction. No doubt it looked too well used to be attractive to any others that might have been interested. In addition, it was clear to the expert eye that the old girl had been adapted. I had engaged an enterprising 'blacksmith' to make it trail behind the tractor, accommodating tramlines. This modern concept was to follow the same lines with machinery throughout the growing season, running down or spoiling as little of the crop as possible.

Many traditional blacksmiths had, over a generation, morphed into skilled agricultural engineers. They had been able to adapt carts and cultivators to do bespoke jobs for farmers. Now that had developed to inventing ways of overcoming challenges that had not previously been required. The carrot plant at Beech Row Farm had been a prime example in separating stones from the crop. I had needed to increase the sprayer width as well as making sure it exactly followed the tractor wheelings without cutting corners as would articulated lorries. My blacksmith carefully measured the hitching point to be halfway from the tractor rear axle and the sprayer axle. The sprayer booms were extended from twelve to eighteen metres[47] and could be folded manually for transporting. This had been a cheap modernisation when capital was tight, and the same pertained now. (Modern spray rigs are now much larger and more specialised, reaching some twenty or thirty metres.)

## More Sheep

It was time to sell the Land Rover. There had been no restriction on keeping it, and if ever challenged I could truthfully say it had enabled me to continue in my chosen profession. I advertised it nationally, explaining it was "as new" and "genuine". The asking price was £14,000 which was comfortably less than the showroom price and it was instantly available. There were a pleasing number of enquiries and I eventually settled for an offer of £13,500.

The sheep enterprise needed to be expanded to become a major part of the business. It was necessary to utilise the permanent pasture to the maximum rather than sublet it to other farmers. This would entail a suitable breed and good quality stock. In the past I had found the North Country Mules[48] to be hardy and prolific enough to produce a good crop of lambs and, crossed with a Texel ram, a conformation that appealed to butchers. My aim was to maximise

---

[47] boom sizes are always given in metric
[48] a cross between a Blue-faced Leicester ram and a Swaledale ewe

income per acre, which might mean catching the early fat lamb market around Easter time if favourable; alternatively keeping them on to almost a year old and selling them as hoggets[49].

August was the time to look for yearling ewes and I asked Henry to find some useful lots. I had spent several weeks improving fences and totally renewing others in readiness for the flock. David, my neighbour's son, had helped when needed and, being self-employed, only issued his invoices occasionally. His willingness to make time when he had other jobs of his own to see to was a great help, and his casual invoicing was most acceptable in what was becoming an expensive time. He helped with the arrival of the ewes, the worming and marking, and in fact on most 'gathering' occasions. Alongside in the same building was a sheep dip and handling race. The work was easier with the two of us. I administered the wormer and David put two blue marks, looking like a number '11', on the shoulder to signify they were our stock. They were then moved up to fresh pasture in readiness for tupping[50].

When we had the first sheep at Woodhead, Rosalind was delighted to be involved practically and helped me move them from one field to another. We had no sheepdog as there were only nineteen old ewes. Rosalind had learned that I encouraged them to follow me by rattling a quarter-full bag of sheep nuts as I stood at the open gate.

"Nip round behind them in case they don't all come," I instructed.

She did this, willing to help. I rattled the bag and they came towards the gate.

"Shoo, go on." She moved towards them but three turned towards her.

"Don't get too near," I called out.

The three stood their ground, uncertain about my new helper. My wife advanced closer which split the trio.

"Don't worry about the one," I called. She spread her arms as if to catch the two still looking at her.

They immediately bolted each side of her and joined their mate.

"You're too close," I shouted. By this time the bunch near me had been alerted to the entertainment and decided to join the party.

"You'll have to go right back," I called.

"It's alright for you; you are only standing there." Rosalind was not enjoying the exercise as much as she had expected.

I shut the gate and joined her.

"Just go back along the fence and fade into the background. I'll give them a few nuts and get them to the gate. Just act as long-stop, unobtrusively."

---

[49] lambs in their second year
[50] mating

I managed to get them to the gate and swung it open. They all followed through... except for two. I shut the gate and joined her. We trotted round making a wide detour to the far fence.

"We'll just stay quiet and let them see the others," I suggested.

The two watched us and then proceeded to graze with no intention of joining the others.

"You need a dog," Rosalind whispered, hoping the two sheep could not hear.

"We will have to have one when the numbers increase," I conceded.

We had lunch and tried again. This time we pushed the big bunch away from the gate as we quietly moved towards them. The new pasture was obviously more important than our discreet presence. I went back to the gate and opened it and walked about forty yards. Turning, the two sauntered straight through to join the others. I had already learned a little of animal psychology which is best translated as 'in my own time'.

That evening Rosalind found a sheepdog for sale in the local paper.

"You have to be careful; it's probably got something wrong with it," I said sniffily.

"They say they can demonstrate it," she replied.

I was pressed to phone the number and ended by suggesting it came for a trial.

Two days later two brothers arrived in an Austin Maxi. They opened the boot and out bounced a crossbred who sat obediently at their feet. (The boot had an extended catch which gave an inch of air to the occupant.)

"What's his name?" I enquired.

"Taff. He's not pure bred but does the job alright." The shorter man appeared to be the owner.

I looked down at the crossbred that seemed to have had a Labrador mother and possibly a greyhound father.

"I must say, he looks a bit unusual," I observed.

"He does the job."

"Why are you selling him?"

"We haven't any sheep now and he misses them."

I must have looked doubtful.

"We rented some fields and they've gone back now," he said. "I'll send him round those if you like?" he added.

I agreed.

"Come-by," he commanded.

The dog was off at a pace, disappearing over the rise in the paddock. In a few moments the sheep were all up at the gate.

I ran over the rise myself to see if any were left behind.

"They are all here!" I announced with a note of surprise.

"He's good like that," the other brother added.

We wanted a dog that would do the simple tasks and at not too much cost; later with a larger flock we might require more. I eventually took ownership of Taff for sixty pounds. He worked well for me with the simple commands of "away" and "by". Rosalind was pleased and relieved.

It was a month later that Rosalind noticed our small flock were all at the gate in the home paddock. She found me in the yard and I went to investigate. We found out that Taff had slipped his lead and must have brought all the sheep to the gate when Rosalind saw them, but there were no sheep at the gate when I got there. I ran over the rise; they were all at the far end with Taff sitting admiring them. I called the dog and tied him up with a tighter notch on his collar. I soon learned that if I lost sight of Taff, I would find him wherever the sheep were. Left to his own devices he would gather them and then exercise them. First to this corner, then the opposite one and, after two minutes rest, to the far end of the field. As far as the sheep were concerned, their grazing had given way to being fast food.

I asked Henry, my go-to sheep and cattle dealer, to look out for some North Country Mules, a hardy and prolific cross that had suited us well on the estate. I trusted him to find good quality at a reasonable price, knowing he would have checked their age and condition thoroughly. Within three weeks he delivered a total of 170 yearling ewes, some a little larger than others depending on the which of three farms they were born on. I was the proud owner of a flock any farmer ought to regard as quality. Now I accompanied Henry to a couple of ram sales. Although I had bought rams previously, it was good to have his comments and confirmation when seeking foundation stock.

We walked up lines of pens looking at Texel rams who were noted for their heavier hindquarters. Some of the owners were brushing their stock and making themselves available for questions.

"Looking for a proven young'un?" The white-coated farmer looked up at us, brush in hand.

Henry gave an acknowledging look and brushed my arm to continue walking.

"I don't know him," Henry confessed.

"Does that stop you looking?" I enquired.

"No, it was his coat."

I must have looked perplexed.

"White coats point to shows," Henry explained. "Shows often mean higher prices."

I was learning valuable pointers. We stopped at a pair of Texels with the farmer half-leaning, half-sitting on the corner of the pen. He looked as if he had come straight from home, in working trousers and large leather belt, topped off with a clean flannel shirt that had only got marginally soiled on the journey. His cloth cap, his working one, had some history.

"Are they related?" Henry asked.

"Aye, twins," came the reply. "Could see they were good'uns the moment they born."

"Do you have any more?" Henry asked.

"Not today, but three or so next month."

"Where are you from?"

"Shrewsbury way." He didn't name the village.

"Got a phone number?" Henry enquired and was offered a rather bent card.

We looked at all the Texels and I jotted down three pens of interest. Henry probably remembered every detail. We bid for our Shrewsbury pen and another couple, less like twins but presenting well. We came home with four rams; Henry having bought them with a hardly perceptible nod.

Henry's invoice arrived about a fortnight later with all the ewes costing £12,240; an average of £72 each, which I thought quite reasonable. There was a separate invoice for the rams; two at £325 and the twins at £300 each.

"We've got a big bill for the sheep," I called out to Rosalind from the office.

"Not too big I hope," she called from the kitchen.

"No, roughly what I expected." I looked at two invoices and added them together: £13,490.

"Amazing!" I rushed to the kitchen. "Thirteen thousand four hundred and ninety pounds!" I exclaimed.

"It is a lot," she agreed.

"Don't you see?" I hung my arm around her. "It's the same price as the Land Rover!"

She turned from the cooking.

"Well, within ten pounds." I was beside myself. "The Land Rover has paid for the flock: both ewes and rams."

"The Lord has provided," she beamed, "and this is His signature."

"Not the fourteen thousand pounds I asked for originally, but what it actually made. Thank you, Lord," I shouted aloud.

The first mule yearlings arrived. Henry reversed his lorry to the doorway and ewes streamed down the aluminium tailgate head to tail, clattering into the handling passageway and into the covered yard where they stayed overnight. It was exciting to see the raw material of the sheep enterprise, now we were into a serious business. The next morning, with my neighbour David's help, we wormed and marked them. Our mark of two parallel blue stripes on their shoulder would identify them as our stock should they stray. The worming would ensure our pastures were kept clean and keep the sheep in good condition before going to the tups.

Our sheepdog, Taff, was sold to a friend with a similar number of old ewes who was well acquainted with his foibles. It suited him to treat Taff as a pet who doubled as sheep-mover when required. We now needed a good sheepdog for our enlarged flock. In searching the local paper I responded to a useful-looking advert. A small girl answered the phone.

"Is Mummy there?" I asked. There was a hesitation.

"I think so," came a plaintive reply.

"I want to speak to Mummy about your dog." I thought this might help in finding Mummy, but there was no sound for several seconds.

"He bit my sister," came the small voice. This information was alarming, but I thought it was still worth speaking to Mummy. Yes, indeed, the dog had bitten the other girl, but it was minor and the mother said at the time the child was trying to pull the dog by its tail whilst it was eating. I gave the dog the benefit of the argument as I could imagine it seeing its breakfast receding in spite of having his four feet planted firmly on the lino.

I bought the well-marked collie, only a year old, for sixty pounds. I was hoping I could rely on him knowing at least the basics and our relationship would do the rest. This was to prove true and he never attempted to bite me.

'Moss' drove home in the cab with me and was sick. I tied him up and played with him, making a fuss and giving him a few treats. I phoned his previous home and apparently he had never travelled in a vehicle before, as an invalid aunt had looked after him when the family went shopping. I had never enquired about travel sickness and was concerned how he would fare as a sheepdog. I returned to Moss to further encourage him and found he was in his kennel. It was a forty-gallon oil drum with three-quarters of the top cut out. The remaining quarter formed a doorstep and kept the bedding dry. He had already taken to his new home and came out to greet me. I had envisaged a time of having to introduce him to the idea that this was where he would sleep. Instead, Moss was showing me his new home. It seemed appropriate to introduce the sheep so I lifted him into the back of the pick-up and clipped his lead to the rack at the front. I could see him in the mirror sniffing the breeze and riding the bumps. No sickness this time. I unclipped him and, holding the lead, encouraged him to jump down. He beat me, gave a shake and looked up as if to say, "What next?"

Erring on the side of caution, we walked around the empty field next to the sheep. I talked to him all the time, which had always been a good contact with dogs. We paused for an affectionate hug every hundred yards. This stroking and patting of the chest was a 'getting to know you' exercise. Next came the walking beside me with no lead. Finally, I got him to sit and walked five yards away, then called him back. This, as I had hoped, was all within his vocabulary. We walked back to the pick-up and drove back. After tea we walked to the rams in their small paddock, the ideal first testing.

"Sit, Moss." He was obedient and focused on the group of four. They of course had seen the dog and were standing to attention.

"Go-bye," I instructed simply. His reply was to run round the group and crouch. The rams walked obediently towards me, Moss following at a suitable distance.

"Sit." Moss did so. I walked to him and congratulated him. I couldn't withhold my delight; he had passed the tests well. I had assumed I would have to teach him from more or less the beginning but he had been well drilled in obedience. The really pleasing aspect was our instant relationship.

# 38

# Lambing the Lot!

Autumn was busy; my mind was focused on making the most of our new sheep enterprise. Other building work and non-vital jobs gave way to organising the tupping time. The rams were now in good condition and fitted with their harnesses on their undersides, ready to be released on the first of October. All of the harnesses had red crayons for the first two weeks, to show which ewes had been mated. The next colour would be blue and the third yellow. This enabled us to separate them later into three groups and feed them accordingly during the six weeks prior to lambing.

As the grass in the pastures slowed in growth, we had to feed them silage, the big bales being dropped into round rings like park railings. This allowed their heads through but not their shoulders. The sheep had grown up with this feeding and were quick to meet me with the forklift and a big bale entering the field. Moss too was keen and his presence cleared a space for me to cut off the plastic wrap before sliding the bale off, upright, into the ring. Not all the ewes rushed for the silage, some preferring to hunt for elusive young blades of grass at the bottom of the feg. Once they were housed in the yards, silage became their bulk ration. I was grateful for sufficient covered yards; it made for controlled feeding and much easier lambing. I had never been keen on lambing out in the fields as some shepherds do. Of course, we have to work in all weathers, but nature has chosen sheep to lamb in the winter; they come into season triggered by the daylight decreasing and gestate for about 147 days. This means they often lamb in bitter weather. The other problem for the hill shepherd is that sheep never mention they feel poorly, or they might get onto their backs and can't get up. They never call for help, so the 'ambulance' (in this case the shepherd) has to tour around looking for trouble. The other peculiarity is the ambulance is needed in the most inhospitable weather, especially at night.

We were able to house the sheep in strawed yards, keeping them within easy view and well fed. As they came in, they were pregnancy-scanned to tell which would have twins or a single. This was done by a specialist, rather than the vet, who had the proper equipment. The operator sat on a fisherman's stool beside the sheep race, armed with a television-like box with a stethoscope-like lead. The skill is in moving the scanner over the underside of the standing ewe whilst watching the screen.

I had to enlist David's help to guide in the ewes down the race one at a time and slam the gate behind them. I was at the head of the ewe ready to open the exit gate and slam it shut before the next ewe thought of a quick exit. The scanner was quick to shout out the result. "One", "two" or "twins", or occasionally "three". I had aerosol sprays to mark one, two or three dots on the head and quickly released the sheep left or right. Our set-up was not fully comprehensive nor was there sufficient space to separate into more categories. As we expected more twins than singles, I let all twins and triplets into the first yard and the others into the further yard. The circus gathered speed as we settled into the task. This was necessary as the scanner man had multiple flocks to attend to in an eight to ten week season. After he had packed his equipment and gone, we ran the 'singles and barren' yard through a second time to remove the barren ewes who would not have any supplementary feeding, only silage.

My routine was now set, concentrating on those in the yards. I told Moss it was holiday time and he would only have to get out of bed for a quick daily inspection of the few barren ewes in a far paddock. I'm not sure he appreciated holidays but he would tell me if anyone came down the drive. I started the mornings by looking over the yards for any possible problems; then, a fortnight later, I fed a sack of sheep pellets for extra protein to the pregnant mums. I started off by trying to shake the pellets into galvanised troughs lying in the straw. After two days I gave up; the rush for the tasty nuts meant I was trapped, unable to get to the other troughs. When I managed to fight my way through, they followed and the same scrum formed. Troughs were turned upside down and expensive nuts fell into the straw.

I soon found that ewes were as diligent as pigs and searched through the litter licking up every nut. I thought of a Plan B: I removed all the troughs and scattered the nuts round the bottom of the walls. This had the merit of all having a fair chance of food; until they got wise to the fact that a rattling bag signalled food. The sound, as it does in a field, calls them to follow, and I was becoming hemmed in again. I took to running round the sides of the yard to beat the rush, but it only lasted a few days. If I had had help, perhaps, we could have shaken two half-full bags starting in opposite directions, but I couldn't prevail on David every morning for just ten minutes. I latched onto Plan C.

Moss was delighted with Plan C. I got him to sit at the yard gate whilst I pulled the string to open the sack. The very sight of the dog created a space as they stood back, staring at him. I started off calling Moss to follow; it worked like a charm. As the sheep got used to Moss's presence they were a little bolder and even dared to ignore him. I was running round the yard shaking nuts as fast as possible. Without any command, indeed I didn't even know the word for 'go ahead of me', Moss took it on himself to run ahead, with me following him. Like a lifeboat ploughing through the surf, I followed in Moss's wake.

Moss also had to guard the yard gateway in preparation for silage feeding. I prepared for the event by arriving at the gate, big bale already speared by the forklift. It was also unwrapped from its plastic, ready to drop straight into the ring feeder. I opened the metal field-type gate, and Moss stationed himself in the middle of the gap whilst I drove in sufficiently far to close the gate behind me. He soon learned that he needed to stand close to the feeder, keeping the ewes from sticking their heads through the bars to grab the first morsels. The danger was in the bale suddenly sliding off the spike and trapping an unwary head under half a ton of silage. The procedure was then reversed in order to exit the yard. Although the feeder was rarely empty, the new bale attracted total attention. I could only liken their behaviour to that of humans smelling newly baked bread at the bakers. As I leaned on the gate, every gap in the bars was filled with the head of a pulling and chewing customer.

The rest of the time was spent constructing individual lambing pens using five-foot-long fertiliser pallets. These were tied together to form three walls and a 'gate' secured with string hinges. Each pen had another improvisation for a 'bucket'; more accurately a well-washed out twenty-five-litre plastic chemical drum cut in half. These were not only free but less able to be tipped over compared to a small bucket.

The time leading up to lambing was the calm before the storm. It afforded me the chance to oversee the yards from the higher 'handling passage', which now had one side as a line of pens. Other pens would be constructed as necessary inside the yards as lambing progressed. I became familiar with the different characters of the ewes as they wandered around their indoor quarters. There were one or two dominant ewes, always prepared to gently head-butt another who had discovered a small hoard of sheep nuts in the straw. One or two were distinguished by their colour markings; a larger than usual black spot on the neck or head, or perhaps the opposite being mostly white or grey. It was notable that some were more placid, nearly always sitting chewing. One could admire the rumination, one mouthful after another. I wondered if there was any thought of green pastures or landscapes from their previous farms.

As night-time visits became necessary to check if there were any early lambers, I was aware of their territorial nature. I noticed some had 'their' night-time area just near the gate or in a corner where two walls met; like the pecking order, it was evident that it was 'owned'. I reflected that the same occurred at pasture; that even returning to a field after some months' absence, they would sleep within a few yards of the same place each night. This was proved to me when I walked early on frosty mornings and disturbed one or two, making them rise and leaving a clear frost-free patch where they had been all night. I guess this is an extension of being hefted to a mountain where 'sheep families' are familiar and very rarely stray to the neighbours' land.

Springtime B&B guests enquired about lambing and my coming and going with bottles. They often asked to see the sheep and of course their lambs. When Rosalind was cooking breakfast, whether a day away from the surgery or at a weekend, she would often escort guests to the lambing pens for a conducted tour. Quite often I would be busying myself with an actual birth that was proving difficult when they peered over the yard rails. I would have to call out a coded note of warning if I was about to deliver a dead lamb.

"I'll be with you in a minute." I did my best to hide the operational end of the prostrate ewe.

"We don't want to trouble you." It was usually the lady of the couple who responded.

"Look at the pens," I called over my shoulder.

Rosalind understood this meant, "Show them the live ones in the pens with mum."

If they showed signs of not appreciating the downside of shepherding, she would take them outside to the nearest field of lambs happily gambling about and a duplicate of the calendar image on the kitchen wall.

"Why have they got numbers?" That was often the first question.

"In case they get lost," Rosalind would answer.

"I thought the mother knew their voice." More explanation was needed.

"They do." She tried to avoid the same 'downside' I was struggling with in the yard. Sometimes a lamb would be found dead in the field. If the lady continued she would get a farmer's wife's reality check.

On other occasions, guests would watch me work.

"Goodness!" – the surprise exclamation of most town guests. "Are they all going to lamb?"

"I hope so," came my fervent reply.

"Lambing the lot yourself?"

"Fortunately, most ewes manage the birth part; I oversee the nursing."

"Can we see one being born?" It was usually the ladies who asked.

The men seemed more interested in the process from lambing, to mum and toddler pen, to transport, and finally to field.

"You must have more than a hundred," the men would observe.

"Nearly two hundred," I confirmed.

"What happens once they lamb?"

"They go into a pen immediately Mum has licked them dry."

The questions would continue, but often I would be a giving a live demonstration which was much the best answer.

"It looks as if I'll have to help that one," I had to announce, if signs of distress or difficulty were evident. "You can go back to the house if you would rather," I offered.

Leaving the choice to remain or leave, I quietly slipped into the yard and approached from the back of the straining ewe. Making sure she couldn't get up, I quickly found two feet; no, three. A little more fumbling and I found the two that belonged to the first lamb. Pushing the wrong leg back, it was possible to pull the two front legs of number one, ensuring the head was resting on its front knees. A little help as mum strained and it was born. I whisked the lamb to the ewe's nostrils whilst stopping her getting up, should she have any such notion. Holding tight onto her wool to keep her lying there, I needed to investigate with my other hand the state of number two. The situation was less crowded and I quickly drew the front legs and head into the 'diving' position; all seemed well. Another heave from mum and number two was born. He joined his sister at mum's head for the same licking and bonding process. I retired to the gate but with a constant eye on the situation.

"Couldn't she manage it herself?" the men would often enquire.

I guessed they considered it rather a messy process being that close to nature. The ladies, if they witnessed a lambing, were generally quiet; possibly thinking or reminiscing.

I went to the twins – one was standing already – and took them both with me, keeping them at straw level as I backed to the nearest empty pen. Mum followed, nose within a few inches of her lambs. The new family were together, unable to stray or be 'mis-mothered' in their individual pen. I put the water bucket in one corner and a wafer of baled hay in another.

"What happens now?" a call came from the yard gate.

"I'm letting things calm down and will look at the pen in fifteen minutes," I called back. There was time to cast an eye over the second yard that should not be lambing for another fortnight... but the odd problem or early lambing could occur.

The guests had returned to the house, no doubt none the wiser but certainly better informed. I was able to continue my routine of inspection and minor servicing of pens. It was a gentle time that shepherds enjoy; nature quietly proceeding on the basis that 'mum knows best'. These yearlings were new to the job but most were perfect mothers with their first lambs. I had to be conscious that some would be fearful and need reassurance as well as physical help. The next vital event was to ensure they were letting their lambs suckle. It usually entailed educating the lamb as to where exactly the milk bar was placed. Once located and the essential colostrum tasted, it was a case of them returning and banging the udder as often as mum permitted.

As lambing advanced from the slightly premature to the real thing, I needed to be on duty at night as well as during the day. My last inspection was about 11 pm. The lights in the yards were left on so that there would be minimal disturbance when entering through the large metal door and walking along the higher passageway overseeing the strawed yards. The ewes were dozing or simply chewing the cud, at peace with the world. It was easy to notice any that were agitated, walking around and sitting down only to get up again. This, together with tight udders, and perhaps swollen and red vulva, indicates birth is about twelve to twenty-four hours away; timing is rarely precise. I moved to the next yard where there should not have been any activity yet, as they had a fortnight to go. Returning to yard one, I tried to assess when the next ewe might lamb; I decided not for at least three hours. I consciously repeated "two-thirty", expecting a routine visit unnecessary before then, and returned to bed. Having two-thirty in mind enabled me to sleep, mindful that everything was OK.

At that time my mind was getting used to my 'lambing clock' mode, with a glance at my watch merely confirming it. Mechanically I pulled on trousers, pullover and socks and, at the back door, Wellingtons. Then I went straight to the yard, only thirty yards away, and quietly slipped the bolt. Everywhere was much the same. I tried to identify the ewe in question; some were walking about, all was quiet. Ah! There she was; no lamb and no problem. I resolved to visit next at six o'clock. Back to bed and the thought of "no problem; just sleep until six", an hour earlier than usual.

It turned out that she came to feed as usual and lambed unaided at noon. As the ewes followed the morning feedbag, the empty space revealed a ewe not interested in eating. She had her head down, nuzzling two lambs, conscious of her new responsibility. With the rest interested only in finding sheep nuts, I was able to pick up the two lambs and backed out of the yard, mum dutifully following with her nose within inches of her young. She now had her own apartment, water and hay laid on.

About a week into the real lambing period, the night and particularly early mornings were busier than the daytime. I had made a practice of starting at 6 am regardless of what work the night had demanded. Often there were a couple of ewes that had lambed and had to be withdrawn to their private pallet-pen before feeding nuts could begin. If fed first, the lambs and their mothers would be separated in the rush, and mis-mothering or even injury could be a real possibility. I walked into the yard and counted five ewes who had given birth; lambs were everywhere! If two ewe-lambs[51] lamb near each other, it is always possible that one ewe will only take to one lamb of her own and ignore its twin. The lone lamb may then be claimed by the ewe who has two of her own, but is more likely be roaming the yard in bewilderment. Another scenario is for a ewe who has not yet had her own lambs to claim that it belongs to her. This over-maternal instinct occurs mostly in older ewes who have had previous pregnancies. Whether they like having a large family or think, "I'll take this one to save all the pain and strain," I am never sure. What I do know is that it is vital to sort out the true mums and their rightful progeny.

---

[51] first-time mothers

On such an occasion I needed help. Standing still, reassessing the situation, the only course of action was to withdraw the couples[52] that I was certain were correct. That reduced the size of the problem; now there were only four ewes and eight lambs. The next clever bit was to ask Rosalind to help me.

"I need a bit of help," I whispered in her ear.

"Now? It's... six o'clock," she peered at the bedside alarm.

"Well, half past six, darling; I need a midwife." This was only half true but it conveyed an urgency, which she understood. In truth I needed a second opinion about relationships. She joined me in the middle of the yard in four minutes.

"Those two have lambed." I pointed to two ewes, side by side and reasonably content, with a lamb each. "Which lamb can you see that looks similar to those two pretending they are 'singles'?" I asked.

"That one is about the same size," she pointed out.

"Yeah, the heads look like a pair," I agreed. "I'll take the lamb, if the ewe is happy, and withdraw them out towards an empty pen."

Rosalind whisked up the lookalike and joined me.

I checked the ewe had milk in both udders and squirted milk all over the lamb's head, pointed it to the source and retreated two paces. The ewe looked behind and turned to munch some hay, an evident improvement on the silage in the yard.

After a few minutes she was content with both lambs. We returned to the yard, where we repeated the same operation with another couple.

"I think the other loose lamb has similar markings although it's a little larger," Rosalind suggested.

I had to admit it looked possible. We drew them out to a pen as before and left them together.

I grabbed a colour aerosol and put a blue stripe on the ewe and twins in the first pen who had settled as a small family. The two new 'twins' were settled in spite of a slight size difference, so we left them to be rechecked later.

"We will get the last two ewes and four lambs out and see how they pair up without the distractions in the yard. We will put them in the large end pen," I suggested.

"I'll have to get ready for work. Next time I could help you do some birthing."

With that, Rosalind left to look after humankind and I turned to the morning feeding regime. It had been a real help to involve my wife and it would be useful to acquaint her further with the lambing operation. After feeding the expectant mothers in the yard, I moved to the new couples in the pens. The lambs needed to have their remaining bit of umbilical cord sprayed, or preferably dipped, in a

---

[52] a 'couple' refers to a ewe and her lambs

two to three per cent solution of iodine. This would stop any infection travelling straight into the vulnerable baby. As I tucked the lamb under one arm and squirted the iodine solution along the cord towards its navel, I mused at the difference between human and ovine progeny: the lamb born onto straw that was far from surgically clean or the one pulled out having had its feet rearranged. Then it would be up to mother to lick the infant dry, all the time stimulating it and bonding. Within minutes it would be standing, albeit shakily, on four legs; a process taking several months humanly to achieve. Walking was a necessary skill on day one, if only to find the milk bar. As the ewe walked a few paces, it seemed prudent to follow. After all, that was where that welcomed drink came from. Those born out in fields would within a week be acknowledging friends that looked like themselves rather than those huge mobile feeding stations. The only similarity between human and ovine, learned by the end of day one, is to bleat and the milk bar comes to you. Lambs go from kindergarten to teenage in about six weeks. Their group of friends increases and independence becomes the norm. The herd instinct is cultivated and peer pressure takes root. Standing in the field, the shepherd sees this unfolding before his eyes.

Two, perhaps three, lambs – feeling well fed and with the spring sunshine on their backs – decided to go jogging together. It was such fun and so liberating that they broke into a run to higher ground thirty yards away. From there they could see much more of the field – and look, there was mum over there. "I'll race you back." This running, ending in another drink, was even more exciting. It had not gone unnoticed by a few other lambs. Soon there were a dozen at it and it was becoming competitive. In fact, it was so exhilarating that a jump just happened; others caught the habit. The adults began to raise heads, much the same as parents raising eyebrows.

"I was quietly grazing and a whole bunch rushed past me."

"That's not all," the neighbour replied. "When you move to another area, they are nowhere to be seen."

"Here they come again; stand firm," the first observed.

"Disgraceful, up to the rise and back, time and again."

"There is no chance to chew the cud in peace."

I broke away from daydreaming to the reality of pens filling up. I marked the ewe, spraying a large 'number' on each side and similarly the same 'number' on junior. Once in the field, I saw at a glance that they were a unit together; if a lamb went missing there was a good chance of rectifying the situation. If, during the regular field visits, I found a dead lamb, then I could record the number, knowing that that ewe now only had a single.

The weather was at least dry, and the first lambers were bonded and fit enough to live in the field. I parked the tractor with a transport box attached in the doorway and carried the twins from the earliest pen, the ewe dutifully following, I held them just inside the small gate to the transport box and the ewe followed. There was just enough room for the couple in the next pen to join them. The box was full and there was little room to jump up and out; the ewes were too busy making sure their family was with them and had no desire to escape. At the field I drove into the middle and simply opened the transport box gate. No second invitation was needed; real grass and freedom beckoned. They regrouped, collected their respective lambs, and I returned and repeated the process. I now had four pens to clean out, disinfect and re-litter ready for the next fresh couple. This process of feeding both forage and nuts, then 'servicing' individual pens, strengthened the relationship between shepherd and flock. As a fairly constant presence, there was no threat or alarm. Equally, I was aware of any unusual behaviour, especially signs of lambing.

The following week was busier and it was hard to keep up with the flow of lambs. I got to the weekend and had to enlist Rosalind's help again; she was keen to help and a quick learner. We talked all the time, which was the perfect tuition. When there was need to assist a ewe, I pointed out the signs and reasoning and demonstrated the technique of catching and laying the ewe down. Rosalind donned a full-length disposable glove.

"What can you feel?" I asked.

"It seems there are too many feet," she replied; it was not something that happened at the surgery.

"Can you feel which way the leg joint bends? I mean, front legs bend at the knee," I offered.

"I think I have got two front legs."

"Check they come from the same chest or else it is possible to have a front leg of each of the twins."

"Will you check for me?"

I got there to hold the ewe from getting up and put on a new glove.

"You are right, but I will help her now rather than distress her later. I have the head resting on those two legs; it was turned backwards."

The commentary ended and a fit lamb was born.

"Keep hold of the ewe and we will let her lick it if she wants to." I placed the lamb by the ewe's mouth. "It is important to check number two is coming properly."

All seemed well and it came easily. I took over gentle restraint of the ewe, who now showed interest in both lambs. I slowly released my grip, allowing her to stand if she wanted to. There was more licking; first one lamb, then the other. We retreated a yard watching nature take over. She had obviously recovered from the birthing and decided standing was best to assert her responsibility as a mother.

We worked well together, Rosalind rapidly becoming a shepherdess, and I let go of the tasks she could handle with confidence. In the house all our conversations were about farming and she loved every minute; it was as if she were a partner in the business. To my embarrassment, her employer, Dr Frank, phoned to ask if she could do an extra clinic if she wasn't farming.

"She's not here at the moment. I'll tell her you called."

"OK, I had better wait to hear from the boss," he accepted.

"I'm sorry, Frank. I'm sure the answer will be yes," I responded.

"Don't worry, old chap. We get a lot of farming talk here." He laughed aloud. "She is all about lambs, not babies, and when the weather's bad we hear about the plight of the farmers."

"I thought you were being serious; she is not quite the boss here," I caught on.

"No, she is the boss here though." Another loud laugh and he recovered himself. "Seriously, she is not the boss; she is our treasure. But don't bother her. I'll see her Monday." Frank rang off.

I had to employ David for a few very busy days. He was skilled in shepherding having learned the job helping his father on their small-holding. We got through the lambing with a good percentage but I had learned not to count results until they were sold. This too Rosalind had picked up, explaining to anybody who would listen that sheep have a death wish.

"They die without ever appearing ill." She would only slightly exaggerate the truth. "I think they have a conference each morning," she would continue. "The head ewe asks, 'Whose turn is it today?' Then they argue. 'It's my turn.' 'No, it's mine.'"

This would cause much mirth in the surgery, the ladies' group in the church, or wherever else she could find a small audience; she was proud to be a farmer's wife.

When they were all out in the fields, it was a splendid sight: ewes content with fresh grass and lambs at the 'gambolling' stage – that is racing, for no good reason, from here to there and back again with jumps of freedom for sheer joy. I too was content that the lambing was over and even the potatoes had been planted by our contractor. The farm was looking in good shape.

# 39

# French Fries

The contractors team had made a very professional job of preparing and planting on the tenancy, just as they had done for me when farming the estate. I took pride in the straight rows of brown earth with that reddish tint, and not a weed in sight. This had all been done whilst I was concentrating on the lambing. Now the first leaves were poking through and it was time for a residual herbicide to kill the weed seedlings and any that would soon break surface, leaving the potatoes without competition. It was a sort of 'barrier cream' that would allow the potatoes to thrive until later when they would overshadow most late-germinating weeds. I was able to spray the crop myself, including the four or five applications against potato blight just before harvest. I kept a keen ear on the weather forecast and an eye on the potato foliage. Humid weather in July would encourage blight, turning the tips of the leaves brown and later killing the whole leaf. The resulting spores would quickly get washed into the soil and infect the tubers. This would render them useless and have to be graded out as total waste or possibly just cattle feed.

I enjoyed inspecting the crops as much as overseeing the sheep. The sheep needed shepherding, which entailed noting their condition, mostly seen in the growth of the lambs and thrift of the ewes i.e. whether they were lame or had any fly-strike. This is a nasty condition when flies lay eggs in the dung of dirty tails in the spring. The eggs hatch and maggots can soon infest the wool leaving a dirty patch. This is countered by dipping them all, and possibly individual treatment, every time they are gathered. In short, a shepherd is responsible for their nutrition and welfare. Somebody explained it as being their "greengrocer, nursemaid and doctor". I would even add 'undertaker' as they seem so ready to leave this world. Relating this to a friend, he said I should add 'barber', and 'policeman' for the times they go missing.

The crops need similar care, with inspections at various times to anticipate yield reductions from pests and diseases. Most farmers use an agronomist, who is skilled in this job and may well be a fieldsman for a chemical firm. They have trained eyes and knowledge of first sightings in the district to spot the first fungus or insect invasion. Importantly, they come up with 'cocktail' suggestions to render the sprays more effective or longer-lasting. The potatoes were a big investment of about a thousand pounds an acre and therefore worthy of very careful attention to detail. The crop needed burning off to control late blight and encourage the skins to set; for example not to be able to be rubbed off as in new potatoes. The skin is permeable protection, discouraging bacteria and disease but allowing the tuber to respire.

Harvesting the crop was done as usual by the contractor and his team. In spite of the massive size of the equipment, it was designed to handle the crop with care. I watched the harvester lifting the entire double row, six feet wide and twelve inches deep, so that it flowed up the main elevator that was then being agitated, allowing soil to fall back onto the ground. At the top of the main elevator, it became a ribbon of tubers falling onto the conveyor and into a trailer travelling alongside. I remembered the old potato spinner; and women picking up every potato by hand before putting them into a bucket and then tipping them into a sack; the back-aching piece work that goaded them on till it was time to collect the children from school. Now the harvester discharge chute was lowered gently by the driver into the empty trailer, to avoid bruising the potatoes, without a hesitation in the forward speed; every moment precious. The harvesting was relentless. More equipment received the loads at the farm; a large hopper embracing the rear of the tipping trailer and gently elevating the potatoes onto the grader. Any remaining soil and small potatoes fell through the first and second sieves, the rest rolling onto the inspection table. The three or four workers there had the busy task of throwing out green tubers and any with cuts or roots. This was to minimise the risk of disease spreading whilst they were stored over winter.

The scene was of constant motion; the frantic hands of the casual labour over the relentless stream of potatoes. I joined the small team in a roving capacity, forking up potatoes that had spilled between trailer and hopper; and moving wooden boxes of rejects, replacing them with empty ones to keep the system going. I also had to keep an eye on the oscillating elevator in the store, edging it backwards to maintain a constant levelling of the potatoes at about nine feet high. It was a gratifying sight to see the harvest materialise, ever growing, to fill the building.

At the completion of the field work, the drivers moved on to their next customer to start the same process all over again. The grading equipment often followed them too, depending on how much the next farmer required to supplement his own machinery. David and I cleared up any soil and spillages, and turned our attention next to strawing the top of the potatoes. It was essential to shake out bales of straw onto the top of the crop as the shed filled. These became a blanket to protect the potatoes from frost and also to maintain total darkness, so as to avoid greening. It allowed the crop to transpire and held back the resulting moisture, keeping them dry. The straw would need adding to and possibly changing as winter progressed.

It was March when the processor asked for deliveries to start, and I got our contractor, Barry, to bring back the grading equipment and conveyors to fill the bulk lorries. The potatoes had come through the winter frost-free and the job was now to reverse the storage process. Now was the time to grade them out of store and onto lorries for sending to the chip factory. Apart from the necessary equipment, I had to find the casual labour to run it. I enquired at the employment exchange and found two Polish workers and a pair of local unemployed men prepared to do farm work. They were all able to find their own transport, saving me from collecting and return them daily.

It was all coming together nicely; the crop had been grown to the tight specifications of the processors, in this case for chips or 'French fries'. The variety had to be Russet Burbank and the dry matter and sugar content precise, in addition to a range in tuber size that was acceptable. On arrival at the factory a sample would be fried for a minute and the colour of the chips measured against a colour chart, much the same as a paint chart for decorators. Their aim was for a pale shade indicating lower sugars. Higher sugars made for brown chips and were unacceptable. I had done this before for my employer and now I had the satisfaction of selling my own crop. The cost of hiring equipment and the tons of daily output needed to make it economical, together with the casual labour being fully employed, made for detailed management. We aimed at grading four loads a day. This would have to be in agreement with the hauliers and the factory. The lorries were timed and dispatched as soon as loaded.

The first day we managed four loads, being about a hundred tons. Everything had gone to plan, the labour had turned up and worked well, the machinery had no stoppages for minor adjustments and the weather was fine.

What had been successfully dispatched became a disappointment at the factory gate. How could the load be rejected? I was used to receiving a phone call as the loads were sampled at the factory intake. The call came through as 'rejected'. Apparently, the fry colours were too dark. How could the fry colours be too dark? The crop had not overheated. I knew that remonstrating with Quality Control was useless. The next load had already left for the factory; I hoped it would be alright. I comforted myself with the idea that the first load from the face of the store may not have been typical of the rest.

The next load was rejected for another reason.

"I am afraid your load number... has been rejected," came the voice of Quality Control.

"I can't understand that. Please take another sample."

"We can't, sir, it's gone."

"Gone where?" I demanded.

"You had better ask your haulier." That was the end of the call.

I was frantic; all I could do was to phone John. I would be charged for the haulage and also have to pay for it to come back to the farm. It would then be unsaleable because of its specialist variety and only fit for animal feed. I knew for every mile travelled it would cost money even to become cattle feed. Fortunately, I knew the haulier well and we had overcome such a problem together in the past.

"John, they have rejected the load." I must have sounded exasperated.

"Yes, it's just turned up in the yard," John replied.

"I can't have the load back; we can't tip it here." I was alluding to the height of the shed and the lack of empty boxes to accommodate twenty-five tons.

"I'll stand it off here and we can speak later." His tone was resigned but I welcomed it.

The next call from the factory was at 5.30 pm; that load was rejected too.

"Can you put the driver on?" I made the request as polite as possible. I waited whilst they called him to the phone. "Fred, can you stand it off?" I'm sure he heard the desperation in my voice.

"I'll ask the boss if it can stay in our yard; don't worry."

I knew it was at my personal expense now, not the established estate's. I would be financially out of pocket. By 8 pm I was beside myself; four loads had been rejected with no hope of a market. They had already cost fourteen pounds a ton for transport – £1,400 lost on my first day of trading – and nearly twenty per cent of my crop was effectively unsaleable.

I spoke to the boss, John. He agreed to do all that he could and would stand down the lorry trailers whilst we looked for a buyer. He gave me the name of another chip processor. I phoned them the next day but without success. There was a black cloud hanging over the farm. All the equipment was in place and idle; we dared not grade any more until these had found a home.

Rosalind was sympathetic but we could not cheer each other up. John tried to get one of the loads accepted on the Wednesday but it failed on another point of quality.

"I could try again on Sunday," John suggested. We knew that on Sunday afternoons Quality Controls were less exacting in order to restart the factory after the weekend clean-down. I tried the other company again; they were prepared to receive a load. I phoned John immediately and he sent a load to Wolverhampton.

The phone rang; it was John.

"Fred has just called me."

I waited with bated breath.

"They have accepted the load."

Gratitude swept over me.

"Are you happy for me to try another load straight away?" John seemed keen.

"Happy! Certainly." I nearly said, "Deliriously happy!"

All four loads were accepted. There would be no huge loss, just a small cost for the extra miles to the other processor. Our prayers of desperation were answered. We had reminded the Lord of His promise to see us through and not go under. We had thanked Him for the Land Rover so why would He let us go out of business now? We had been so grateful for His blessings, but why was life such a rollercoaster?

The paperwork came back with the details and Quality Control's test results. Not only were they accepted in full, but we received a quality bonus which covered the extra transport cost. Our faith in His promises was restored, and that bonus had the Lord's signature.

As I looked back over the years, I could see God had saved me so often. I actually knew the answer as to why life was a rollercoaster; a church minister had once told me that testing times strengthen us and they increase our faith in God. In nature I had noticed that trees in a woodland plantation grew up together tall and straight. Then, in a thinning operation, or by clear felling a section, the trees are left vulnerable to external forces. A severe wind will blow down those that have not been tested by it previously. I knew in my heart that testing enables us to be stronger. I had to have faith in God's promise of keeping us throughout the tenancy.

In the middle of a crisis it is difficult not to struggle and to have doubts; that is the normal human reaction. However, I had enough history to understand that the Lord will never break or go back on His promises. I had taken the tenancy because I had committed my future to Him and He had opened up the way ahead. In human terms I could never have contemplated such a move; indeed, even management jobs seemed unobtainable. Church people often refer to God's blessing but it is never a smooth path; there are always ups and downs. I liken it to porridge; tasty, nutritious and satisfying... but at times stodgy, cold and sticking to the saucepan.

## Managing the Labour

The rest of the grading-out and sales went without further trouble. Fulfilling the contract, my confidence in producing the right quality was restored. I worked closely with the casual labour each day to ensure quality and to react to any emergency. Occasionally, the local men were less reliable in turning up for work or would be a few minutes late. The Polish women and man were not related in any way but never failed to be on time. In fairness, the younger Englishman, Tom, would send his wife or daughter when he was not available. This was better than non-attendance but no explanation for absence was ever given. The Polish lady turned out to be a librarian but was working in the UK for a year or so to gain income. The five pounds per hour rate on farm work was substantially more than she earned as a librarian at home. The man who had left wife and family behind in Poland was a school teacher but seemingly on an annual contract basis. He was working here to pay off his mortgage, which he expected to do in five years.

It was noticeable that whenever there was a slight stoppage of the grader, the two from Poland were immediately looking under belts and chains to find the offending stone jamming it or a broken link in the drive chain. The Englishmen would lean against the straw bales in the adjacent barn until it was mended. It wasn't long before I noticed a new car parked in the yard. As we chatted, heads down grading out rejects, I asked whose car it was.

"It's mine," replied Tom.

"Looks good," I observed without looking up.

"I sold my old one to Jim here." Jim was a man of few words and just grinned.

"We came in the new one to try it out," Tom explained.

A week later they arrived in the original car. To pass the time whilst studying the flow of tubers passing along the inspection belt, there was light-hearted banter above the sound of machinery.

"Not come in your car today, Tom?" I enquired.

"No." The cold reply told me there was no more to be said.

The next day Tom did not turn up but Jim arrived in the old car.

"Is Tom ill?" I asked Jim.

"No, his car has gone." Jim had a plain, simple approach in any conversation, answering the immediate question but prompting another.

"He never phoned; I expect to know when you can't work," I said testily. "Why didn't he come with you?"

"He's had to take the car back." Jim offered another short sentence.

"Back where?" I had to poke further.

"Back to Birmingham." Jim was factual but I needed more.

"Look, Jim, I don't want to know his private life, but if I had known he was not coming, I could have found someone else for a day or two."

"They 'ave rumbled him," Jim answered.

I started all the machinery, fearing it would take a little longer to fill the waiting bulk potato lorry. It emerged, little by little, that the new car was supplied because of his 'disability'. Tom had claimed he could not work because of severe back pain and so was receiving disability payment. I was therefore astonished that he had taken a manual job requiring standing at a conveyor belt all day; even more surprised that the employment exchange had recommended him. There was plainly a need to join all the dots for the truth to emerge. In Jim I had the succinct answer: he had been "rumbled". No doubt the authorities had eventually caught up with the deception. We never saw Tom again; Jim signed for his friend's pay that was due up to his absence and continued to turn up alone in his old car.

The potato enterprise had grown and settled after the first dreadful shock of rejections. We still had the odd load that failed but eventually was accepted. The income was reducing our bank overdraft and, equally importantly, giving confidence that the cropping was making the farm viable. I had been used to the ebb and flow of money in and quickly out; that is farming. The challenge had been to build the business from virtually nothing and to know it was moving forwards.

The oilseed rape experiment was even more successful than the yields we had achieved lower down on the estate. I had ploughed a level field that was 840 feet above sea level, where critics had said it was meant to be pasture. After decades of grazing animals, surely it was going to be fertile, but I had not taken soil tests. The seedbed had been perfect and the seed well rolled in. It grew well and responded to the necessary sprays against pollen beetle and light leaf spot. At harvest my contractor combined the crop and I did my best to keep up with carting the rape back to the farm. We were both astounded at the speed the black seed filled the combine tank. The yield passed two tons per acre and was eventually weighed out at 2.30 tons per acre; a vindication for growing the crop and another help to the cash flow.

During the potato marketing in the spring, the large lorries carrying twenty-five-ton loads had difficulty in getting up the slope out of the yard and along the hard track to the main road. Good as most drivers were from a standing start, they had no more than two lengths of the vehicle before pulling around a ninety-degree bend and up a significant slope. They had to select the right gear and, if possible, keep the tri-axle on the unit raised to ensure maximum traction. The yard, and track out, was only stone-hardened and tamped down over the decades. If the powered wheels spun, the lorry would get stuck. It then required very careful reversing and a second attempt made. A further complication was that some makes of truck were much worse than others. I had to warn drivers on their first visit to the farm not to allow wheel spin or the resulting depression would present a further hazard. It would have solved the problem if the entire driveway had had a tarmac surface, something the landlord would not contemplate and I could never afford.

# 40

# Daylight Robbery

In July a van drove into the yard and out stepped a man in a clean white paper boiler suit.

"My men have a load of tarmac that is surplus. Have you any use for it or part of it?" he announced.

"Possibly," I replied cautiously.

I was surprised, having thought he was the 'man from the Ministry' to take a sample or make an inspection. I was wary of such visits; hardly knowing what sample or which Ministry, as they seemingly morphed from one title to another. My mind could hardly take in a white overall and tarmac.

"It's quite genuine, sir. Road standard," he asserted. "Let me just direct the lorry."

With that he turned to his van and produced a walkie-talkie.

"What area were you thinking of, sir?" he asked.

"I may be interested in part of the road being surfaced; it depends on the price and quality." I laid down careful guidelines.

At that moment a lorry, duly sheeted to keep the heat in, came into the yard. I walked up the road to the top of the incline.

"There is a problem with heavy lorries getting up to here," I pointed out. "It would need to start here and go back to the yard as far as possible. How much a yard do you charge?"

"Four pounds a yard, sir," the foreman answered.

"That is out of the question; I'm not interested," I said.

"That's our normal price and it's a professional job."

I was sure it needed tarmac because we had already had problems trying to tow lorries with the addition of a tractor and heavy chain. The question in my mind was, was such an expense mine? I was sure the landlord would say it had been perfectly satisfactory for the previous tenant.

"I will agree to £3.50; that's it," I asserted.

"I will have to ask the boss."

We walked back to the van and his radio device.

"We can do it," he agreed.

"At £3.50?" I insisted.

He had a clipboard in his hand.

"I'll have to get your signature." He offered me a pen. "Name and address please, and write £3.50 in that box," he instructed.

It all seemed a very ordered and professional outfit. The three men who had come with the lorry were set to work by the foreman. I noticed another phone call being made and minutes later a pedestrian roller arrived on a trailer drawn by a pick-up.

I watched the job as it went on apace and the lorry was emptied. The finished job was tidy and not skimped in depth. I walked up the drive, pacing out the yardage. The foreman produced a measuring wheel from his van, checking its accuracy.

"I expect you would like a cheque now." I turned towards the house.

"We don't accept cheques, sir, only cash," the foreman replied.

"How much is it? I asked.

"Watch as I measure it again, sir." He cancelled the clock to zero and pushed it across the road.

"Four yards," he called.

"I mean the length," I said.

"OK." He pushed the wheel to where they had finished laying the tarmac; we both peered at the reading.

"Ninety-six," I read aloud.

"Times four," he added, getting a calculator from his pocket.

"What do you mean, 'times four'?"

"Well, ninety-six times four is 384 yards... times £3.50 is..."

"Wait a minute, we are talking about ninety-six yards." I realised I had shouted.

Two of the men walked over to join us. The foreman produced the contract I had signed.

"It's all down here in the small print," he said.

"It's ninety-six yards of road," I insisted.

"Bill, check this." The worker moved unnecessarily close to squint at the contract.

"That's right, boss, always is." He was a little taller than me and twice as wide.

"It comes to £1,334." The foreman showed me the calculator.

"I would have never have started the job on that basis," I blurted out.

"That's what you signed for." He showed me the paperwork.

The other 'heavy' sauntered across and stood too close to me on my other side.

"I can't afford that," I said flatly.

"It's all legal and agreed," the foreman asserted.

"I haven't got that sort of money in the house." I was getting concerned. "I'll have to give you a cheque."

"The boss said cash." The first heavy gripped my arm.

"He plays rugby," his mate informed me.

"So did I," I insisted. Although true, I realised it was not going to improve the situation.

The foreman intervened. "You'll have to go to the bank and get the money."

Bill had not released his grip. I was in an impossible position, outnumbered and out of touch with the world. This was robbery.

"I'll have to get my cheque book to draw out money," I insisted.

"Bill, you go with him," the foreman directed.

He walked into the office behind me; I took the cheque book out of the drawer and locked the back door as we left. He climbed into the pick-up beside me.

It was a twenty-minute drive to town and I entered into small talk about rugby as if everything were normal. It didn't calm my mind that was racing to find a way out. What could I do to let police or bank staff know a robbery was taking place? I wondered about giving Bill the slip once I parked the vehicle, but how could I be sure he couldn't contact the foreman or indeed any other gang member?

Even if I got home without the money, they could arrive at the farm on any future day and threaten us or steal whatever they fancied. I looked around to see if there was a policeman anywhere; predictably not. Anyway, Bill might have been as fleet of foot as me. I reflected that even prop forwards could run if the goal line was near.

We entered the bank. There were three queues; I opted for the middle one. No escape now; he was right behind me and I noticed the occasional touch of his arm or clothing. He had watched me complete the cheque book before we had joined the queue; could I now hold the book, refusing to let it go as the clerk tried to pull it under the glass screen? Perhaps I could mouth "No!" without anyone else seeing.

"This is a large amount, Mr Jennings. Are you sure you want to withdraw it as cash?"

I wanted to say, "No," but at that moment Bill's foot accidentally kicked my heel. I simply nodded to the clerk. He counted the notes very deliberately.

"Do you mind a few fifties?"

I wanted to say I minded every one of the notes, but simply stared at the enormity of the £1,350 being counted out.

Back in the pick-up I took sixteen pounds from the bag and put it into my pocket. The bag itself I put in the recess beside the steering column, in view of us both. My fate was sealed; I could not imagine any way of reducing the payment or negotiating a discount. I handed the bundles of notes to the foreman keeping the cloth bank bag. He counted every note. The lorry had gone and Bill settled himself in the foreman's van. I just watched them drive over the new tarmac and away. I went into the house and made a cup of tea. What could I tell Rosalind? I felt such a fool; I had expected to pay for the job but not such an amount, and how foolish not to have noticed the small print. Why didn't I have the courage to blurt out, "It's daylight robbery"? I thought of phoning the police but had not even noted the vehicle's number plate; anyway, the only paperwork that existed had my signature on it. I was totally deflated and found I was shaking.

I could not even tell Rosalind. I couldn't lie but hoped she would never ask what it cost. (Dear Reader, you are the only one who has ever heard of this event.) I went out to examine the new road surface as Rosalind came down the drive.

"Don't drive over it!" I held my hand up in a mock expression of danger. She stopped and got out.

"What's happened here?" She smiled. "It's wonderful."

"A lorry load simply turned up," I said.

"Where from?"

"It was just surplus to a job," I answered.

"Well, it is just what you needed, isn't it? That's lucky." She went in to start cooking.

I walked over the new acquisition, at least pleased with the appearance. No doubt there would soon be some lorries that would test it.

Although Rosalind never questioned the road surfacing, I had great feelings of guilt. I saw my own foolishness in not suspecting the deception, not asking how the tarmac became 'surplus'. I fell for the professionalism of the foreman; the list went on. The greatest guilt was that the Lord had provided money when really needed and I had suddenly squandered a great sum. I carried a concern that the tarmac men might return and cause even more problems, stealing bits of equipment by offering derisory sums and pressurising me into agreement. It occurred to me then that the sum was so near to the potential loss of £1,400 that the four first loads of potatoes had cost in haulage. In that case, the Lord had taught me to have faith; He had agreed that I should farm until retirement and affirmed that by not only selling the rejected loads but every one with a quality bonus.

This tarmac event has stayed with me and I now view it as His provision. Undoubtedly it was needed in order to continue growing potatoes; there was no alternative exit from the yard except up that road. Never did a lorry fail to get away with a full load thereafter. Never did a pothole appear. As I look back twenty-five years later, I do not believe anyone has ever had to resurface it. I suffered no injury except to my pride. In hindsight, even the expense of the job did not adversely affect the performance of the farm; it could even be said that it enhanced it.

It was plain that the potatoes were the big money earners, providing the right quality was achieved. Consistently getting the best results was not only down to crop husbandry but controlled winter storage. This would require a new building and that would be expensive. The question of finance was rearing its head again. I had fields that would allow fifty acres of potatoes on the 250-acre farm but only on a tight rotation of every fourth year rather than every fifth year in the rotation. I resolved to go for it but I knew the costliness of buildings. Clear thoughts surfaced as I fed sheep at pasture. The world slowed down as I walked around them. In the pastoral peace away from the yard, buildings and business, I wondered if I could buy a sort of kit and do the building myself. I would need some help from David, but could manage the site preparation with the big bucket. The asbestos cladding might require outside help but it was worth trying to build it ourselves.

The site was reasonably level and I soon skimmed off the grass, coming to a clay subsoil. The next necessity was to peg out the corners of the shed, making certain it was absolutely square and level. I took great pains to establish the desired 'finished floor level' guided by the adjacent store which we had adapted and used for potatoes. The two stores would be side by side. I had no theodolite[53], only a fifty-yard tape and a spirit level. Guided by the adjacent shed, I started with a straight line and accurately marked the position of the end stanchions[54], measuring from centre to centre. To get the opposing corners square, I originally used binder twine from corner to corner. The strings were knotted at exactly the same length, forming a giant 'X' over the floor area. By constantly adjusting the pegs at the approximate site of the far columns, I found the precise square. This was confirmed by the tape measurements becoming equal on the diagonals. It was not the quickest method, and no doubt ridiculed by the experts as a "farmer's bodge", but it worked.

The footings for the columns were dug and ready to be filled with concrete as per the plan. We had to make a plywood template with four holes drilled in it to replicate the foot of the column. This was to accurately position the six long bolts that would finally secure the column. The bolts, head down, each had a small plastic pocket around them and dangled downward from our plywood template. With the template exactly where the foot of the column would be, we poured concrete around the polythene pockets. A day later, when that was set, the polythene pocket was burned away, leaving a void. This was filled with very wet grout to exactly 'finished floor level'.

This was the defining moment; the foundations of the portal frame were in place with six bolts at every bay protruding through the concrete. I had to trust the meticulous measuring was accurate and that the holes in the flange plate of the column would drop over the bolts. I left everything for three days to make

---

[53]  surveying instrument
[54]  columns

sure the concrete had cured. David helped me to bolt the roof truss to the top of the column as we had decided it was safer to raise the right-angled structure together rather than just the column by itself. The forklift came into its own; one fork under the arm of the right angle and the other close to within three inches of the outside face of the column. A heavy chain secured it all to the forklift's backplate. Slowly and with great care, I gently raised the forklift. It was just clear of the ground. I moved it forward by extending the boom. David had his hand doing little more than resting on the steel upright, to be aware of any slippage. If he sensed any movement he could immediately signal me to stop and lower it four inches back down to the ground.

The procedure was slow but safe, moving inches towards the six bolts protruding from the footings. The forklift had all the weight and it was easy to poke the bolts by hand with a spanner to enter each hole into the column flange. The structure still being held by the forklift, David threaded the nuts onto the bolts and made them finger-tight. The first column was up and reaching into thin air; that would become the apex of the roof. Flushed with this success we quickly moved to repeat the operation with its opposite number which would form the other corner of the shed. Soon we had it up and secured. I put the big bucket on the forklift and raised David up high to thread the bolts through the two flanges meeting at the apex.

"The bolts don't reach," David shouted down.

"What do you mean, don't reach?" I called back.

"They are not long enough," he replied.

"They are the right ones; there are no others," I asserted.

"The flanges don't meet."

I got down from the forklift and looked up; there was a gap of at least four inches.

"They should be touching each other." I was incredulous, voicing the obvious.

I lowered David down to the ground, letting him climb out of the bucket. We stared at the gap.

"If we slackened the bolts on the columns..." David hesitated. We both knew that was not the answer.

"The measurements must be wrong," I assumed, with an air of utter defeat.

We measured it with the tape; they were exact.

David went home and I went down to the sheep. I leaned on the gate. The sheep did not notice me; all was well in their world. It was often the way; I was by myself. They were engrossed in living, which for them was very largely eating or chewing the cud. I was trying a more complicated style: eating when I had to and not chewing the cud. By that I mean thinking, devising, trying new things, getting life half-right. They were content within their own boundary; competing for a tasty few leaves but flocking together when anxious, then resuming their feeding and ruminating. As I looked over the contented scene, I wondered if I had got it all wrong. Mankind chases all day long only to sleep and in the morning continue to chase again. I thought of the Bible verse, "But godliness with contentment is great gain. For we brought nothing into this world and it is certain we can carry nothing out of it." (1 Timothy 6:6-7)

It came to me that I should ask my son-in-law, John; he was used to buildings. He promised to come at the weekend.

I was still despondent as he and I stood in the middle of the site, the meagre single sheet of an A4 plan in hand.

"There are six twenty-foot bays and I have measured it so carefully," I explained.

"Let's run the tape over it again," he said. I agreed in silence, having done it several times. We checked each footing down the length, twenty feet centre to centre.

"That's OK," John said. "Now across."

We measured again.

"That's out," he announced.

"I know; that's the problem!" I replied.

"It's sixty feet, four inches," John confirmed.

"I made it sixty feet exactly," I claimed.

He walked over to me; I was still holding the tape.

"Where did you measure from?" John asked.

"The centre of the column," I replied.

He then explained to me that measurements are always taken centre to centre down the building's length, but outside dimensions are taken across the width.

I looked at him in amazement. "How daft is that? How am I supposed to know that?" I was flabbergasted. More than that, all my careful measurements were to no avail. "Whatever can we do now?" I asked.

John examined the bottom of the column.

"We will have to move it in and across on both sides, using just four bolts and not the original six that we had made holes for."

"Will that be safe?" I enquired.

"Yes, it will all be bolted together as one unit and, with the sheeting and roofing tight, it will be fine," John assured me.

We spent the rest of the day undoing the columns and moving them two inches closer. Then we erected the next bay and installed the roof purlins between the trusses. This, John assured me, would make it absolutely safe, whatever the wind overnight. The bolts were tightened with spanners but not too tightly. Final tightening would be achieved at the end of erection, which David and I could complete without John's help. All was saved; I could breathe again, I had learned from the expert. John was amazed that the measurements were what I intended and that the building was truly square. I was duly humbled.

The portal frame now completed successfully, David and I did the asbestos roofing and side sheeting down to seven feet from finished floor level. We managed this using the Manitou forklift with its extending boom and ladders. We could work using the large bucket as a platform, getting to it from a ladder tied against the boom if more convenient. There was a rush to complete the new store before the potato harvest. Moss, my sheepdog, was getting less exercise. He had always associated me with machines ever since I had brought him to the farm in the pick-up. He now took delight in sitting on the driver's seat whenever I was not doing so myself. This was useful at times, especially if he was running loose; I only had to start the engine and he would come racing to me. Moss's ownership of the Manitou seat was fine for several months before we discovered a downside.

# 41

# The Farmer's Wife

The role, I should say *relationship*, of a farmer's wife is so important that it could cover many chapters, if not a whole book. Here I have to restrict myself to just an extended chapter but at least demonstrating Rosalind's involvement in almost every aspect of the business; the downsides and justifiably the upsides.

Almost by definition a farmer's wife is his shadow; at least, that is how it was in our relationship. I can think of no greater compliment and little point in trying to itemise specific tasks. To be a shadow implies total 'togetherness' in body and mind, unanimous in passage and purpose.

She brought us tea, placing the mugs on the Manitou floor whilst Moss was 'driving'. In a flash he bit her hand and drew blood, not to mention a scream. I came straight down the ladder to the scene.

"He bit me." Her hand was shaking. "I only put the tea on the floor; I didn't climb on the step." She was crying with shock.

I admonished the dog and tied him to his kennel. Then I returned to examine her hand. Fortunately the shock proved worse than the injury.

A couple of days later I was under the Manitou adjusting some cables with Moss at my side, when Rosalind kindly appeared again with tea, which she placed on the floor of the machine. In an instant, Moss leaped up the step, biting her as she let go of the mugs. I shouted at the dog and banged my head as I extricated myself. I felt Moss's collar and he was still chained to his kennel. This was bad news; he had turned into a biter for no apparent reason except being totally possessive of me or my machine. I remembered my first introduction to him had been the four-year-old girl telling me, "He has bitten my sister." At that moment the estate gamekeeper came through the yard on his quad bike and I told him what had happened. I asked if he knew anyone who might want such a dog. Surprisingly he said yes and he would come for him the next day.

I was now in urgent need of a new sheepdog, so Rosalind scoured the papers. Perhaps she felt, although the innocent party, the desperate need of a replacement for the sake of the farm.

"Do you think we ought to have two dogs?" she asked after dinner, her head still in the small ads.

"Find one for now and see how he or she performs," I reacted quickly. "If that one goes well, the same breeder may have another," I added thoughtfully.

She ended her searches with one phone number, which I readily used. It was a farmer whom I didn't know some twenty-five miles away, but I asked if I could see the dog as soon as possible.

"Come tomorrow if you like." He was brief and to the point. I took directions and agreed to go over at 10 am the next day.

The dog was chained up to his kennel, as is usual with farm sheepdogs. I bent down to make friends with him.

"Is he a good worker?" I asked.

"Yes, he can do the job. I'll put him round the sheep in the field behind you," he offered.

The dog did not need any encouragement and at a word was away along the hedge although I could see no sheep. In a minute about forty ewes appeared over the rise coming at fair speed towards us. Another command and the dog lay down behind them.

"Well, that wasn't bad," I said, not wanting to raise the price of the dog too much.

"I told you he'll do the job for you," he said.

"Did you breed him yourself?" I enquired.

"I don't go in for that," he said briskly.

"It's just I see his markings are not the usual collie," I observed.

"Do you want the dog?"

I wondered what had triggered the sharp tone.

"Is there something wrong with him?" I asked.

"He does wander off," the farmer admitted, "but he does a good job."

A doubt was creeping into my mind.

"We haven't talked about price," I suggested.

"Nothing!" came the sharp reply.

"What do you mean, nothing?" I was getting unsettled.

"Look, I told you, he goes off. Do you want him or not? I don't want anything; take the b***** dog," he insisted.

In spite of his aggression, or perhaps because of it, I said I would take the dog.

"What's his name?" I thought to enquire.

"Russ... Russell."

"Thank you. One more thing, just tell me the magic words you use for left and right."

"Away and bye," he said, effectively terminating our conversation.

I lowered the pick-up tailgate and Russ regarded it as an invitation to jump up. I clipped his collar to the static lead fixed to the headboard and we were off.

I drove home wondering if I had done the right thing. Russ had obviously been a problem but he had collected the ewes in fine fashion. It crossed my mind that he may have been mistreated, but he didn't seem afraid or nervous. The next thought was, why wouldn't the farmer take any payment? It was a contradiction in terms: 'farmer' and 'free'. I thought of some generous farmers in my experience and the great help they had often given me, but also the odd one who had wanted payment for the smallest item. I chose to look at the positives: here was a dog that gathered sheep as well as any, and I was desperate to find such a helper; plus the bonus, I hoped, was something for nothing.

I drove up the farm road stopping at our first field, unclipped Russ and issued the magic word, "Away." He did just that, shot away as he had done earlier; minutes later all the ewes came up to me standing in the gateway. It was a perfect demonstration. Although I had seen him do the same for his last owner, I was so relieved and happy that Russ had done it for me. We had only met each other an hour or so previously; he had not even travelled in the cab with me. I was amazed; he stood in the gateway of a strange field with an unknown man and a voice he had never heard. My voice was new to him, so surely I could expect him to obey other male voices. This was immediately important as we were about to go to relatives for New Year, having always worked over Christmas. My friend John, who worked on another farm, had agreed to feed and check the sheep for three days. As it turned out, Russ worked for him too.

Russ was assigned Moss's oil drum kennel and was attached by a long chain which he took to immediately. The next morning I found him in his barrel lying on the cold metal with all the sacks meant to be used as bedding pushed in front as a doormat. I took the hint and found three fresh sacks and burned the old ones. For all his rough and ready experiences, he obviously wasn't going to have another dog's old blankets. He was crossbred with mostly a thick white coat and a few black patches. Half his nose and one ear were black and three large black patches were distributed randomly over his back-end. It seemed to reflect his nature; rough and ready, his own character and proud of it. We had an immediate rapport. Russ settled in and took to running ahead of me round the yards creating that gap in his wake sufficient for me to shake the sheep nuts for the ewes to find at their leisure. I was careful to tie him up whenever we were not working, and he never wandered off. Around the sheep he was fast but not too close; obeying three simple commands, including "lie down". What more could I ask? Rosalind loved him but, like all our sheepdogs, he never came into the house.

It was about April and we had finished the lambing except for about ten 'tail-enders' left in the yard. By this time, I was starting in the mornings, visiting and feeding those in the fields with their lambs, with Russ keeping close to my heels and riding as usual in the pick-up. I simply fed the few in the yard and went to tie up Russ. *He was gone.* He had been around my heels; maybe he had chosen to sit in his kennel as he did when I went in for breakfast. He was not there. I called, and walked around the yard and buildings.

"The dog has gone!" I announced as I strode into the kitchen.

"He can't be far," Rosalind offered.

After a quick breakfast I walked around the yard calling again… There was no sign of him. Of course, this is what had frustrated his previous owner. He was a wanderer, but where had he gone?

I phoned three of our neighbouring farmers; they had not seen him. I was getting worried and drove to the sheep in every other field I thought he might be in. I returned to the farm office just as the phone was ringing.

"I think we have your dog here."

My relief was palpable.

"I got your phone number from his collar disc," the lady continued. "He has been walking around our stables."

"Where are you?" I asked.

She mentioned a house and stables near a wood I was not aware of.

"Thank you so much. I will pick him up straight away. We are at Woodhead."

I was about to jump into the pick-up when I ran back to find a bottle of wine. Surely that would be an appropriate 'thank you'.

It was over two miles by road and I found him chained to a post in their small yard. I thanked the lady and presented the bottle to her.

"There is no need for that!" she protested as she received it. "He is lovely and friendly," she added.

Russ was ready to jump up into the pick-up as if he had been waiting for transport. All was forgiven and our relationship restored.

It was some three months before Russ went missing again. This time I had not noticed and was only alerted by the same horse lady phoning to say he was with her. I had to repeat the humbling process and went off to collect him.

"We have a bitch on heat; that must be the attraction," she volunteered.

"I am so sorry; I will tie him up as soon as work is finished."

The third occasion I was annoyed and phoned the stables as soon as I missed him. I arrived in the stable yard to see him chained and lying down as if tired of waiting; I fancied his expression was, "What kept you this time?" I offered profuse apologies and a bottle of wine. That evening we decided he must see the vet and be castrated.

The day came and I left Russ at the vet's, collecting him at teatime.

"He's fine, just needs rest. A model patient," the vet assured me.

He was very sleepy and I had to lay him on the front seat and drive back carefully. He had a lampshade to stop any licking of the wound and was feeling sorry for himself.

"He can't be left outside in that oil drum." Rosalind was ever the nurse; in fact, she sounded like matron. Russ spent the night quietly on a blanket in the kitchen. In the morning he could stand but preferred to lie, looking at us with doleful eyes whilst breakfasting. Rosalind moved his blanket under the table in the corner, saying he needed more time to recuperate.

Russ thought differently and later disappeared.

"I thought we had lost him," Rosalind told me. "I came to find you, but he was in his kennel. I don't know how he got in with his lampshade on." She looked perplexed.

"It's a good sign. He wanted to be home; he's never been in the kitchen before," I said.

"You are hard on him." Rosalind was in nursing mode.

"Animals are animals; we love them and respect them but they are in their natural element outside." I sounded harsh.

"Well, I am pleased he is happy," she concluded.

Russ soon recovered and was working the sheep again with his old vigour. I thought of his exploits and was glad he would now stop his wandering; at least I hoped so. It occurred to me that he had always disappeared at the same time of day. He had done his work around the yard, helping me feed sheep, and then in a flash disappeared. Looking back, he was always so near me at that time, almost under my feet, and then gone. No doubt nature was calling him but I realised he was kissing me goodbye. His nearness was saying, "I have done my bit; now I'm off." In fact, he seemed to know I would always go and collect him; he never wandered to anywhere else.

# 42

# Accidents Happen

The new potato store was finished including the concrete floor; only the sliding doors were needed for completion. I was relieved that even if they had to be fitted in September or October, the crop face could be sheeted from any frost. Cereal harvest was about to start and the potatoes were needing fortnightly blight sprays. The sheep had all been dipped a month after shearing and the farm was buzzing. We had time for a day off in Ledbury with the girls before the rush of harvest. The day was fine; the girls had fun around the castle and the freedom of a family together, a rare event. Although I enjoyed it, my arm was aching, which I put down to the fact that it was resting from work and finding it an unusual experience. I had learned to ignore aches and pains in the pressure of getting jobs done and it only catches up with you when you stop and have the time to think about it. Twenty-four hours later, however, I pointed out to Rosalind that my lower arm was quite red.

"If it is no better tomorrow, you must see the doctor," she suggested.

I was spraying potatoes the next day, but she came to see me before she went to her surgery.

"Let me see your arm." She undid my shirt sleeve. "It's red the other side of your elbow now; I'm going to make an appointment for you." It was obviously an order.

"OK, I've just got to finish spraying this field and I will come after that."

I sprayed another tankful and realised I would only just catch the end of the morning surgery.

I showed the doctor my arm.

"Have you cut yourself?" he asked, looking at a well-worn arm with various scrapes and blemishes.

"I don't think so, not really. A bit of a nick dipping sheep maybe," I replied.

He called his partner in from the next room. He rolled my sleeve up further; I knew it was redder than yesterday. With only a nod to each other, my doctor said, "You must go to the hospital now, *today*. The receptionist will book you in right away. Just walk straight to the hospital reception; they will be expecting you. By the way, take a night bag; they will probable keep you in." The doctor turned back to his desk.

Back at the farm I climbed on the tractor and continued the blight spraying. I finished the field but was concerned about the 'night bag'. If they were to keep me in, it might be two nights, and I had too much to do on the farm. My immediate concern was to finish the spraying; that didn't want to wait a single day. I decided to do the next field; at least the potatoes would be safe from blight for another fourteen days. I continued all afternoon and was just completing the last field when Rosalind came driving up to the field.

"I just got home and the phone was ringing." She was agitated. I was wondering what was so urgent.

"It was the hospital; they want to know where you are," she gasped.

"I had to finish the potatoes," I justified.

"I didn't even know you were going to hospital; you never phoned me at the surgery."

"Sorry, I thought…"

"You didn't think at all," she admonished me before I could think of an excuse. "Don't you know this is serious?" she shouted.

"Tell them I am coming, and please pack a few things because I'll be there overnight."

I didn't hear her reply which was probably a mercy.

I immediately continued up the rough track back to the yard but had not quite reached the gate when there was a loud clatter of metal behind me. The whole spray boom assembly had dropped back. It was worse than I thought; the framework holding the boom assembly to the tank had fatigued apart and was dragging on the ground. I couldn't even drive the tractor home. Immediately I knew I would have to leave it all there and so ran back to the house. Rosalind drove me to the hospital.

The first examination was a reality check. I couldn't get my shirt off, nor could the medics; they cut it off my arm. I was hooked up to an intravenous drip and spent a sleepless hospital night. The next morning I was able to use my mobile phone to ask David to retrieve the tractor and sprayer and to stand by for harvest. Although not in pain, I felt in chains. What a stupid time to be in hospital; added to which it was brilliantly sunny and harvest would be only days away. I could get out of bed and sit in a chair, provided I took care of my 'coat stand' with the inverted plastic bottle of antibiotics. I soon found it was permissible to move to a restroom or even through the open fire exit door to a grassy patch. Appealing as it might have been, the downside was that the nurses came there for a relaxing smoke as it was technically outside the ward.

My real concern was the feeling of imprisonment away from the harvest. After the first day, I found I could extend my horizons as long as I had one hand on the 'coat stand' and wheeled it with an appearance of needing to travel somewhere. I chatted to other patients, who were invariably more ill than I, and it gave me very limited exercise. By the third day, I had hit on the idea that I could avoid taking up precious hospital bed space by having the 'coat stand' at home supervised by a fully qualified nurse, namely my wife. Matron did not agree.

After a week, feeling as well as I could remember, and guilty for it, I was desperate to get out. Rosalind visited in the evenings, which was like an oasis. She brought refreshment for any deficiency in hospital catering and good cheer, not least the progress of the combine. The contractor had started cutting the barley and David was running the trailer loads back to store. Rosalind also started the education process of teaching an ignorant farmer that my condition had caused real concern. Septicaemia was very serious and I could not leap straight back into work, harvesting or not. I was later taken further to task by a senior nurse in the church who thought I had been cavalier to the point of stupidity. Although I couldn't claim I had never been stupid, I did not feel I had gone out of my way to contract it.

My sojourn in hospital had taught me that nobody is indispensable, even during harvest. I had learned this in management lectures and even told others that the world carries on if the prime minister dies. I reasoned that on a restricted capitalisation of the farm business, at least I was saving a man's wages, provided my physical labour did not inhibit good management. Besides, I enjoyed the physical involvement and the joy of seeing it through to completion; a satisfaction few factory workers can experience. I returned home weak but able to manage operations, if only from the office.

A few decades ago some urban dwellers looked on farming, by its very nature, as slow. The image was stereotyped as leaning on a gate waiting for something to happen. The advent of country holidays, tourism and the recent rash of television programmes has largely corrected that myth. Since I left London and lived and worked in the industry, I have only known it as dynamic. There is constant change, activity, progress, mixed with excitement and disappointment. When dealing with animals and the elements, plus birth, growth and renewal or death, it is dynamic. It is this quality that has kept my interest, even fascination. I have no regrets but a profound gratitude for the privilege of being involved in agriculture. Every day is full of incidents, large or small, good or bad. Just as things seem normal and the farm is running as expected, something happens.

Routine shepherding may seem slow to the urban dweller; a question of moving along at nature's pace, having time to ruminate, even the occasional doze in a field of hay on a summer day. I doubt it was ever thus but modern sheep farming is a succession of major operations organised to deal with large numbers as efficiently as possible. We are conscious of animal health and do our best to treat problems whenever we confine them for worming or when drafting[55],

---

[55] selected out of the flock to move to better grazing, usually on another farm

taking the opportunity to treat fly-strike or foot-rot. It is easy to see and catch a lame ewe in the collecting pen and pare the infected foot.

One such day, I was on my own but could not let the ewe go untreated. I collected a paring knife and violet antiseptic aerosol from the vet cupboard. I cut out the foul tissue and went to spray the foot. The aerosol nozzle was gummed up. I tried another can but it was the same. I could not leave the foot untreated and thought it would be worth ten minutes cleaning the nozzles, as the vet had advised, in warm water. In the kitchen I filled an old saucepan and quickly rubbed them with water. The cold water didn't help, so reluctantly I popped the saucepan on the Rayburn to warm gently. The phone rang; I was beginning to wish I had never started the job. I dried my hands and went to answer the phone in the next room. I was just about to lift the receiver, saying I would phone back, when there was an explosion of such magnitude that I froze. The noise was deafening followed by complete silence. I realised it must have been the aerosol. I hesitated to even peer around the kitchen door; surely the whole window would have blown out. I knelt down and pushed the door in case the second canister had not yet exploded. Miraculously, the window was still in place and the glass not even cracked.

The saucepan was teetering on the edge of the cooker and the walls and ceiling were violet. In fact, everything was violet: worktop, utensils, china, even the clothes on the ceiling airer. There was no sign of the aerosol canisters. I rushed back and released the sheep into the yard; this was going to be a long job. I started by finding all the rags I could muster. The worktop was the first to be cleared; I piled as much crockery as possible into the sink. The worktop cleaned easily with soapy hot water, which was a relief. I then noticed tin fragments the size of confetti; there was nothing bigger than a postage stamp. I thought for a moment of what might have happened if the phone had not rung. I was duly humbled; my stupidity was unbelievable, but the vet had suggested the 'helpful tip'; I had had no intention of getting the water hot. There was no time to wonder further; this had to be cleaned before my wife arrived home. I washed the china and utensils, but the walls, floor and ceiling were still more violet than white. Sheep and any work outside were cancelled; this was the priority.

Efforts to clean the walls or ceiling only changed the violet hue from vivid to a slightly less vivid. I knew Rosalind would be in no mood to discuss shades of damage; I would have to repaint the kitchen. I started on the ceiling with the emulsion we had. It barely did more than register good intention; at least it was a shade paler than the walls. I heard her car come into the yard and thought it best to meet her at the door.

"I'm painting the kitchen," I heard myself saying.

"What for? I thought you were doing sheep today?" was her astonished reply.

"Well, there's been a bit of an accident." I felt like a guilty schoolboy marching behind her to the scene of the crime. Fortunately, she was speechless, unable to recognise the room she had left that morning.

"The foot spray exploded," I explained. "This is just the first coat."

"You heated it up in the saucepan? You must be mad!" She was obviously a detective.

"I know; I only went to pick up the phone and *bang* in no time at all." That was succinct but hardly good enough. "I'll do at least two coats and maybe three," I offered.

"I'll leave you to it; I'm getting fish and chips." She turned and left.

Accidents happen so quickly; some we understand, others remain a mystery. Life on a farm is never dull or merely pastoral.

Rosalind had lost her cat, Thistle, who had disappeared for more than the usual twenty-four hours. He lived outside as a matter of preference and a predilection for mice. We had missed him coming on walks, although our walking around the farm together had been occasional. When we did find time for a walk, we never looked for the cat to accompany us. It was Thistle's constant oversight of his domain that he noticed us. We gave up looking for or calling him, and it was unlikely he would be found by distant neighbours a mile or more in any direction from us. The likely conclusion was he had met a sticky end, either run over or lost the battle with a fox.

When we did have time for a walk it was often in the direction of the beef cattle, who rarely had need of treatment in the farmyard; hence Rosalind was not acquainted with them. As the business grew, it needed trimming to keep viable. I thought of introducing store cattle as potentially more profitable than sheep. It would be an extra enterprise based on utilising grass and subject to rather different market forces than lamb production. I asked Henry, my friendly dealer, to find some suitable stores. The vogue for producing beef was Simmental crossed with other beef breeds and he soon delivered a dozen that looked promising. It did mean we had to check fences, making sure they were of sufficient height and had no weak places. It fitted in well with pasture management as they required four to seven inches of grass leaf whereas sheep thrive on two to four inches.

The enterprise essentially hung on buying and selling store animals at the right price. Occasionally some of the bunch were sold as fat (I prefer the term 'prime') straight for slaughter. At other times the auction price at market was greater for the animals that had "more growth in them". This was when buyers in late spring had grass they were desperate to utilise rather than conserve, and judged they could put a hundredweight or so of extra flesh on them, so turning a profit. The year and the seasons moved relentlessly on from harvesting both corn and potatoes. The autumn beef stores had settled in, and I could do the smaller jobs that are always pushed out by the major weather-dependent operations.

I was anxious to improve the pole barn where we had graded the potatoes. It was a simple tin-roofed shed held up by eight telegraph poles. There was only a single row of sheeting on the weather-side and an earth floor. Originally used for storing straw bales, we had used it as a sheltered working area when grading potatoes both to and from storage. I loaded some remaining straw bales into the forklift bucket and took them up to our main Dutch barn. I was offloading the bucket – and there was Thistle, asleep. It was one of those notable moments that makes the day. I bent down; Thistle was dead. It looked for all the world as if he were sleeping, but after six months of absence there he was. It was unbelievable; four legs stretched out, head gazing across the yard as if sunbathing, his body and fur unmarked as if the sun had only just set. There he was, somehow passed into the 'Great Cattery in the Sky' and dry as a chip. Rosalind was pleased to know the cat's end was apparently so peaceful and preserved as well as any taxidermist could. We buried him in the garden.

The next day I ordered a load of scalpings and proceeded to rake and level them to make a floor in the tin barn. It would enable the grading equipment to stand level and be easily moved and adjusted. I needed to roll down the surface, making it almost like concrete. I had been alone on the farm all day but the job now only needed a pedestrian vibrating roller to finish it off. I drove to town to hire the roller. The only machine available had just come out of the repair shop and the engineer had difficulty in starting the engine. After several swings of the starting handle, the diesel engine fired up, and he quickly steered it up their ramp onto my low car trailer. He said, "Now it's had a run, it should start easily again."

Back at the farm twelve minutes later, it would not start. This was annoying as there were only a couple of hours of daylight left. I could not start the machine even to drive it off the trailer. I had everything in place; the trailer was only two feet high and the loading ramps were in place to get it down to ground level. I tried again and again; then it fired. I walked backwards to the ramp boards but it just dislodged one of them as it left the trailer. I was standing on the ground, my feet each side of the two boards, gripping the roller steering handle. It was suddenly an emergency. The roller had passed the point of no return. I had to use every ounce of strength to keep the roller on the remaining ramp which was only half the width of the roller. It was coming down; I gripped the handle bars. It was six inches from the ground, still coming; it would not fall now, but I took another step backward gripping hard. The roller came onto the ground.

In an instant the roller itself stopped moving, but the inertia of the handles took my hands to the ground. I had touched my toes at lightning speed, still gripping the handle. *Crack!* Something snapped. I flicked the roller engine off. I was in real pain; I knew this was serious. I hopped to the side of the pick-up, now gripping the side to support myself. I could not walk. I could not bear weight on my right leg. I clung there, feeling the back of my thigh swelling. "I cannot have broken my leg," I reasoned. "I must stand still until the pain passes."

I gradually opened my eyes. "What am I looking at?" I wondered. It looked like the roof of the shed, the underside of the corrugated roof sheets. It was as if I was talking to myself. I realised I was lying down with my back to the floor. Why would I want to look at the roof? I looked down to my feet; the pick-up was about five feet away and I was flat on my back. I couldn't move at all without impossible pain. I needed help. The light in the shed was on; it was dark outside. The passenger door of the pick-up was open; why was that? I was lying just inside the open double doors. I remembered I had tossed my phone onto the bench seat of the pick-up in order not to damage it whilst working. I tried to move again; I could only shuffle on my back providing I didn't attempt to sit up. I thought Rosalind must be home by now. She would never think of looking for me. I shouted for help, at the same time knowing nobody would hear me.

I would try to reach the phone. I shuffled to the open door of the pick-up. Still on my back I reached to feel the phone; there was no way I could reach more than six inches across the passenger seat. I felt a hammer handle. My mind was working overtime. I tried to use the hammer to reach further. The phone was there somewhere. I felt the hammer encounter an object; I knew it must be my phone and carefully edged it nearer. I left the hammer and grasped the phone.

I phoned the house; there was an agonising wait. Surely she was there?

"I've had a bit of an accident." I didn't want to frighten her but she detected the urgency in my voice.

"Where are you?"

"In the potato shed on the floor." The phone went dead.

At least my only lifeline had held. I knew I was totally helpless; at least she would get help. Rosalind came running.

"What's happened?

"I can't move." I wasn't interested in trying to explain anything. "It's my leg."

"Have you broken it?" she asked.

"No, I've torn something, I think," I stammered.

"I'll be right back," she called out as she ran for the house.

It seemed an age but could only have been about five minutes before Rosalind returned breathless and with a blanket.

"The doctor is coming." She covered me up and, kneeling, hugged my head against hers. There were no more questions but I could feel silent tears.

It could only have been ten minutes and a car roared into the yard. The doctor could see the lights and drove up to the shed. He did some quick tests and found that I was very cold. Returning to his car he came back with a silver foil sheet.

"What happened?" he asked.

I explained all the unloading actions and the 'pike dive' that my body was forced into. He gently felt the underside of my thigh, causing me to scream.

"I'm sorry; it is tender."

He seemed surprised. He got up and phoned for an ambulance.

"I going to give you some morphine; it may make you feel a little sick but will ease the pain."

I was grateful for any help.

"I'm just glad you came so quickly," I said.

"I shut the surgery, knowing the Wellingtons were always in the car." He smiled as we waited. "Rosalind sounded urgent. It didn't need much comprehension. When a call comes from a farmer, it is always serious... especially when his wife is an SRN," the doctor added.

"I'm sorry to get you out like this," I apologised.

The ambulance took twenty-five minutes and I was feeling cold, but I was pleased Dr Grey stayed with us. The crew discussed getting me from a lying position onto a chair or stretcher. I had to insist I couldn't sit upright. They came back into the shed with a full-sized trolley stretcher, and with one lifting under my arms, the other did so under my lower legs. The sudden pain was worse than at the time of the accident. My involuntary scream was enough to wake the dead.

Rosalind was told to collect a night bag and make her own way to the hospital. My journey seemed to take forever; there was no rush or siren, and I felt as if I could be sick at any time.

At the hospital the staff did not seem to understand that I had not broken my leg, but I was so relieved that I was in a bed and lying down. Their concern was more for the considerable bump on my forehead which must have occurred as I passed out and fell to the ground. On account of this, a nurse shone a torch in my eyes several times during the night to examine my pupils. My concern was solely my leg. It appeared there was little they could do in hospital, and after four days I was walking with crutches. The final diagnosis was that my hamstring had torn to such an extent that the immediate and large internal bleeding had led to me passing out. I was now back home and resigned myself to a gradual mending providing I took care. It could have been worse.

My farming journey could only have been fully achieved in partnership with my wife. Without her it would have been lonelier and less productive. It started in my last year of managing on the estate. She had arrived in Shropshire because she alighted from the train there. She had decided for a complete break from hospital life in London and reversed Dick Whittington's itinerary. Rosalind never told me why she collected her two suitcases and got off the train there; she had never visited that station previously. In fact, she had no relatives, friends or any connections with the small town. I have often wondered if the rural countryside had appealed or if she was just tired of the journey; her only comment was that it seemed "OK". This begged more questions than it answered but the reasons why never seemed important; I am glad that she did get off there.

Although we knew each other informally from the doctor's surgery, we had actually met through a dating agency, the sort before computers, where interested parties wrote letters. After being matched as possibly compatible, dependent on how we answered the initial questionnaire, it was up to us to make the running. We both found that much could be discovered from a letter but even more at our first tentative meeting. Our common Christian faith was a great platform, honed by life's knocks and abrasions; we were confident and yet incomplete. We came to believe we needed each other. Rosalind was prepared to launch into a completely new field (pun intended) and I could see her many qualities. These were of course not related to the physical labour of farming but the more important partnership role of supporting the farmer. This she accomplished with great insight and caring.

The first blessing was decluttering the large farmhouse, making a dwelling more like a home; the subtleties of things in their right place, rather than heaps often in many places. Office items, such as invoices and seed catalogues, found they were trapped there. Small hand tools, such as moisture meter, penknives and shepherd's crook, disappeared from kitchen to workshop. Following this logic, I was somewhat surprised to find my evening armchair, which fitted me perfectly for watching television or sleeping, also turned up in the workshop. Apparently, it was "a disgrace" and, although the office and workshop were part of a large extension, it should really have been burned.

The other notable and welcome change was the daily routine that arrived with my wife. There was a common start time to the day whether she was working at the surgery or not; in each case breakfast was laid and prepared for. Of necessity the timing of the first meal of the day was up to me. Lunch and dinner were fixed at one o'clock and six o'clock respectively. This would assist catering and be a known time when phone calls could not be received. Rosalind did not strike people as a perfectionist or a 'matron', but her order helped my life considerably. It was a sort of hospital precision to facilitate various operations; just what I needed.

The operation of the B&B meant further sharing. Rosalind looked after the guests' breakfasts and servicing the rooms at weekends when we had most of our visitors. I had to cook breakfast on weekdays. It was a shared venture that amused the regulars who got to know us.

"Is your wife ill?" an anxious voice rose as I approached to take their breakfast order.

"No, she's gone to work," I replied.

"Do you do the cooking as well?" the guest continued.

I was not sure whether she was surprised I did two jobs or that my culinary skills were doubtful. Rosalind had set out a help-yourself cereal trolley that is mostly used by establishments today. My role was to cook the required choice of cooked breakfast. This required quite a bit of juggling as the choices were numerous. Eggs were offered in boiled, poached or scrambled form; perched on white, brown or granary bread. Added to this was the possible inclusion of sausage, mushroom, tomato and fried bread. By special request the night before, kippers were on offer. The notice required had nothing to do with catching them but allowing them to thaw out.

In order to serve up to six guests more or less at the same time, my preparation was to place various colours of bread on the worktop next to the toaster. Bacon, prepared mushrooms and cut tomatoes were in line in readiness. Eggs were still in their tray with cup and mixing bowl beside them. The consummate aid in all this was the Rayburn, which had two hot plates for cooking that could accommodate any temperature depending how near the pan was to the centre. It also had two ovens; hot or only tepid. Rosalind had come to understand that the tepid one was really used as an incubator for orphaned lambs. I had to develop an order, slotting in the 'quickly' cooked after starting off the 'slower' items, and then keeping things hot without overcooking them; a matter of keeping all the balls in the air. In practice it seemed to please the guests, and I enjoyed the challenge.

Although I quite enjoyed breakfast days, they required absolute cleanliness. I would start early in working clothes and check the stock, which might entail mud or, even worse, dirt. This was necessary, as 10 am is too late if a ewe is on her back or with her head caught in a fence. There would be a race to wash and change all my work clothing to do the breakfasts; similarly, the reverse procedure to become a farmer again. The reward for all the work entailed in the B&B business was chatting with guests about activity on the farm and hearing some of their amazing lives. Rosalind took great pride in explaining the hazards and disappointments of farming, not least the disparity between farm and retail prices.

Apart from saving me time in lambing, Rosalind was a great help in collecting sundries whilst shopping. This varied from a can of herbicide from the agricultural merchant when I needed to be sure of finishing a field, to staples and a roll of barbed wire for fencing. I was pleased when she had a mobile phone as, in addition to it making her feel safe, it was a great help in contacting her for emergency supplies; providing it was switched on!

The real joy was that my wife was an integral part of the business; we were in it together. This came to the fore during the lambing after my hamstring injury. I had returned relatively quickly to light work, but lambing did not fit into that category. Gone were the crutches, and walking was fine but I had difficulty in bending down and certainly was incapable of lifting anything. I was still feeling the tenderness and really frightened of it happening again. David was a great help in doing the heavier jobs but could not be with me all the hours of lambing.

I was inspecting a yard of ewes and found one needing help. David was away on his own work but Rosalind was home.

"Please can you give me hand?" I called through the kitchen door.

She came out as I was reassessing the scene from the yard gate.

"I need to catch her." I pointed to 'her' with my crook.

"You can't do that," Rosalind said.

"We can together," I replied. "Stay close to me and grab her round the neck when I catch her back leg with the crook."

Part of the crook was like the traditional bishop's crosier but the other end was a narrow 'v' that could accommodate a rear leg. As we approached, the ewe was more concerned with us than actually lambing. She walked steadily away. We followed; she walked with more purpose. The others in the yard were moving with her. It soon developed into a circular rodeo around the yard. This was the last thing pregnant ewes required. I decide to stop and plan a joint action.

The yards were divided by a large concrete trough and overhead wooden hayracks for wintering cattle.

"I'll hold a hurdle if you walk very slowly behind her," I instructed. "Bring two or three along the wall with her."

The first walk past failed, but all remained calm. At the second attempt I managed to jam her and another against the concrete trough.

"Quick, hang on…" I dropped the hurdle and squeezed her tight. At least I had upper body strength. "I need her in the trough."

"You can't do it and I can't lift her," Rosalind protested.

"Just stand directly in front of her and hold tight. I can lift her weight straight up," I instructed.

We got her level with the top of the trough and pushed her over, feet sticking out towards me. She lay in the cattle trough as if it were made for her, comfortable and unable to roll out. Rosalind kept a heavy hand on her, reassuring both the patient and me. I managed with the birth, standing upright and sorting out the various lamb legs as if at an operating table. The twins were put by her head and she licked them just where she was. I continued to hold her, marvelling at the strength of instinct to bond even lying horizontally. Rosalind held the lambs whilst I pulled the ewe to the edge and rolled her over to the ground. She followed her new family to her own clean pen as if it were entirely natural to give birth this way.

My wife had risen to the occasion as if she had been born to it. I'm sure the surgery would have heard all the details the next day. Although I did not want her to be involved with day-to-day farm work, she was happy to stand in the gap when it really mattered. It was a marvellous arrangement to call upon. Farmers, like their animals, are hefted to the land. They are part of it; whatever affects the farm affects them. The farm business involves the whole family. The farmer, male or female, needs care as well as nourishment. When things go wrong or seem out of control, he or she needs a listening ear. The worst scenario, such as an outbreak of foot and mouth, is a graphic example; support is needed from the whole family.

The often unsung contribution of a farmer's wife or partner is in dealing with visitors to the farm. My wife seemed gifted from the start, no doubt in some measure acquired at Kings College Hospital and the local GP surgery. Presumably there is a close link between shielding both doctors and farmers from interruption or simple aggravation. In the middle of an operation (whether human, ovine or bovine), it is a definite "No!" to letting anybody near the scene. Equally, there is a skill in determining the real worth of the enquirer to the business. A salesman may well be low on the list of priority visitors unless he or she is bearing that urgently needed can of herbicide or antibiotic. Even in that case, prudence may dictate that it be left at the back door rather than risk them setting foot in the yard. This gifting is born out of a close relationship with the farmer and the business; particularly when the man from the Inland Revenue calls.

## Visit from the Tax Man

In our second year at Woodhead Farm I received a letter from the Inland Revenue saying I was due for a check on my tax situation. Paying tax was of no concern as my big problem was trying to make money rather than the tax it might attract. Nevertheless, I informed my accountant, Mark, who said it was routine for such a visit to be paid to people who had just started out in business. It was arranged that he would attend to answer any questions that I couldn't. I felt it would give me moral support and them an opportunity to see first-hand the various enterprises. Being rather proud of what we had achieved, and having very few visitors, it seemed a good idea to invite them to lunch. The appointed time was 12 noon so it would fit in well to see the farm for an hour beforehand and discuss it after lunch. Rosalind took a day's holiday and cooked a chicken; it would be mixture of business and pleasure. The three of us – tax man, accountant and I – fitted into the bench seat of the pick-up and toured the fields, stopping to inspect the few sheep around at that time and the various crops. I was pleased to give a running commentary on what we hoped to achieve. The weather was fine, if rather cool, and the simple farm lunch a success.

After lunch Mark showed the accounts which consisted of more expense than income. Then there was a series of questions, mostly personal.

"I want to get a picture of how you live up here. You have virtually no income." The revenue man was straight to the point.

"My wife buys all the groceries," I replied.

"Does she?" He seemed surprised.

"She has a full-time job as a practice nurse," I added. It occurred to me that although she had cooked lunch, it had obviously not been appreciated. "She is nothing to do with the farm," I said indignantly, not wanting to implicate her in any way.

"How many potatoes did you eat between October and the end of the year?" he asked.

"I've no idea," I blurted out.

"How many lambs?" he asked.

"None! What is this? Have you come here to insult me?" I couldn't help it.

Mark fortunately intervened, saying this was all new and a straightforward, simple start-up.

"The lambs are the size of dogs. I couldn't eat them even if I wanted to." I felt I had to justify myself. This man was really upsetting me, but he continued on personal matters.

"Where do you get your hair cut?"

"My wife does what's needed." I tried to at least have a calmer exterior.

"Who pays for a newspaper?"

"Nobody. We wouldn't have time to read one and we don't have one."

"You realise I have the power to refer you to a tribunal?" he threatened.

I looked to my accountant.

"I've done nothing wrong," I insisted. "I'm absolutely honest; I have even showed you everything." I told the tax man I would go before any tribunal.

Mark tapped my arm. "Peter, I know you are absolutely honest but you can't ask for a tribunal."

The meeting ended and the Inland Revenue man with it.

I was angry that they would send a man that seemed to have no idea of farming. Mark told me that it is part of their training to get up your nose.

"But surely they have some idea when they meet an honest man," I said.

"Some are very clever criminals," Mark assured me, but it didn't help.

"Well, I don't want to see him again."

"You probably won't. It was because he couldn't see how you lived without wages."

I apologised to Mark.

"I was afraid you might have hit him," he smiled.

"I knew better than that, but I was tested," I admitted.

Rosalind listened to the whole story as amazed as me. She did her best to unwind me, saying, "However unpleasant, he couldn't find any fault." It took me until the next day to unwind but she was right. I was glad I hadn't hit him.

# 43

# Shearing and Harvest

Shearing comes before harvest but both jobs vie for ascendancy in a farmer's mind in June and July. I had always been aware of keeping farm costs down rather than driving to solely increase production. Indeed, the management aim was to seek optimum size of enterprises within the business. The cost of hiring a contractor for harvesting grain was considerable as well as problematic when the weather had been bad, calling everyone to seek their services when it improved. I thought a second-hand combine, of less capacity than the latest model and able to be used exactly when we wanted, would be a logical decision for us. The relatively small capital outlay would soon be recouped.

I found an old second-hand Massey 780 model in need of a complete overhaul but, after a little negotiating, costing only £450. My concern had been the condition of the engine, but after fitting a new battery it started the second time. It sounded fine and I reasoned that combines, which only work for a few weeks of the year, can hardly be abused as they run at maximum revs all the time they are in work. I was familiar with the model as I had driven one in the sixties.

Having my own combine was a psychological step change. Yes, it made good financial sense, but it felt the hallmark of being one of the farming fraternity; an independence from anyone else's business decisions and the ability to harvest when I judged nature intended. It was the final part of the jigsaw that sealed the picture and value of the business. In the winter months, whenever there was a wet day, I worked on renovating it. I started by opening up all the flaps, removing the knives and screens, and giving it a good shake. The movement of the threshing drum and sieving mechanism was enough to make the machine rock. This, coupled with the winnowing fan, blew away every cobweb, quite literally. I opened the shed doors and there was the dust of ages blown out of the throbbing machine. Eventually I replaced every knife section and aligned or replaced the 'fingers' in which the knives run. Every greased nipple and bearing was checked and, if necessary, replaced. Finally, the elevators moving the grain and all the belt drives were tightened or replaced. Suffice it to say, like a bird taking a dust bath, the old girl shook and felt refreshed.

That harvest she proved her worth; the hard work of restoration was amply rewarded. The cutting and threshing, when finely adjusted in the field, produced a good clean sample, equal to a modern machine. I had forgotten the joy of combining as we used to do it. The days were sunny and bright, and the birds, indeed the whole of nature, were singing. Once the dew had gone and the straw felt dry, it was time for bait; twenty or thirty minutes of sheer pleasurable anticipation. The machine was ready to go, but no pressure; another half an hour would only improve harvesting conditions. I would often sit on a sack and lean against the large land wheel[56]; I would be sitting in the driving seat for quite long enough later.

At ground level I was actually closer to nature. The cut stubble from yesterday's work was a regular high street of activity. Small birds were collecting their own harvest of tailings[57]. Now and again they would snatch a tasty insect making its way to what seemed to be nowhere in particular. If there were any butterflies I was mindful it was warm enough to be at work myself; then I thought it was seldom I got to take pleasure like this. Another piece of Rosalind's fruit cake wouldn't wait till teatime; anyway, it would have been rude to have returned any of her excellent cooking.

I had to start work but that was no real hardship; quite to the contrary, it had its own pleasures. The machine had been set up the day before, but after only a hundred yards it was best to check that good grains were not being blown over the sieves nor was any greenery being left in the sample. There I was, perched above the crop, watching the standing straw being cut and consumed by the elevator taking it all to the threshing drum. There was no cab; the fresh air was breezing past and all the scents of summer were rising with the dust. Later in the day it was always prudent to wear a mask as everything became drier and dustier.

The background noise was the roar of the engine running at a constant speed, the machine swallowing the crop and disgorging the threshed straw in a neat row behind. The valuable harvest was filling the grain tank immediately behind my seat. I could see David on a tractor and trailer driving around the headland. He was coming up behind me ready to collect the first load. This was done without stopping the operation. He just pulled ahead and changed into second gear; he would then adjust his speed only by the throttle to keep the trailer under the discharge chute. The unwritten rule was that he was responsible for filling the trailer evenly by a touch of the throttle. The driver of the combine was responsible for switching the on/off grain delivery lever from tank to trailer. If the trailer had to stop for any reason, the combine driver would shut off the discharge and continue harvesting. If the combine had to stop suddenly because of a blockage or breakage, the trailer also had to stop, as if attached by an umbilical cord. If the combining had to stop in order to unload, it could cost two to three hours' working time in a full day.

---

[56] wheel of a plough that runs on the unploughed land
[57] cut and shrivelled grains blown over the sieves with the threshed straw

Our first year of reaping our own harvest was most successful and saved the cost of it being done by a contractor. We had control of harvesting when it was best for us, when it was dry enough and not needing costly drying in store. I appreciated my personal involvement in the crowning activity of a year's work. This was heightened by the old combine not having a cab and real levers to operate; the noise of the engine powering everything like a beating heart. The life of the machine was more akin to a jockey nursing the best out of his steed; perhaps the thrill of a sports car, compared to an automatic saloon.

Of course, the contractor's modern combine is a super tool; a tool of latest efficiency covering acres at great speed and monitoring every activity from height of cut to amount of grain loss over the sieves. Remarkably, the latest combines seem to know where they are in the field and I bet will even make tea; or is that next year's model! The cabs now are air-conditioned with sprung and padded seats adjustable to every farmer's back. The audio is not the engine but the latest chart-topper, and communication is available to whomever you wish. The onboard computer advises the 'pilot' of every aspect and optimum performance. Apparently, it can be clever enough to place an order for a part, such as an alternator, before it is recognised as wearing out.

I confess huge admiration for the latest combines and covet the comfort of the 'pilot', particularly when the weather is less than one expects of summer. Etched on my memory are the days of dust enveloping the open platform and clogging the driver's every orifice. The sports car driver needs goggles and they really need wipers. I remember an exceptionally wet harvest time in the sixties when some fields could not be harvested at all. We waited for anything approaching even damp weather as long as the straw would go through the combine without clogging it. It was the first day of the new year that I, as a contractor, was able to combine the last field. The ears that had not dropped off were showing signs of sprouting and I had to wear gloves and two coats to complete the salvage operation. I could not even have dreamt of the modern cab.

Shearing had to come before the combine could be put to work. There was now a large enough flock to require professional shearers. I could no longer pay a neighbour or casual help to shear a few each night after they had finished their own work. In the first days with only a few dozen sheep, it was OK to get them all into the yard, shear half of them and repeat the operation the next night, or even a couple of days later. The handling of a small bunch was easy to keep together, shorn and unshorn, grazing them together, collected together.

Fifty years earlier, shearing was almost a local festival in the more traditional sheep areas. The larger farms had buildings to accommodate large numbers of sheep and the shearers to do the job. Smallholders could join in by labouring; moving sheep to and from the shearing platform whilst young, fit men sheared them. Among the shearers there was a competition to be the quickest without injuring the sheep. The slightly slower men would counter with arguments about the quality of their job versus quantity.

"Easy for you young bloods only taking 'arf off." – a reference to any tuft of wool left on the ewe.

"Do yer cut yourself shaving?" – a shout about a cut seen on a freshly white sheep.

It was good-humoured banter underlying the competition among the farming fraternity. There was a pride in the 'best', whatever the task, and self-esteem among peers. It was evident at all the shows of produce and livestock, and even weekly in the markets, that reputations were made or ruined by the quality on display.

We were in different times and circumstances back then; the business now was to be as efficient as possible. Accordingly, I looked for shearers from New Zealand. These were young farmers skilled at the job and wanting to see the world. Some would be spending two or more years moving through various European countries before finishing the season in the UK and then the Baltic States. I managed to engage a solo New Zealander who had difficulty getting into the UK. The phone was answered by Rosalind.

"HM Customs. May I ask if you are expecting Mr Peers to be visiting you?" He was polite and to the point.

"Oh yes; it's alright, he is our shearer," Rosalind quickly confirmed.

Unfortunately, it was not alright as he had no work visa, and my dear wife had innocently confirmed he would be working, albeit for a day, maybe two. Later a mobile call came from the shearer saying, "I am sorry but I will be with you sometime Wednesday." Apparently, it would take forty-eight hours to get from France into Germany and a flight from there. This he achieved without a hitch. It was disappointing that officialdom had not been informed that there were no out-of-work English shearers and that the only way to find one was from abroad.

We were ready for him with sheep already yarded in the dry overnight. This was important as even a dew would make shearing almost impossible and a rolled damp fleece could not be kept in a woolsack a number of months before dispatch. David had helped to set up pens next to the platform and partitioned off part of the passageway ready to receive a dozen ewes at a time for the 'roustabout'. That is an Antipodean term for the man who collects the animal to be shorn. It is his responsibility to see the shearer always has a sheep to hand.

The roustabout has to grab a ewe from the adjacent pen, turning it quickly onto its rump, without letting any others out. With a deft lift and skid, holding the animal upright, it is passed into the hands of the shearer, at the same time collecting the last fleece from the plywood platform. This has to be thrown onto the makeshift table, any daggings[58] are pulled off, and the fleece is rolled, with the 'arms' used as ties. The roll is pushed down into a suspended wool sheet used like a large sack. This leaves just enough time to repeat the operation. The shearer is king of the operation; dressed in vest, jeans and moccasins, the legwear being coated in months of lanolin and surely able to stand upright unassisted. We provided two sheets of plywood, simply laid on top of the concrete, as his platform; essential for day-long foot comfort and care. Other essentials hung from any convenient beam but definitely within arms' reach. The nearest was the on/off pull chord for his electric handpiece[59]. Two feet away swung his bottle of water, which was in direct line of the electric fan, cooling both bottle and shearer. The other essential was the counter, which he clicked as he straightened his back at the detachment of a fleece. No doubt every time this happened there was the rewarding thought that a pound had dropped into his piggy bank.

Finally, there was the vital alarm clock which was timed for two hours. This is the universal signal for a ten-minute 'smoko'. However many shearers, they all break together but must complete the sheep they are shearing first. Although I have never seen any modern shearer smoke, it is the standard break to get through the day and get maximum numbers shorn.

David's job was to fill the holding pen and clean up any dirty sheep with hand shears. I kept the shearer supplied with sheep and rolled the fleeces; the shearer completing the operation. We were all exhausted by the end of the day. Remarkably, nearly two hundred sheep were sheared in the day in an effort for the shearer to start at another farm the next morning.

## Dipping the Flock

Some six weeks after shearing, the sheep have grown enough wool to 'hold' the dip. This is to ward off sheep scab, ticks and parasites, including blowfly. It is another carefully planned operation requiring a small team. At Woodhead the dip was an integral part of the passageway bordering the two main yards. It had been made out of concrete when the yards were built and had a drain plug plumbed into the bottom running out to the home meadow. All year the top was covered over with three-foot-long mini sleepers acting as a race[60] for worming, injecting, or otherwise treating and drafting sheep. The tank was twelve-foot long with a sloping floor enabling sheep to walk out at the far end.

It was important to retain a sense of humour as the best-laid plans rarely proceed smoothly. At that time of year, just after shearing, the flock was together, ewes and lambs. The expectation is to run them *en bloc* through the chemical dip. The ewes can remember the pantomime last year that resulted in

---

[58] dirty, wet wool cut away from around the tail/anus of a sheep
[59] shears
[60] single file treatment of animals

them getting wet; to the lambs it is a new experience. This entails having to urge the adults to get wet again by pushing and heaving them when they hesitate. Once in the water, the dipper, armed with a hairless broom, pushes each head or neck downwards to submerge the entire fleece before the sheep paddles to the upwards slope and on towards the drain pens at the far end. Although this is for their own good and well-being, many are reluctant as they only remember getting really wet.

The lambs, however, take two different approaches. The first few, out of total ignorance or bravado, leap in unaided. The next, seeing what happened to their friends, are hesitant, but having more wool, being unshorn, have something for the dipper's assistant to grab. It is probably the ovine equivalent of pushing somebody off the top diving board. The next lambs, witnessing what is going on, opt for the straightforward approach – a giant leap – in the hope of clearing the length of the trough without touching the water. This is occasionally dangerous for the assistant at the starting end. The lambs give no notice of when they may take off. I have witnessed the assistant gripping a lamb's fleece, expecting it to need encouragement, when in an instant it decides on the all-in-one jump. Truthfully, the assistant has been known to go in with the lamb, the result being a win-win situation: the lamb didn't achieve the distance and was successfully dunked, and the assistant never suffered from sheep scab.

This was the first time we had used this dipping system, and before we started I noted that there was no bung in the outlet pipe from the dip. Nor was there was any threaded cap or bung that could be operated remotely. I had tried the day before to fashion a bung out of wood but realised it would never seal fully, nor be removable, and the dip would have to be emptied by the bucketful. In my hunting about a garden shed, I came across the girls' tennis gear, including a set of old balls. Just maybe that would do as a bung. I tried a ball in the outlet pipe; it was too big. I stood in the dry tank desperate for something smaller. I went back and collected the box of balls; some were well worn, older than others. I pushed the baldest hard into the outlet; it fitted perfectly. At least it would now hold water even if we would have to bucket it out afterwards.

I filled the dip overnight and it was still full the next day. The planned dipping went ahead as described above but we had a crisis after only about a dozen ewes had been dipped. It was my fault but events often happen so quickly that instinct kicks in. I was always conscious that money was tight, especially early in the enterprise, and I had used nearly all the expensive chemical hoping it would suffice for the entire flock. Suddenly the water level was going down; it could only be the tennis ball.

"Shut the race gate," I yelled and jumped straight into the dip.

I grabbed the ball floating on top and, holding my breath, buried my head in the dip and jammed the ball back into the pipe. Fortunately, it had not lost much; some £250 had been saved from running down the drain. We realised that a ewe we had tried to restrain had landed a direct hit (i.e. her foot) on the ball that was doing its job half-protruding out of the pipe. However, it gave us the answer to draining the dip; with a careful feel with a length of roofing batten, one could locate the metal pipe and then the half-protruding ball to dislodge it.

## A Proper Sheepdog

I had to have a heart-to-heart with Russ, my best sheepdog yet. I thought it would be good to discuss matters with him whilst we were watching the sheep.

"Russ, time for another look at those sheep."

I unhooked his chain and he needed no further invitation. I lowered the tailgate of the pick-up and he was up.

"We are just looking," I said to him as I settled on the grass and he came to my side.

This chat was for my sake as much as for Russ's. It was to make me feel better when big changes were about to take place.

"Look, old fella..." I stroked his head so he knew he didn't have to get ready for work. "I'm thinking there are a lot of sheep now and you could do with a bit of help. No offence to you," I added quickly. "I'm getting older too. I think we could do with a puppy to help you out."

He turned his head, as if really listening.

"Of course, he will need some training. I hope you will see to that," I continued. "I think it will be good to put an oil drum next to yours so you can keep an eye on him. Be kind; make a friend of him. You see, it can be a bit unsettling on your first farm and not knowing anybody. I will send him for a bit of basic training, but I need you, Russ, to show him the ropes here." I was still rubbing his ears and making a fuss of him. I doubt he was listening, but dogs, especially sheepdogs, have a habit of knowing more than you give them credit for but not talking back.

We drove back without actually collecting the sheep to the gate. He stayed with me for an hour as I tidied up the sheep penning. I then collected his bowl – he knew all about that – and I put the usual measure of dry feed in and soaked it with water. Russ never seemed bored with his staple diet, but certainly liked any meat bones Rosalind could provide. I chained him up but he was concentrating on eating, or should I say swallowing? Dogs work on the principle of getting it inside them and worrying about indigestion later... if at all. But I did wonder if he appreciated knowing about a junior partner arriving.

I picked up the new puppy; he was a beautifully marked collie, four months old and from "very useful parents". Rosalind made a real fuss of him but always with Russ at hand. I had insisted he start in his own kennel and that was his home, never the house. She saw the sense of this. The puppy was an immediate success with Russ. Although they were two male dogs together, after the initial introductions that only they understood, they were perfect friends. I fancy Russ sorted out the pecking order and 'Fly' was happy with that. Although later somebody told me that Fly was a female name, he could have no other; from his first outing he was rocket-propelled. In the field Russ and Fly would run together – I mean *start* together. Fly, having set off, had to keep looking back to see where his guide was. Russ did his usual routine regardless of Fly. The moment Fly noticed a change of direction he would be at Russ's side; it was an uncanny master-son relationship.

I made arrangements for Fly to have professional training and took him for his first lesson. We arrived at the farm where I expected the trainer, Joe Maitland, to take over.

"Shall I unclip Fly?" I wondered if he wanted to make friends with him first.

"No, I won't be talking to Fly; I need to talk to you."

I must have looked puzzled.

" *You* need the training, not the dog." He was completely blunt in order to reinforce the concept. "The dog knows what to do, if he's got it in him. Just a few don't have much idea," he added. "He's a sheepdog by nature. What he's got to do is understand your language."

It was beginning to make sense.

"Now walk up there about five yards with him."

I was beginning to wonder which of us would be rounding up the sheep.

"Now tell him to sit," he instructed.

Fly already knew what to do – it was me being trained. It was increasingly likely that Fly would be sitting and I would be showing him how to run!

"Now he's sitting, unclip the lead and be ready to repeat the command and, if necessary, hold a hand close to his face if he attempts to get up."

Fly seemed to understand completely.

"Now walk slowly backwards. Keep looking at him... That's good."

Fly stood up but didn't move.

"Go back, make a fuss of him and do it again. Go back a little further each time," he was instructing me again.

I noticed that Fly was good at sitting and I was getting better at walking backwards.

"Now call him to you."

I used his name and he came, wagging his tail vigorously. Pleased as I was with his response, I thought in his enthusiasm Fly was congratulating me.

"It's best to use his name in case you are working two dogs; don't just call 'ere," the trainer told me. "Now that is enough for today; just practise that time and again. Those are the fundamentals: 'Sit!' – or some prefer 'Lie down!' – and 'Come!' to his name."

I resolved to say "Fly" every time I put his food bowl down.

The second lesson a week later was to go out left or right and collect sheep. It was impressed on me that I should stand where I wanted the sheep to be. Fly should always go and fetch the sheep to me. If I stood in a gateway, I would only need to step smartly to the side and they would run into the new pasture. Well, that was the theory.

"The usual commands are 'Go-bye!' sending them clockwise and 'Away!' for anticlockwise," the trainer insisted.

I stood with Fly at my left heel looking down the field. "Bye!" I shouted. He leaped forward about ten yards and looked back. I was told to go up to him and repeat it, standing on his right and 'shooing' him in the clockwise direction. After a few attempts Fly understood; he wasn't to look for Russ but to get on with it himself. I then stood on his left and commanded "Away!" shooing him anticlockwise.

"That's all there is to it, but it needs constant practice." And that was the end of the second lesson.

Fly was a good student and full of enthusiasm. The third lesson was to try all this with actual sheep; he needed to collect them even when they were out of sight. Joe, the trainer, was aiming at training a really useful farm dog rather than a trials specialist. We moved to the next field, which rose and then dipped away apparently without sheep.

"There are twenty somewhere; they're usually at the far end," Joe asserted. "I hope you can stand still, no flapping of arms, and just give the command." He was instructing me again.

Fly needed no second command; he was off, tight to the hedge, and then out of sight. I waited, anxiously peering ahead. Suddenly sheep came galloping over the horizon and slowed down to a stop by us. I then noticed Fly lying down behind them, tongue out panting.

"Good. Have you taught him 'Steady!'? If they'd been in-lamb they'd be lambing now," Joe cautioned.

Fly was a quick learner and gathered sheep like a proper collie. He worked with Russ in harmony but now he was first there with Russ following him. It was pleasing to watch as we grew our flock; Fly first over the horizon raising a number of heads, then just as they might be thinking "Shall we bother?" Russ appeared fifty yards behind. "Look out girls; we're off!" Russ had no pretensions of being boss; he seemed to be happy as elder statesman.

# 44

# On the Crest of a Wave

It was good to feel established; the financial position felt comfortable. At least there was a small reserve, and if that would not get us through the next downturn then we could borrow a little more. The crops were yielding well and we had one particularly good year selling potatoes. We had eventually reached nearly four hundred ewes and could not expand any more.

I took care to thank the Lord often for honouring my prayer that started the impossible venture. I realised I had not made any covenant with Him; only God makes covenants. They are His promises, a sort of contract of working together. He answered my cry and through all the trials was still guiding us and enabling us to continue. I had to have faith and never doubt that He would lead us through to the end.

There was much work to be done and no room for complacency. Farming always demands effort but when it is rewarded there is no better occupation. These thoughts surfaced as I was driving my restored combine through a particularly heavy crop of wheat. It was one of those harvest mornings when the sun was bright and nature vibrant; the day promised all that one could possibly hope for at harvest time. There was every chance these fourteen acres would become thirty-five tons in the barn by evening.

I had no help from David that day and would have to keep stopping at the trailer and, when filled, drive it to the store myself. The grain was filling the combine's tank and I was hoping to reach the empty trailer before it overflowed. It was actually gratifying that the yield was so good. I lifted the header, moved onto the track and drove towards the trailer.

Sitting high on the combine, next to the engine, I thought there was a hint of a smoky smell. I looked down as I throttled back and changed gear; it *was* smoke. Stopping, there was the flicker of flames right down beside the engine. Chaff that always accumulated there was alight. I tried to get my boot beside the engine to stamp it out but it was too hot. I stopped the engine but the engine block was too hot; I was sure to burn my leg badly. As I stopped the engine, the flames grew stronger. I started it up again and drove straight to the trailer, unloading the grain. Strangely, the fan on the engine, running at full revs, somewhat suppressed the fire. Empty, I drove into the next field, which was pasture. I stopped the engine and the flames advanced; the small fire extinguisher was not effective. The combination of grease, oil and burning chaff was unstoppable. I tried to disconnect the battery that had now shorted out the wiring around the engine, and a fresh source of fire started. I could do no more than carry my toolbox down the steps as fast as possible.

I phoned 999. "Fire!"

I knew the alarm would be ringing in the fire station and the firemen would be dressing on the way. I stated the postcode followed by details of the farm. It would all be passed on to the driver as they headed in the right direction out of town. It was a remote field with only a hard track once the tarmac surface finished a quarter of a mile away.

I sat on the ground watching the fire getting stronger. I was heartbroken, with the only consolation being that at least the burning combine was standing in a grass field and not in the standing crop.

The firemen were marvellous and easily put out the fire. They had even driven across a stubble field, against regulations, to reach me. There was no more danger. It was as if the crest of a wave had broken and had receded; all was still. I sat forlornly for a while, stunned; the day that had promised so much had effectively ended. I drove the tractor and trailer home and unloaded it in the barn. There was no hope of repairing the combine; I phoned my contractor, Barry, asking him to cut the rest of the harvest.

It was after harvest had finished that I returned to the combine to assess what could be done. I had no heart to spend another winter trying to restore and rewire everything. The cost of getting an engineer to do it was surely more than the machine was worth.

It was another nice day, which was a painful reminder as I lay underneath the stricken machine. I had come to assess how to retrieve it without using its own power and to see if there was anything left to salvage. It was a forlorn hope but it couldn't stay as a wreck in the pasture.

It was a windless day as I lay down flat on the ground, right under the middle of the combine. I had an adjustable spanner to undo anything but I didn't know what. What could be salvaged? Putting a chain around the back axle and towing it backwards was probably the only way of getting it back to the yard. I lay on my side, chin at grass level, thinking that this was a sheep's view, munching off fresh grass before moving on to another tasty patch; that was their life.

The grass blades themselves were part of nature's miracle provision. A single blade twitched a foot from my eyes yet there was not the slightest breeze. I was in no hurry. As I looked at it twitch again, the same blade, I was transfixed. Whatever could cause that; a passing ant? There was no fly sitting on it. In the total stillness, what could make a single blade twitch only eight or so inches from my face? I moved an inch or two nearer, stopping only six inches away. Something that looked like a needle was coming up from the soil. It was touching the blade. As I watched, it came up further, resting on the blade for a moment.

A leg, possibly two; it was resting at 45° on the blade. In no more than a minute its wings materialised before my eyes. It was a crane fly. I could still see the needle-hole it had emerged from; it had unfolded from a hole the size of a pin. A few flexes of the tissue-like frail wings and it was off. My mind was totally absorbed in the scene; I had witnessed the birth of a crane fly.

What had prompted that birth? What set of circumstances, stimuli; what power had come together to raise the 'needle' vertically? The crane fly had gone but I lay there marvelling at what I had seen. How did it know what to do? There was no adult to teach it the first details of flight or survival, and what sort of brain can there be in a head smaller than a pinhead? I wondered what triggered the desire to mate, or even feed?

Of course, I couldn't suggest any answers and wondered if scientists had investigated such things. I settled for the privilege of witnessing such a miracle. I have not come across anyone else who has witnessed such an event in the wild. In the midst of my depression, it reminded me of a phoenix rising from the ashes. Surely everything is temporary. The strongest castle eventually becomes a ruin. I was aware that the whole of nature is a cycle of birth and death. My hopes rose; I had been lamenting a dead combine, but the contractor's machine had completed the harvest. Had the Lord of the harvest demonstrated that He was capable of caring for the most insignificant of births, even that of a 'daddy-long-legs'? The reality was, His promises to me were still holding true.

We had suffered many disappointments and apparent reversals in the business but the blessings and provision had also continued. We were sure difficulties had strengthened our faith, even preparing us for future knocks in life. Rosalind had suffered her own knocks and was about to receive another punch.

"I think it's final." There was a note of resignation as she looked into the office on her return from the surgery. I looked up, waiting for more information.

"My job, I mean." She only offered a tantalising phrase. "The new doctors want to get rid of me."

Dr Frank had sold the practice to a young couple wanting to make their way in life and naturally there would be some changes. It now seemed Rosalind was going to be one of them. She had shown them the ropes and introduced them to the necessary contacts in a spirit of fulsome cooperation. However, she was part of the 'old', almost as insignificant as Dr Frank; she also had to go.

"I will have to find another job; I can't retire just yet." She settled into the spare chair the other side of my desk.

"I knew you said relations were strained, but that sounds a bit beastly after all you have done," I sympathised.

"I'm not bitter but they want to do their own thing." She was trying to be positive.

We prayed there and then, asking God for guidance. We had both found that He answers prayer; that was how we had found each other, both relying on Him. We had committed our lives to trying to follow Jesus and He had always answered, in His own perfect way.

There were no practice nurse posts anywhere near; it looked bleak. Rosalind needed a job. It was an important part of our budgeting and essential for her self-esteem; she had never been unemployed before. She worked out her term of notice; there were only three days to go.

"I've found a vacancy in the local paper," she practically shouted as she banged the car door.

"Is it some surgery miles away?" I asked.

"No, and I haven't got the job yet," she was bubbling, "but I have got an interview."

"Already?" I exclaimed.

"I phoned straight away and it's so near."

"You sound as if you have got it," I cautioned, unable to understand her confidence.

"It's not a surgery; it's a nursing home. They want a nurse in charge, under the owner."

The interview was successful. The Lord had answered again; it had His signature on it – a change of direction but perfect for our circumstances. There was a settling-in period like any change of job but the calmer, even restful, atmosphere of the home was therapeutic.

"Don't you miss the medical work?" I asked.

"Not really; I'm still dealing with people."

"But not so stimulating," I countered.

"Don't you believe it; I'm challenged all the time." She smiled over her evening mug of coffee.

"I suppose, instead of me telling the patient what to do, they tell me." Rosalind smiled as she explained, "I go down there for a lesson. When I think about it, I used to give all the instructions and expect patients to take the right pills at the right time, or change their habits. Now I meet more resistance."

She continued reliving an incident:

"Freda Smith helped me yesterday. She insisted on showing me the dining room. Struggling up from her lounge chair she steadied herself, catching hold of my arm, pulling me towards the dining room. 'I know where it is, Freda; it is where you have your meals,' I told her. 'You are new here, dear,' she said undeterred. 'I am showing you, this is where we have our dinner. When the bell rings we have to come here.' I took her back to her chair, satisfied she had done a good turn, when another lady caught my coat whispering, 'She's always bossy.'"

Rosalind was on a roll.

"We have some colourful characters. Yesterday I had to separate two men who were fighting over their chairs. One was sitting peacefully in his armchair in an anteroom, and a nurse had told another man to go in there because he was interfering with a card game, not realising there was only one armchair in the side room. He tried to pull out the peaceful one, who was gripping the arms as if his life depended on it."

"Sounds as if it is fun every day," I grinned.

"Now the patients are insisting on their rights and keep telling me so," Rosalind finished.

I concluded her new job still revolved around people and that was the essence of her vocation: nursing.

We were beginning to get used to 'waves'; first the gentle swell then swifter, the crest raising us higher, sweeping us along, only to then drop. The buoyancy vanished; it seemed we would be drowned by the following crest. The farm output continued to be favourable and the yields of crop and stock were maintained; the slight disappointment was the downturn in prices. It was slow at first with lower prices per ton of grain and also for lamb. However, farming fortunes have always been cyclical, and we hoped they would soon improve. I trimmed expenses but there was little to cut out or reduce. The annual cropping could hardly be adjusted to favour the higher gross margin of potatoes as they were now grown once in the four year rotation. Like many other farmers, we carried on with tightened belts.

The new millennium was approaching and there was an air of optimism in the media. It seemed significant, a turning point in history, not merely a fresh century but a new millennium. The year 2000 was more than new; it was avant-garde. Parties and public fireworks were planned and the future seemed bright. The mobile phone system was blossoming and the advertising of one network insisted "the future's bright; the future's Orange".

We were encouraged to light a beacon on all high ground to send a message around the nation welcoming the new millennium. Accordingly, we joined with neighbours and built a huge bonfire at Woodhead on our highest field. The ladies had contributed to a winter picnic worthy of the occasion and fortunately eaten around a large fire. In the dark we watched as fires were lit, and tried to pinpoint where they were. It must have been similar to the beacons' warning of the Spanish Armada; now not in impending disaster but in celebration and hope.

The next morning some may have been a little hungover, but the milking and feeding of stock on farms carried on as usual. I remember from my days of milking that cows are a great leveller. Whatever the day of the week or public holiday, they file into the parlour, eat cattle cake and chew the cud, with their brown soulful eyes that contentedly say, "It's what we do." Their excitement is tied to fresh grass in the spring; having been confined in winter quarters, they celebrate with a great dance and leap for joy, which is so infectious that each one catches it as their feet feel the pasture. The farming carried on as usual but the returns did not improve; the next year was even worse.

## Foot and Mouth

The disease was first reported on 19th February, 2001 at an abattoir in Essex; the date is etched on the memory in the industry. It was discovered out of the blue during an inspection of an abattoir, but where had it come from? That was the question on every farmer's mind. The news channels gradually opened up on the topic as the disease quickly appeared over a large part of the country, causing great alarm to all livestock farmers.

Since Christmas we had moved our ewes into the yards. This was to save damaging the pastures in wet winter conditions and to promote early spring grass. It also made sure their nutrition was kept up by feeding them silage and protein concentrate. Left to winter grass, some ewes will ignore even good quality silage and pick at any rough, barely nutritious grass to the point of wasting away. In the yards they have no choice but to eat silage and, soon getting the taste for it, they thrive. I thought how fortunate they were, safer than in open fields, but had a nagging doubt in case the disease spread like wildfire in the confined space.

It was immediately the topic of every conversation. There were general references on the news about the way the virus spread and precautions that should be taken, but would they be enough? Our vets sent a letter to all their customers, but there were still questions we really needed answered. Looking back, the questions were not necessary. We knew enough; we knew nothing was guaranteed. The concern was palpable; it affected every livestock farmer, all cloven hooves, even wild deer. We had a lot of deer in the woods; they grazed the pastures at night. It was a welcome relief that the ewes were all in the yards. But the rams were not! We had no more housing; perhaps they would be alright. I talked about this with Rosalind; at least it was better than bottling it all up.

"The rams are still out; I hope they will be alright," I said.

"They have got plenty of fresh air," she replied.

"But it's airborne as well as contact," I added.

"Nothing is foolproof." She was trying to comfort me.

"Ahh! They'll all be killed," I blurted out. "If there're any cases here, they all have to be slaughtered."

We sat in silence. It was as if a blanket of despondency had been thrown over the whole of farming.

There was no cure, although on the continent they used vaccines with some success. The policy in the UK was to slaughter all animals where an infection had occurred. This apparently had the merit of having absolute confidence that in the future animals could be sold here and abroad, guaranteed free from the disease. It was particularly useful for pedigree breeders as, should a vaccine have been administered, a later blood test might have given a positive result just as if they had contracted the disease. The other downside to vaccination was the multiple mutations that occur; plus, an animal that recovers is often less thrifty and unprofitable. However, total slaughter was a sledgehammer blow both to the business and to the life of the farming family.

I phoned David who would normally help in busy periods; he had a small flock of his own which his father mostly looked after in his retirement.

"We can't meet up," I heard my own despondent voice.

"No, we can't, for both our sakes." He was no brighter. "Dad is really fed up."

"We are some way off lambing." I tried to lift the tone.

"The auctioneers say it's stopped all their marts."

"It affects us all, even if we haven't got it," I added.

"They say it started in pigswill," David said.

"I guess anything is possible, but they are going to ban that now."

Our talk was not productive but we knew we were isolated.

"I'm going to put a postbox at the end of the lane and a notice, 'No callers'," I announced.

David asked to keep in touch on the phone.

I phoned another neighbour.

"Ernie, it's Peter."

"How yer doing?" His gruff voice was recognisable anywhere.

"OK!" I responded.

"Yer lucky then; nobody else is." He was rarely downbeat.

"Do you know anybody who's got it?" I thought he might have some news.

"No, but my cousin in the Lake District is near some."

"Has he got cattle?" I knew it was bad up there.

"He's got a few single sucklers," Ernie replied. "What about you?"

"I never bought stores for this winter; prospects didn't look too good," I said.

"That was lucky; bit less to worry about."

Ernie had rather more ewes but no cattle.

"What happens if we get a case now when they are heavy in-lamb; compensation, I mean?" I asked him.

"Must have the true value of a 'couple'," he said straight away. "I only hope the union will stand up for that."

"I just want to keep my head down and let it all pass over," I said.

Ernie felt the same; there was little we could do.

I had placed a twenty-five-litre chemical container, with one side cut out, by the door of the shed. It was filled with disinfectant and a brush dangled next to it on string, the farmer's approach to hygiene, to be used before any dare to enter. I looked carefully over the yard each morning, trying not to make a sound that would disturb the sheep. I asked myself if there any were limping or showing other symptoms. Sheep are generally more difficult to diagnose than cattle. I looked for any blisters around the mouth but that could be confused with orf[61]. I walked into the yards and moved very slowly; the sheep soon took little notice and I eventually felt confident there were no foot and mouth symptoms. My day had subtly changed: there was still the routine that goes with keeping livestock but no external sounds; no people, a quieter world. Rosalind was still able to go to work, but no postman or other delivery was possible. The world had moved away and a 'foot and mouth curtain' seemed to have come between us. The B&B guests had been stopped, although we didn't have many bookings that early in spring anyway. David and other farmers would not be moving from their holdings. It added to the isolation.

News came somehow, in this febrile stand-off, that cattle on the Welsh border were affected. It was coming nearer home and we were now included in a ten-mile zone. Soon more details came from the local press and the network that exists between the farming fraternity. Some of the details were second- if not tenth-hand but generally ratified by the media. There were pictures of up to a dozen white boiler suits descending on a farm and cattle crammed into yards. I imagined the anxiety of the cattle at white ghosts cajoling them rather than the farm staff. I was used to taking utmost care of any animals I delivered to an abattoir, believing they were sensitive to aggressive handling.

I was told that often the first course of action was instructing the farmer to stay indoors as the Ministry team would be taking over full responsibility for the cull. This too must have been a terrible imposition: absolute helplessness in your own yard; the fate of your own livestock, the ones you have reared and cared for up till the day before, in someone else's hands; farmers' dogs left chained up, unable to be used by the strangers, their owner imprisoned in the house. What was happening? The next operation was the systematic 'humane' shooting and the dragging of carcasses to the nearest field or loaded onto a bulk lorry to be transported to a communal pyre.

Inevitably there were incidents where inexperienced drovers without the aid of dogs gathered animals, particularly sheep, and lost control. If sheep are packed tight and meet field fences only designed for defining boundaries, something has to give. This may be the fence or a woolly maverick deciding to jump; the result is the same – total disarray. There were reports of some sheep under pressure breaking into the neighbour's field. Such possibility of contamination immediately condemned his stock to be slaughtered as well. It was all too terrible.

It meant the animals would be slaughtered and the carcasses burned on the farm. It meant the farmer was powerless, and effectively under house arrest,

---

[61] a viral skin disease that can be spread to humans by handling infected sheep and goats

whilst a Ministry team corralled and killed all the herd or flock, or both. Although compensation according to the value of the animals would eventually be paid, some farmers must have felt as if their world had come to an end. They were immediately out of a job with nothing to do except walk through empty buildings. They could not buy healthy animals again until the disease was over and the compensation had been paid. Equally, where would they find suitable stock and at what price? Especially those engaged in pedigree breeding stock had lost their gene bank that could have been the work of several generations. It was not uncommon to hear of suicides where life had simply not been worth contemplating. Gone was income, with no prospect of when it might return. Most farmers were unemployable, at least in the short term. Driving the school bus would be out of reach without a passenger carrying vehicle (CPC) driving licence. To drive a forklift truck in a factory required training and passing a test, although many had driven their farm's forklift for years. Gone was their self-worth; gone was their world.

As culling increased, we could see smoke rising across the valley; it was five or six miles away but definitely funeral pyres. I pointed it out to Rosalind when she came home, and we just felt sorrow for the farmers involved. During that working day, moving from one job to another, it was an involuntary action to glance westwards to the fire. Occasionally I smelled it, no doubt as the wind changed. After two days I noticed a second fire a little further to our left. The smoke was black and spiralling upwards; I thought of neighbours who would be much nearer and their reactions.

"There is a new fire," I announced to Rosalind.

"Poor people," she replied with a tone of resignation.

"I was thinking about the smoke, wondering if it was dangerous," I mused.

"I'm sure they would be careful," she said.

"I mean, can it spread contagion?" I asked.

"It seems to spread so easily," Rosalind offered wearily.

"Precisely," I concluded.

It was the next day that we noticed another fire. I was becoming transfixed.

"That's the third and all in a row," I observed.

"It could be the smoke is to blame," she agreed. "It could be a coincidence or spread by vehicles or some birds or deer."

"It could be anything, but my guess is it's the smoke. Look, each time the fires have been to the left. We see the direction of the wind and behold the next day or so there is a fire next to that," I concluded.

"We had our first lamb this morning," I told Rosalind as we started dinner.

"Is it alright?" Her midwifery concern was aroused.

"Twins and full term," I smiled.

After the meal she came with me to the pens. All was well. Mum stood up and both youngsters noticed the milk bar was available.

"I'm not thinking about foot and mouth," I said. "I'm concentrating on our own affairs; this is our lamb harvest."

"That's it, be positive," Rosalind agreed.

The lambing soon gathered pace and our system of birthing in yards and transferring couples to single pens worked well. As soon as possible I took singles to one field and doubles to another. It was prudent to get them out and into their natural environment. The ewes and lambs had their numbers sprayed on and I ferried two couples at a time in the transport box as usual. Although I had a little help from David towards the end of lambing, I was drained by being on duty night and day for six weeks. Fortunately, I was buoyed up by ewes managing without needing much of my intervention. There were only a few yearlings, lambing for the first time and therefore requiring extra shepherding. Any problem ewes from the previous year had been drafted out of the flock. Additionally, I was running on the adrenalin of a good lambing percentage of about 176 per cent.

## Flaky Farming

Producer sale prices were mixed, with prices fluctuating after the last cases of foot and mouth in September. Many sheep had been slaughtered but there was some consumer resistance to meat. The whole industry seemed in a state of flux following the shutdown as if suffering a psychological shock or crisis of confidence.

Several interest groups seemed to be competing for the high ground. There was a move towards 'organic' production but little certainty of what that meant. Imported organic vegetables were not necessarily grown under the same criteria as home-produced crops. It was uncertain whether 'organic' potatoes meant no chemicals were used. In fact, chemicals were permitted to control potato blight to more or less the same rate as conventional crops. Some countries advocated Bordeaux mixture, being copper sulphate and slaked lime, a man-made poison applied to the foliage. Some imported 'organic' lettuce was top-dressed with nitrogen. At the same time there was new interest in vegetarianism and even veganism. There was a general movement towards all things natural and consideration of the importance of nature, which we are still applauding. However, this did not square with producing more of our home-grown food as a country. Self-sufficiency had been vital in the time of the Second World War but there was a growing demand for a more continental diet.

All these straining points were a confusion to the primary producer who was tempted to invest in heavier and greater capacity machinery in the hope of increasing output and reducing cost per item. The heavier machinery was a great boon but often at the cost to nature by loss of soil structure. This we were seeing in ploughed-up permanent pasture to grow clean-skinned potatoes. 'Cosmetic' vegetables, washed and plastic-packaged, required irrigation; another call on nature. Supermarkets were growing in size and with their buying power were naming the price they would pay producers. In the dairy industry it was hastening the movement towards ever-larger dairy herds in an effort to achieve economy of scale. Smaller producers were squeezed so much that at times they were having to sell milk for less than it cost to produce.

We had to decide what our prospects were and how we would manage the changes.

"It's coming up to rent time again," I wearily informed Rosalind after another evening in the office.

"Is the rent going up?" she enquired.

"No, but it takes some finding. We are treading water and I can't see how we can increase output."

"You can't work any harder," she sympathised.

"There is no real prospect of prices picking up," I added despondently.

"We have only a few years until the tenancy finishes and we retire," she tried to encourage me.

"There is one option; it may be possible to rent just the land here and not this house, and, say, the home meadow," I suggested.

"How would that help?" she asked.

"If that happened, the landlord could rent out this house and a field for a fancy price to somebody wanting a country life with two horses and we would only pay to rent the fields. The landlord would take more total rent and we would save about three thousand per year."

"I would miss the rent for my cottage," Rosalind cautioned.

"Yes, but we would be better off for the last three years we were here," I added.

"How would you manage the farm?" She had hit on the imponderable. I would have to do a detailed budget.

I would have to get rid of the sheep and sublet the pasture or just sell hay or silage from it. It would also entail ploughing up some forty acres of borderline arable fields that I previously considered unsuitable for modern cultivations.

I floated the proposition to Robert, my landlord. He responded immediately.

"The answer was no," I told Rosalind when she came in from the surgery.

It was a week later that I broached the subject again.

"I think it's best for us to pack up early."

"What do you mean?" she asked.

"I think we ought to give up the tenancy."

It sounded so simple. I was proposing giving up what other people would be fighting for. I had known of people offering key money to landlords and paying grossly inflated rents to get hold of a tenancy.

"Is it as bad as that?" Rosalind had come to understand farming and feared I must have been concealing bad news.

"It's not too bad yet, but I don't intend to lose money farming," I said with finality. "Things are all changing and we are not in it like traditional family farms; we can't struggle through any depression in the hope of keeping things for the next generation. We have had some good years and I don't want to lose money and end up in a couple of years more or less where we started."

She just looked. I could see her eyes filling up. She came over and hugged my neck, putting her head against mine.

"I'm sorry. It's not your fault; it's farming," she whispered.

"If you agree, I'll give up the tenancy and we can see what the Lord has for us. He has provided for us and there is no shame in leaving a tenancy after ten years."

"Of course. We will be just going to the cottage a bit earlier." She brightened up a little.

"I can give notice now, a year ahead." The decision had been made.

# 45

# All Change Again

I sent a formal letter requesting the ending of my tenancy two years before its natural termination. It was not well received, but I guess change is very often uncomfortable, unsettling. When everything is proceeding in the expected way, we call it normal. Nothing seemed normal now; the landlord and tenant system had suited both parties for hundreds of years with minor adjustments. Now agriculture was changing, driven by many pressures coming together. The commodity, or farm gate, prices were being squeezed downwards. This was resulting in farmers trying to produce more without increasing costs, hence a market surplus.

It seemed to me that there could be no reversal of the trend. These changes had influenced our decision to give up the tenancy. We were not in the race to farm at all costs; I had achieved my goals and enjoyed it. We had no dynasty to maintain, no next generation to satisfy. We had the flexibility to change and new things to do. My releasing the tenancy a couple of years early only hastened changes that many estates had in mind. As the squeezes mentioned above tightened, and tenants retired, fields were often reallocated to existing tenants. This enabled tenants to scale up production without the estates losing rent; the simple expedient of the same area of land but fewer mouths to feed. Woodhead was unlikely to be relet as a single unit.

We had to prepare for the rundown of our business and the eventual retirement sale. Farming continued with an eye on using as much of our consumables as possible. Any crop sprays were carefully underestimated even if it entailed collecting the odd can to finish the last field. Similarly, no more equipment was purchased and the workshop was run down. The same happened with sheep wormers and injections. The retirement sale was planned for early September with the ewes in good condition for going to the rams.

I needed to grow potatoes but on the basis that they would be dispatched more or less 'off the field'. Contracts for this were secured and similar plans were made for all grains to go at harvest. The B&B came to a natural end simply by not taking any bookings after the end of August. It was all falling into place. There was no sadness; it was a planned progression. Moving to Rosalind's cottage would be better as it was even nearer her work and I had plenty to do ahead of me. The consultancy business that had grown around me I would continue to do to a greater or lesser extent. It had all started informally whilst I was managing in Wessex, when local friends and acquaintances sought my help. At the time many houses were changing hands and people, mostly with London connections, were buying properties in the area. Farm workers were getting thinner on the ground and the urban affluent were seeking 'the good life'. Although we were never in a social network, the local farm manager was the go-to contact where practical issues were concerned.

It started with advice on keeping a horse in, or perhaps the deer out, of the small field that was attached to their property. In some instances what had appeared so enticing when purchased could later become a source of concern. Not everybody had recognised that the field was part of nature and therefore subject to change. The worst case of misunderstanding occurred to an acquaintance of mine who thought he had sold a country house to a couple who spent time abroad. The house they were interested in had a glorious view across a field of wheat to open countryside. Some ten weeks later they said they could not complete the purchase because the outlook had changed. It had been a glorious field of wheat harvest when they first saw it; weeks later, returning from abroad, it was all grass. It transpired that harvest had finished and that the fields had "some bare earth", others "young grass"; the sort of grass that would become next year's wheat! He did not mention his prospective client's address in London but I assumed it must have been several storeys high. Whilst relating this he had actually sold a similar property where the people had moved in. Sometime later they complained that cows kept walking down their lane making it dirty. It was easily explained that the cows from the local dairy farm grazed the fields in question and then moved to other fields that were not beyond the dairy farm's property, but in any case the cows had an appointment twice a day with the 'milkman'. So much for the idea of a painted landscape; I guess I might make similar gaffs if I suddenly parachuted into the Stock Exchange, especially on finding the 'stock' did not have four legs.

Back on my patch I was able to suggest to our new enquiring neighbours some suitable fencing for a couple of horses and who might do the job for them. I similarly answered a distress call about a septic tank that was not behaving like the mains in London. These practicalities were easily sorted out by most country dwellers but to newcomers they were insuperable. Furthermore, they often offered to pay for such advice, for half an hour's work with drainage rods, which we regarded as just doing a good turn.

The enquiries even moved to "What can I do with all the grass that is growing?" The horse had gradually been disappearing from view as spring growth accelerated. I suggested a simple grazing agreement with a farmer who was short of grass to legally cover both parties. On other occasions it was easy to arrange with a farmer who was making hay or silage to include one more field whilst he was cutting his own. The business grew into advice on diversification on farms and the maintaining of farm records. A fresh look from an outsider often unlocked ideas for busy farmers who were rushing ahead, because they had "always done it this way".

Changes were happening for us as we planned leaving Woodhead and moving into Rosalind's small cottage. We talked of making the cottage larger. We had both been used to living in a large farmhouse and had spent ten years living three-quarters of a mile off a tarmac road. During the day there was not a single dwelling in sight; on clear nights we could see pinpricks of light spaced out on the far valley some miles away. Although Rosalind had lived in her cottage before we were married, I could not imagine what village life would be like.

At the moment most of our thoughts were on the closing down of our time spent farming. As harvest neared, I tried to use the calm before the storm to take time to enjoy the fields and various viewpoints. It was always better to take the dogs with me; at least, *I* enjoyed it even if *they* were hoping to gather sheep. We walked the boundary, stopping at various places that didn't go anywhere. Often it was only fifty yards from our usual passage between fields but now there was time to pause on the sloping grass looking into the woods. It was a moment to reflect; conifers tall and straight, unmoved by world events. I thought of those men who had planted the saplings sixty or so years ago; imagining the hard work, them carrying a bunch of three-foot saplings, spade in hand. Pacing out the spacing up the slope, a few stokes of the spade and 'heeling' the saplings in. I pictured the men I had first worked with; a cloth cap with greasy peak, trousers and jacket taken from 'Sunday best', now only fit for work. Nothing waterproof; that would be a sack with a foot of baler twine joining top to bottom corner to become a shawl. I doubted many of them ever moved from their estate house. House and job would have gone together and they would generally have been pleased with such security. How would they, having started with horses and becoming reluctantly used to tractors, have imagined the power giants of today?

I walked home across the top field; there was the familiar oak, solitary and loved by sheep on a hot day. It must be four hundred years old, grown from a sapling; who would have planted that? Why plant one in the middle of a pasture? Perhaps there were originally more trees, or even an ancient hedge line. I was reminded of the fragility of man compared with the centuries of the oak; and my tenure little more than a decade before moving on. Looking back, Woodhead Farm had moved on into the twenty-first century during my tenancy. The buildings were larger, the yard bigger to accommodate huge trucks. I was aware of the landscape and vegetation as I walked back to the house; I doubted that had changed. The raw materials of nature had not changed much; I had simply done my best to work with the elements. The crops were a testament to nature; I had only been the cultivator, and now someone else would carry on. There would be more minor changes; minute in the aeons of time, but then we are all 'tenants' as far as the Lord of the harvest is concerned.

## Sale Time

All my spare time after harvest was spent preparing for the farm sale. It was made a little easier knowing the priorities and pitfalls of just over a decade ago when I had undertaken the closing sale on the estate. We marked out the lines for the various lots and the sheep penning with the help of the auctioneers. Access and car parking was also planned, with traffic flowing in one direction. We cleaned and stored as much equipment as possible ready for the great day, concerning ourselves that the last week was bound to be frantic.

I had decided to keep the Manitou forklift with its attachments, my pick-up and car trailer. The same applied to the small hand tools which I might find useful. I had decided that, although retired, I would still keep a connection with farming; this would be mainly through various consultancy clients and would become a source of income. I had a yearning to run a few beef cattle if I could find a couple of fields to rent. The thought of leaning on a gate and passing the time of day, in the tradition of retired farmers, was appealing, especially if a few of my cattle were grazing in the background.

The plan was to sell the 'dead stock'[62], starting with the usual minor items and leading up to the cultivating equipment and then tractors. The sale of livestock would follow more or less without a break. The auctioneers favoured this as it would keep the purchasers together. It would be a relatively small dispersal sale but, with good quality sheep included, would be of significant interest to a wide selection of farmers.

I submitted a detailed list of sale items in the approximate selling order to Glyn and his fellows in the firm. He suggested a few blank spaces for items that were worth splitting, and I agreed the inclusion of a few additional items of machinery from other vendors.

In the final few days, the sheep were moved to two adjacent fields and drafted into yards overnight. This gave us the chance to run them through the handling system, separating the younger one- to two-year-olds. This involved examining teeth and udders as well as casting an eye over their feet in case of needing obvious treatment. I managed to get David to help and his father, Ron.

Ron was one of the old school, having learned his livestock craft from the practical apprenticeship of working beside someone who had done it all before. Ron was ever conscious that he had the same responsibility to educate the next generation. I asked Ron to examine the mouths and David to operate the gates; a job requiring lightning reactions to thwart the liveliest youngsters.

---

[62] equipment

"How do you expect me to mouth these? Yer fed them on oats?" Ron quipped knowing full well how to handle sheep.

"I thought I'd ask an expert," I called back.

Ron wrestled with a few more but was always wanting banter to ease the day.

"I wish I 'ad teeth like these," Ron commented.

"You did 'av, till you went to that horse dentist," David couldn't resist adding.

A few more sheep passed muster as I bent over the race, one hand on the ewe's hindquarters and the other feeling her bag for any lumps.

'Horses' – the word had been making its way around Ron's mind, triggering another old-time subject. "This job is like 'orses."

We were waiting for the explanation.

"Sound in wind and limb," he added.

"What's that got to do with sheep, Dad?" David felt he had to respond.

"When you buy an 'orse, it needs to be sound in wind and limb," Ron insisted. "Good lungs mean good power… and sound legs converts that power. What you have to do is try the 'orse trotting; don't buy an 'orse led by an old man walking," Ron continued.

There was another young ewe trying to butt Ron under the chin rather than give him access to her dentures; he won by raising her 'cheeks' enough to see them.

"A young man can hold the bridle or lead-rope and go as quick as possible." We hoped Ron had finished.

Rather than prompt any more gems, I noted the sheep's number and David and I walked them all into the near field. The few broken-mouthed ewes were led into a calf box. If an older ewe had no teeth and was in good condition, she was eating better than a ewe with just one or two teeth left. This was because the gums met and were able to pull off grass. The older ewe, providing she was in good condition and with pliable udders, could well do another lambing or even two.

By the end of the day, we had sorted the one- to two-year-old ewes to the near field and the older, sound ewes to another field on the other side of the drive. The next day we got the rams in and made sure they were 'sound in foot'; they also received a little grooming with hand shears and 'curry comb'[63]. We kept them in the yard overnight ready for the big day. I could only hope we had done enough and that the final movement from field to the sale pens would go without any maverick breaking out.

---

[63] a brush for removing dirt

The day was fine and all the machines were well presented in their appropriate order as per the catalogue. I had walked with Rosalind, an hour before dusk, to see it all for the last time.

"Won't it be sad for you?" she enquired.

"Yes and no, but I want to do it," I replied without emotion.

It was impressive and appeared much more numerous than I had expected. All that we had purchased, except for the Manitou, was there.

"I didn't know you had so much," Rosalind commented.

"Now we know why we had an overdraft!" I smiled.

I had mixed feelings but no real regrets. Walking up the rows, it was as if they were on display and standing to attention; a sort of decommissioning, job done.

"I confess I feel quite proud," I said unapologetically.

"So you should be," said Rosalind, ever the encourager. "There will be all the sheep as well." We passed the waiting empty pens. "I do hope you have a good sale, darling." She turned to kiss me.

"It is us together; I couldn't do it without you," I said.

We were getting rather sentimental.

"The future is bright. It is what we have planned; we have not been thrown out," I asserted.

The phone had rung all evening with questions about various lots. "How many hours has the Case 885 tractor done?" "Has it been regularly serviced?" "Is it tidy?" I wondered if the next question was going to be "Has it had a lady driver?" but remembered I was trying to sell the tractor. I tried to briefly outline that we had used it for mostly light tasks and employed contractors for the major work. Others wanted more details about trailers which would be evident to all the next day. In spite of tiredness creeping on, I tried to be upbeat. It occurred to me that hearing a voice, rather than just reading a catalogue, conveyed a certain something about a person. We construct mental pictures about the age and personality at the end of a phone.

"What did they sound like?" Rosalind asked

"Well, like a farmer, I suppose," I could only respond.

"Was he interested?"

"I guess so or he wouldn't have phoned," I suggested.

"Just like a man!" she retorted.

"I can't make anybody come; I can only answer their questions."

She was obviously used to answering calls to the surgery and forming a mental triage. "How bad is your cough, Mrs Smith?" followed up with, "Do your false teeth fall out?"

The sale day was dry again and it would be dry underfoot as well as overhead. I need not have worried about anything; all appeared well. The auctioneer's men joined us in the sheep movement and filled the row of pens with young ewes. The first pens held the good younger stock and the older ewes were next. The poorest were destined for the draft market in town. I didn't want to spoil the general quality by the inclusion of the poorest dozen.

There was nothing more to do except hang around; an hour of anticlimax. Everything was as ready as possible and the sheep were all penned. The cars were being directed to the top of the field and early birds were making their way along the lines, intent on an unhurried inspection before it became crowded. I was just there trying to look available, if indeed strangers from afar would even guess I was the retiring vendor. Glyn was busy with his staff, setting up the desk in the rear of my pick-up and the small tent that would house the accounts staff.

The car parking had moved into the overflow field and the sale lines were becoming full. As one or two locals called for my attention, others assumed I must be the farmer and formed a small knot for insider information. "If I bought something could I leave it overnight?" "If I had the rolls, have you got anything to lift them onto a truck?" The other concern revolved around security overnight. I had to assure them that the moment a purchase was made, it became their property and consequently their responsibility.

Glyn, after the ringing of the loud market bell summonsing the start of the sale and a few obligatory taps on his headpiece mic, launched into the introductions.

"Welcome to Woodhead Farm, and we thank Mr and Mrs Jennings for favouring us in handling this notable retirement sale." He went on to give details of requiring full payment for all lots purchased and the responsibility of immediate movement unless prior arrangements had been secured.

"You see a full array of good quality farm equipment, well presented, and we start straight away with lot one." Glyn was in motion.

Unfortunately, the first few lots, as always in farm sales, hardly warranted the great build-up he had given them. In our case Lot 1 consisted of a heap of wood that would have served well on the fifth of November. Lot 2 was hardly more valuable, being any scrap metal that could not be sold as an item. Fortunately, scrap metal was always attractive to specialist merchants and made a good price.

Lot 3 was my old, sturdy workshop bench. It reduced in value from ten pounds down to two pounds, at which point I stepped in and secured it. I had originally purchased it at the estate sale, a decade earlier, for the same price. It had given a further two decades of service, becoming as essential as my favourite armchair.

Fortunately, these opening lots were, as always, to get momentum going, generating decision-making and the quick reaction that auctions thrive on. The next lots were useful sundries of hand tools, spray chemicals, a medicine cupboard complete with various wormers, spray markers and application guns.

There were also fencing posts, ancillary tools and 'gas guns'[64]. All these led up to tractor implements and eventually the 'heavies'.

It was important to get at least a good market price for 'heavies', the serious implements and machines that are currently commercial. The deep cultivator: a frame carrying up to a dozen stout tines, that can break a 'plough pan'[65] and acts as the first rough cultivator on heavy ground. It would find a home on any farm, costing little to maintain and available when lighter equipment just wouldn't do the job. David's father, Ron, had pulled my leg saying, "That cultivator is only for bad farmers," waiting for me to react.

"What do you mean, bad farmers?" I knew that would be a trigger for something.

"If the land is too wet to work, yer shouldn't be on it," Ron said.

"You only say that because you haven't got a tractor big enough to use it!" I joked. It was unfair as he only had a small pasture holding but I knew he would find an answer.

"Horses could pull that all day," came the retort.

"Yes, but how many, six or eight?" It was all nonsense but we both enjoyed the banter.

A year or two earlier, Ron had appeared at the farm whilst I was just creosoting a saw-bench which would hold a significant branch when using a bow-saw. Rosalind had brought out a cup of coffee and stayed to be sociable. Ron examined the bench in great detail, congratulating me with such gushing terms that I knew he was up to his tricks.

"That is beautifully finished, just the right height." He walked around the other side. "That will last a lifetime. You could handle a chainsaw on that bench." He half-turned his back on Rosalind. "You really are good to your wife; she will love that," he said.

Rosalind took no immediate notice, whilst he laughed and I simply allowed a slight grin to crease my face.

"You wait until I see you at the surgery. Whether you come for an injection or constipation relief, I will remember," she threatened Ron, and went back to the house.

Back at the sale we were on to the implements. The heavy cultivator was as well shod as the power harrow, both selling well. So was my adapted crop sprayer which would reach across modern tramlines, eminently commercial until one can afford a contractor to do the spraying. The crowd moved on, both serious bidders and interested spectators. Glyn had all the specifications of the portable crop drier, emphasising its usefulness on both large and smaller farms where grain was stored in rented buildings or without mains electricity. I

---

[64] bird scarers
[65] a compacted layer in cultivated soil resulting from repeated ploughing

warmed to his sales technique and wondered if underbidders wouldn't be forming a small queue at the main dealer's premises later.

The old Belarus tractor sold for double the £600 I had paid a decade earlier to, I think, a vintage enthusiast. Then the modern Case tractor, suitably cleaned and now started for at least the sixth time today. There was great interest from both smallholders and those who could warrant a smaller workhorse in addition to their current 'stable'.

Glyn handed over to his colleague as the crowd broke up, some to make payments whilst the livestock farmers moved on to the sheep pens. I was relieved that no sheep had escaped and now there were sufficient hands leaning over the pens, feeling the condition of the ewes under the long wool, to deter any thought of it. Some were 'mouthing' the nearest head they could reach, making sure of the age and that 'grass-harvesting' parts were sound. They checked the incisors at the front, not the cud-chewing section at the back of the mouth. Four adult teeth in the bottom jaw approximated to two years old; and eight teeth, approximating to three years, was called a 'full mouth'. Other prospective purchasers had done the same before the crowd had moved from the machinery. The usual trilby hats and cloth caps I knew from the weekly livestock market were there. They always jumped at the chance to see the farm where stock had come from and make judgements about the 'home' that had nurtured them. It also gave a chance to reminisce on previous tenants and their farming ability.

Glyn's colleague, Morris, started the sheep section with the same ingratiating introduction that Glyn had used. I wondered if they learned it as a matter of company policy by way of advertising that they had been chosen, as auctioneers, above other competitors. On the other hand, I liked to think it was a polite recognition that they valued the business. Morris opened, as auctioneers do, with a rather flattering suggestion that the first pen was worth fifty per cent more than any others he had ever sold. Realising in an instant that the prospective purchasers were there when he had last held a gavel, he dropped down by five pounds before he received so much as a nod. Auctioneer and experienced buyers were now on equal footing and business could commence. He reeled off the bids in one pound steps. Having started at seventy-five it was soon eighty-five pounds as buyers wanted to get in, on the assumption the first lot was often the cheapest.

Morris sensed a steadying rate of bids and dropped in fifty pence steps without slackening pace. He wound down to twenty pence steps.

"87.50; 88; 88.20; 88.40; all finished? 88.60..." *Knock!* His small gavel hit his clipboard. The teller noted the price and the purchaser's name. Most were well-known regulars but retirement farm sales often attracted strangers from some distance. This, coupled with extended families, often required confirmation by eliciting a few suggestions. The auctioneer had long overcome any doubts by asking additionally for the farm name. This we often copied in conversations, referring to Jones 'Chapel House', Mason 'The Gables', even Jennings 'Woodhead'.

The rams were sold as individuals and the sale was soon over. A long queue formed at the accounts tent whilst others of the same family were securing the lots they had purchased. The lines were a jumble of pick-ups, car trailers and tractors, all vying for their purchase and leaving the mêlée. The essential bit of paper to exit the farm was the receipt of purchase "fully paid".

I thanked Glyn, Morris and their staff and retreated indoors. We had decided to have a meal at a restaurant rather than chance a broken evening with more phone calls. We settled down, emptied of energy, just looking at each other across the table.

"It's all over." Rosalind was the first to speak.

"Yes, we can't go back." A smile of relief crossed my face.

"There is plenty of future." She reached across to grip my hand; we were both exhausted.

"A bottle of red wine, I think." I raised a hand but the waiter was already on his way. It was a great evening of unwinding. Going out to dinner was a rare treat; we resolved to spend more quality time together now the farm had gone.

## Fly Away

The next morning was different; indeed, we had expected it to be, but it was strangely empty. We had not flown away leaving everything behind; Rosalind had gone to work as usual. I had stepped into an empty farmyard with no stock to care for, no machinery to repair or prepare for the next task. I untied the dogs and walked to the sale field. There were two large items left that I knew would be collected later: the portable corn drier shortly, and the gang of ring rollers about lunchtime. I would clear up the pieces of litter and shut all the gates when every item had gone.

We walked two more fields to where the pasture sloped steeply towards the valley. Russ and Fly were close at heel, but there were no sheep to be seen. The cool autumn air told us to keep walking. The dogs did not seem to expect a workout today. I doubted they had connected the fact that the sheep in pens were disappearing forever; surely there would be others. I bent down and briefly made a fuss of them both. We enjoyed our relationship and I was sorry they were not going to have the pleasure of working sheep today. There was a subtle change; the farm was all there but its life had gone. Perhaps if we had been in the pick-up, as usual, the dogs would have thought of nothing else but arriving at the sheep field.

By six o'clock it seemed I had achieved very little except minor tidying up. I had no heart or energy to do anything outside, so after dinner I settled down to watch television.

"I've been thinking about Fly and Russ." I introduced the subject out of the blue.

"No wonder you haven't done a lot today." Rosalind chided me after evenings of saying, "You must spend less time working."

"There is nothing for them to do now," I continued.

"Well, they will just be pets," she said.

"They're sheepdogs; that's their life," I asserted.

"Can't they retire just like us?" Rosalind insisted.

"Not really. Working is their life; it's what they want and need, the purpose they have been trained for."

There was a silence, but neither of us were interested in the TV.

"I think Russ will become a pet, he is getting too old to run after sheep ... but Fly is in his prime. I think we will have to sell him," I suggested.

"Sell him? How could you?" Rosalind was more animated than she had been all evening.

"We owe it to him; it is bred in him, absolutely part of his life. It's the kindest thing for him," I insisted.

I advertised a "useful young collie due to my retirement". It was with a heavy heart but I knew it was the best I could do for Fly. There were about five phone call replies giving me some idea about the situation he might be going into. I had bought an extended car boot catch which latched within an inch off being completely closed. This was the way most trial dogs travelled rather than standing in the back of farm pick-ups. Fly took no time in learning to hop into my car boot and the lid shutting, closing on him except for ventilation.

I was expected to give a demonstration of his abilities, so we drove some twenty-five miles to a specialist sheep farm just over the county border. I was introduced to the farmer and to his 'friend' who apparently judged sheepdog trials.

"I haven't trained Fly for trials," I admitted. "He just does a useful farm job."

It was with some trepidation that I asked what they would like demonstrated as I couldn't see any sheep.

"There is a bunch of ewes at the bottom of the field. Get him to fetch them." The farmer was very matter of fact, verging on hostility.

I walked some five yards forward as the two of them seemed intent on sharing comments. Fly for his part showed no signs of the pressure I felt.

"Sit!" I quietly commanded, which he simply obeyed.

"Away!" I commanded.

Fly needed no second invitation and disappeared down the left-hand side of the field at some speed.

I waited, staring at the empty view ahead, not daring to avert my gaze. Then a bunch of at least fifty sheep, for no accountable reason, hastened towards me.

"Slow," I shouted.

The sheep didn't hear, but Fly immediately lay down. It had the desired effect. The sheep slowed to a trot with no dog behind them, and Fly the motivator was just in view.

"Get them a bit close," the farmer instructed.

"Steady," I called out.

Fly simply stood up, which was the perfect signal for the sheep to move another twenty yards closer.

"Sit!" Fly obeyed; it was better than clockwork. I called the dog to my side.

"Get him to push them back over the brow," the farmer directed.

"Sit!" I said as I walked towards the top of the slope. I had only walked some forty yards and moved a few paces across the field.

"Fly, away!" He stood up, which the sheep immediately noticed, and trotted towards me. It was the correct command and correct response. The flock passed me by down the slope.

"Sit!" I commanded and Fly was ten yards from me, having achieved the task. I walked briskly to him and back to the 'judges'.

"Get him to run to the right side and stop before they see him."

"Fly, go-bye!" I instructed emphasising the 'bye'.

"Sit!" He dropped like a stone, flat in the grass.

"Call 'im back."

"You give 'im the wrong instructions; 'Away' is anticlockwise and 'Bye' clockwise," the judge said.

I felt like saying I was left-handed which, although true, may not have helped the sale.

"All I can say is, I trained Fly and we understand each other."

"Why do you call him Fly? That's a bitch's name," he asked

"Cos he went like a rocket the first time I instructed him." I felt distinctly uncharitable to them.

"What price do you want for him?" the farmer asked.

"He's worth five hundred; he has got a long life before him and knows the job," I replied.

"Way over the top," came the comment.

"I would accept £475," I said flatly.

"Too much," he said.

I turned and opened the boot lid and Fly jumped back in.

"Don't be so hasty," the farmer called out.

It was clear that I had had enough and was certainly not bluffing.

"You were the first to respond to the advert and the first people to see the dog." The implication was clear.

"I'll give you a cheque for £475 and ask you to hold it for two or three days whilst I see how he settles," he immediately offered.

I agreed to this and we shook hands. Three nights later the farmer phoned me and told me to present the cheque.

Rosalind and I were sorry to lose Fly who was a most remarkable dog. I tried to be casual, insisting it was for his own good. After a couple of weeks I felt I must see Fly again to make sure he was OK.

"I'll tell you what," I announced to my dear wife, "I would like to be sure Fly is happy. Do you want to come?"

"No, I'm sure I would want him back." It was honest and no doubt the best answer.

I phoned, asking if I could call and see Fly had settled in; it appeared to be no problem.

I drew into the yard and approached a Land Rover next to a barn, expecting to meet the farmer.

"Fly!" He was lying in the back of the vehicle, immediately getting up on hearing my voice. Of course, we greeted each other. I was careful not to make too much fuss of him, unsettling his new relationship. I turned to look around for his new owner. Fly simply looked at me and jumped back into his new vehicle. It was absolutely clear that he had settled in, and I retreated without a word. I didn't need a translation; I understood 'canine' as well as he understood English.

I found the farmer in the barn and told him I had seen Fly and that he seemed fine. I mentioned his real attachment to the Land Rover and the fact I had not unsettled him.

"I'm pleased with him; in fact, my cousin wants to know if you have any more like him?" His tone was friendly and in no sense begrudging Fly's price. I could only tell him Russ was too old, but I was pleased to find Fly well at home.

# 46

# Stream Cottage

Stream Cottage was Rosalind's treasured possession; it was all that one pictures in the quintessential English countryside. Built in 1832 of local stone, with a slate roof and a millstream flowing around two sides of the garden, it was as if it were planted on the edge of a village going nowhere. For Rosalind it was like returning home after a twelve-year absence. Her old friends and neighbours had never been very distant in thought or miles; birthday cards had kept relationships going at arm's length. The occasional visit she had made, to administer the letting, had kept her up to date with the village. There had been no new houses built because nobody had seen the need or had the desire to apply for building permission. In short, change was not made because it was deemed alright as it was. This was not to imply that it was stuffy or backward. Far from it; much was going on.

The village hall was used by the Whist Club, Women's Institute, painting classes, Keep Fit and much more. It was the venue for every committee as well as parish council meetings, a venue for harvest suppers and any excuse for communal get-togethers, especially any involving eating. At the time we arrived, the hall was being modernised and extended, mostly by villagers' personal efforts. What was there to dislike about such a community?

My concern was about our cottage; it was too small, and right on the main road. I use the word 'main' advisedly as it was perfectly possible to walk down the middle of it without impeding a motor vehicle or cyclist. After Woodhead, three-quarters of a mile off the tarmac, we were now one yard away from a road; yes, the end of the dwelling was within three feet of the side of a single-decker bus that passed on a Tuesday. It delivered a few villagers to the nearest town, collected them two hours later and repeated the trip seven days later. I had to confess to Rosalind that it was the psychological shock of being on a road that unsettled me, rather than concern about possible structural damage.

We both settled into our new circumstances; Rosalind with less distance to travel in her last four years before retirement, and me with my long list of maintenance and improvement jobs.

"I do find it rather cramped here compared with the farm," I started gently.

"We have been used to more space, especially on the estate, but I lived here before," she said.

"Precisely, dear, but now there are two of us." I paused, not wanting to start an argument. "Wouldn't you like a bigger kitchen?" I asked.

"Well, yes, now you mention it, I would." Rosalind brightened.

"It could be extended a foot or so to bring it in line with the roadside wall and five feet towards the garage." I had actually measured it.

"That would be useful." She was wistful.

"Actually, we need a bathroom upstairs; there is no water at all up there," I emphasised.

"I've never thought about it; we have a bath and toilet opposite the kitchen. It would cost a lot to alter," she observed.

I drew a rough plan the next day which sold the principle that modernisation was necessary. We agreed that my brother-in-law Richard, an architect, could draw up proper plans, making sure it would pass planning regulations.

In the meantime I continued with the farm consultancy, advising on diversification enterprises to supplement incomes and readjustments of traditional farming. Increasingly there was a demand for coping with the 'Single Payment Scheme' which the government was developing and which involved complying with minimum standards for crop production, animal welfare and the environment in order to qualify for a subsidy. I was also trying to rent a couple of fields and run a few beef cattle to keep a foot in farming.

I managed to rent permanent pasture from an otherwise all-arable farm in the village. The land sloped and had a few trees and wet patches. This was Yeoman England; medieval towns and villages standing since the Middle Ages, owing their prosperity to the wool trade. It was as if they continued to stand in defiance of modernisation, which had failed to even influence them. The fields had evolved into modern farming but with patches that refused to accept large machinery and insisted on nurturing fritillaries. It was this sort of small field that accommodated my newly purchased Welsh Black stores, chosen for their quiet temperament.

It was a joy to cross the road and say good morning to the dozen all-black bullocks. I was soon accepted as a friend; no doubt helped by a few beef nuts. Friendship was a practical relationship rather than an oversentimentality in my retirement. I was conscious that I could not call on help to collect them into a corral for veterinary inspection except by persuasion. I managed to get two to eat from my hand but others needed to 'graze' their handful of nuts from the ground. My two 'close' friends were 'Hairy Ears' and 'Sniffy'. Now that I had moved from livestock units to casual small-scale retirement, I had decided to give the animals names. Hairy Ears got his name from a veritable bouquet growing out of each ear, right from where sound ought to be received. Sniffy had the constant habit of licking his nose as if his great tongue were a windscreen wiper for clear smelling. These two would even allow a friendly rub behind the ears whilst they swiped off a handful of nuts.

I constructed a strong corral and got most of them to enter, but never tried slamming the gate shut behind them in case it destroyed their confidence. Inevitably the time came for a TB test, and I could not rely on Russ to help; they seemed to have had a 'bad dog experience' at the back of their minds and would not tolerate any canine in the field. Frank, the local cattle dealer who had purchased them for me, offered to help me corral them for the vet's first visit. He arrived on his quad bike with a dog. I dealt with the dog issue as soon as the vet appeared by tying it up with Russ. We soon discovered that the cattle also had an issue with quad bikes.

"Where did you get these from?" I called to him.

"My lot don't mind the quad." Frank bypassed the question and I didn't pursue it.

I held the gate open as the cattle were moving swiftly towards it. At that moment Frank, riding the quad like a jockey, appeared over the rise behind the cattle. The effect could not have been greater if he had fired a gun behind them. They stampeded past me and the corral to the roadside hedge.

"These are not used to a bike; I don't care if yours are," I shouted in shock and fear.

"We can try again." Frank was still on the bike, revving the engine occasionally in case they may have forgotten he was behind them.

"We will have to walk them round," I insisted.

We slowly pushed them back to the far hedge to gently walk them towards the corral again. The cattle turned in the right direction but immediately repeated the rodeo as if the first time were a dress rehearsal. We were left spellbound.

"They've got it on 'em," Frank said, as if it were my fault.

"It's no use; we will have to leave it for today. I'll speak to the vet," I called out.

For the next four days I tried putting nuts in troughs inside the corral but it was difficult to persuade them all in. Soon the first eight had eaten the nuts but with four animals still standing outside watching. It was time to enlist the help of two neighbouring farmers. We walked behind the bullocks, four abreast as if linked by a rope. They walked in as if for a picnic; I quickly shut the gate. We guided them into the short race and the cattle crush. The vet cut off a small circle of hair on each animal and injected a small Tuberculin dose.

Three days later we tried the same procedure for the vet to measure the size of the resulting 'bump' with callipers; too large a bump indicating a reactor[66]. "First get your animals into the crush," so the manual might have said. It was not that the cattle remembered the quad bike or dog, but that three days earlier they had had a sharp prick instead of nice beef nuts. It called for reinforcements and the whole morning to complete the testing. It was the beginning of the end

---

[66] failed the test for bovine TB

as far as keeping my nice cattle; although we had no reactors, it just was not practical to muster busy neighbours and expensive veterinary services without farmyard penning. Disappointed, I kept them until an autumn sale.

## Just an Extension

The suggestion of enlarging the cottage matured, or more accurately morphed, into a possibility. It was no longer out of the question, as Rosalind came to the conclusion that two people in a house needed a little more room than single occupancy had. Apart from a larger kitchen, she agreed that it would be an improvement to have water upstairs. My brother-in-law, Richard, being an architect, took in the whole building. In his mind he was not in the business of adding a slightly bigger 'box' to an existing one, in terms of the kitchen. He drew up plans envisioning life in the whole dwelling. In due course a large envelope arrived with plans in triplicate, beautifully presented as "before" and "after". We spread them on the dining-room table, the only surface large enough to take them.

"This is now." I pointed to the single-storey kitchen with a lean-to roof.

"So this would be the new one." Rosalind moved to the next sheet. "What is that?" Her finger moved across to a toilet in plain view.

"That is the utility," I explained. "It will take toilet and handbasin as well as a washing machine."

She looked up at me, "What about the bath?"

"That's upstairs," I said.

"The stairs are here." She pointed to the obvious treads next to the utility room. "But they are actually in here."

This was undeniable as we were in the dining room and the stairs were three feet away going diagonally up the wall.

"Richard has moved the stairs to make it better upstairs, and it gives us about three feet extra in this room." I opened the first-floor plan.

"Look, there is the bathroom and there's an extra bedroom on top of the kitchen... which is currently single-storey. We will have all that on top of what we have now." I hoped I had sold the idea.

"But that's not just an extension; it's half a house!" Rosalind exclaimed, half in disbelief and half in dismay at the apparent loss of her cottage. "We can't afford all this; it will cost a fortune," she added, looking at me disapprovingly.

"Look at what we will have." I pointed out that the extra bedroom had its own en suite and across the landing there was a bathroom, emulating a hotel. "We *can* afford it; I can do most of it myself," I assured her.

"You can't build a house; anyway, you haven't got the time."

"I can do most of it and I've got the Manitou and car trailer still," I insisted.

"Well, make a start; it does look lovely." Rosalind was firing the starting pistol.

Planning permission was granted but with only adding five feet extra to the cottage's present 'footprint'. I marked out the new boundary that defined the future for both of us. The first real work was preparing to live on a building site; I started by making the kitchen smaller. The temporary roadside wall was made with sheets of shuttering ply, with the electric cooker junction box screwed onto it. The plans indicated footings nearly three feet deep had to be dug before the first block of the wall could be laid. I noticed that the building inspector back in 1832 had only specified a four-by-four-inch timber laid straight onto the clay soil. As I dug the trench for the footings, I wished I could have congratulated him on both the quality of the timber and his sound specification, which was still holding up the two-storey cottage some hundred and seventy years later.

I managed with a builder's line and a good spirit level to build the block walls to first-floor level. The tricky items were the very precise holes for windows and the new back door, to be fitted much later. The old front door was the other end of the house and never used, if ever opened at all; it was blocked by the armchair in the lounge. Common practice by several generations had never used the proper front door as it was hung with thick curtains from ceiling to floor to keep out the draught. It was only to be opened if royalty or the parson were calling and then only with due notice. The back door, like most country properties, was the door for everybody else, including the postman who would collect letters as well as deliver them.

I must mention here the excellent postmen and women who served us. During the various stages of the building work, Ron and his colleagues went beyond the call of duty, even giving a brief hand. I found that when I came upon a two-man job, I could often work around it until the next morning. Once, this entailed holding an eight-by-four sheet whilst I secured it and later a four-metre worktop spanning the width of the kitchen without it snapping at the hole for the sink in its middle. Ron's greatest contribution was helping by providing two extra hands (I needed four) to reassemble part of the Manitou engine. We spent twenty minutes heaving and struggling, ending successfully but with grease from the waist up. I would have offered him a shower if I had already installed one at that stage, but he cheerfully made do with copious rags and degreaser, plus a bottle of wine.

The postman's information was equally helpful in terms of finding out where to source building sundries from. He knew where there was a portable electric cement mixer when mine refused to work, and surplus window lintels at a job two miles away. Equal thanks were extended to delivery drivers from the builders' merchants who knew a quicker way do some plumbing or the "new spray foam" to fix window frames. The building inspector realised he was dealing with a farmer trying to do a builder's job and was always ready to enlighten me. This had the merit of free advice and the guarantee of him passing the job next time he inspected.

It was satisfying to overcome potential problems even if slower than professional tradesmen. Rosalind, needless to say, welcomed seeing the gradual progress, but I heard from a friend that the nursing home noticed her nervousness as she packed up each evening. Apparently, her apprehension was at what she might find on arriving home. This happened at a number of critical stages, such as the only entrance becoming two gangplanks across a new 'ditch' to get into the house. Equally, the absence of a front door for a couple of nights; she insisted on a temporary blockading of the stairs whilst we slept. I might add that the reason there was no door was because I had first to fit the doorframe. It had become something of a joke at her work as to what deficiency she might have suffered overnight.

The walls reached eaves level and I needed expert help with the roof construction. The house extension would have two smaller apex roofs at right angles to the existing roof. Fortunately, my friend Spencer had been a lecturer in technical construction and was more than able to instruct another friend and me on building a cut roof, cutting the timber on site as distinct from using factory-made trusses.

The fun started with the plans requiring a steel joist from the new concrete block wall spanning back to rest on the original house wall. Naturally, experts like my friend Spencer would think in terms of a mobile crane for the job.

"That's the beam they specified," Spencer confirmed. "It's hefty; we'll need a crane for that."

"I've got one," I answered, pointing to the Manitou.

I could see doubt crossing Spencer's face.

"I've erected several steel beams with it." I clearly wasn't convincing him. "We will have to be careful not to knock the new block work," I cautioned.

I tied a substantial rope around the beam and wrapped the forklift tines, making sure it was balanced and not able to slip. We tested it about a foot off the ground, giving us both confidence. I drove imperceptibly to the corner of the extension; Spencer had his hand on the girder to detect any movement.

"Stand clear! I'm just going to raise it," I called out. Spencer moved several paces backwards. The hydraulic lift was smooth and there was no swinging. It was at the right height; I gently extended the mast and lowered it onto the block work.

We both breathed a sigh of relief. It was resting on both the roadside wall and the end wall. We went upstairs onto the new chipboarded floor and very carefully lifted and edged the beam with our shoulders. "Just a few inches will do," I called to Spencer at the other end of the beam.

"OK, lift rather than drag," he confirmed.

Eventually it was in place; we checked the measurements from every angle, and then checked again.

"That's about it." I could hardly believe the tape.

"Spot on! Well done!" Spencer congratulated me.

"I won't tell you how many times I've measured everything," I smiled.

"Well, the new roof will rest on this and it will certainly carry the weight." Spencer was satisfied.

The roof was felted, battened and slated. It made a huge difference to the outside of the cottage and a psychological confirmation that the work was not beyond us. The internal work could now proceed independently of the weather and was ever nearer completion. My wife could hardly wait.

## The Kitchen Expands

Rosalind returned home to find me on my knees in the middle of the kitchen.

"Where has the wall gone?" she gasped.

"Most of it is outside," I quietly informed her.

I was proud of the difference as I hammered away at the base of the last wall. Two stone and brick walls had been wheelbarrowed out and up to my neighbour's field as hardcore. The next day Rosalind had a second surprise, returning home to find her kitchen had disappeared. More precisely, the bottom half had. We had discussed the possibility of this as a new floor was needed, but to see it gone was a shock.

We now had crockery in the dining room, as well as the fridge; other household items could be found in the garage.

"Where did you put the tins?" she called from the dining room.

"What tins? I asked.

"Sardines."

"In the garage, I think…"

"I thought we agreed: food in the dining room and cleaning stuff in the garage." She was not amused.

"Well, I thought there was plenty of stuff in the dining room; something had to go to the garage," I called back.

"I happen to want sardines. Where in the garage?" She was quite definite.

"They would all be together." I tried to make light of it.

"If they are all together, I'd appreciate you finding them," she instructed.

I could well understand her frustration and was working as fast as possible to get back to whatever constituted normal. It might have been easier if we had lived in a caravan in the garden but, it being four feet higher than the drive, it was inaccessible to any transport heavier than a child's tricycle. I found the sardines, predictably at the bottom of the chest of tins.

I used ready-mix concrete and 'floated in' the floor throughout the extension. This meant we had three consecutive dinners at the local inn. Each evening Rosalind filled in the proprietor's wife with a progress report, eliciting much sympathy. I could only counter by suggesting a discount as we had become regular customers.

"I've been looking at floor tiles and they have got some lovely ones at the Tile Centre," said Rosalind, visibly brightened.

I took the catalogue and joined her on the settee, our only available seat.

"These are the ones I would like" – she hesitated and dropped her voice – "but they are the most expensive."

I didn't respond but noted they were a variegated brick colour which would be pleasing and easy on the eye. I felt she deserved the best; the cost was not to be an issue.

"They are really cottagey." She looked up with hope in her eyes.

"I agree; after all your inconvenience you deserve the best," I asserted.

"I want you to like them."

"I really do; they are three different sizes laid in a repeating pattern," I observed.

"That's the charm, isn't it?" she agreed.

I was wondering how difficult it would be to lay them in the correct sequence without finding at the end of the job that one tile was sideways or there were two small ones in the place where one medium-sized tile should have been.

Laying the floor tiles in the kitchen went without a hitch and delighted Rosalind.

"I am glad you like them. I do too."

We peered into the kitchen.

"We must leave them overnight to be sure they are set," I warned.

"Let's go upstairs."

"By the way, I've got to collect the stairs tomorrow." I tried to make it as casual as possible to avoid another dispute.

"That's good." It was a rather restrained reply.

"Yes, I'm getting fed up with the ladder," I agreed. "We badly need the stairs but it will delay the kitchen units a little."

"I can't wait for the stairs," she burst out.

"They are made in two halves and I will try and get Colin to help me."

I hoped this would be an encouragement to her. Colin was an old friend and had helped us many times over the years.

The only stairs had been removed to increase the space in the dining room and an aluminium ladder had been put in their place. Rosalind had arrived home, noticing the alterations immediately.

"I knew the stairs were going, but how do you expect me to get to bed?"

"The ladder is quite safe." I stepped on the second rung and shook the ladder, but it was hardly convincing.

"I can't go up there; I'll have to sleep down here." She looked around the lounge-diner; large as it was, even the floor was crowded.

I couldn't remember Rosalind with tears; they started gently, suddenly bursting like a dam. I wrapped my arm around her shoulder and steered her head to mine. I waited; it was best to remain silent. Sobs slowed as if the reservoir were emptying. How could the ladder have caused so much grief?

"There, darling; don't take on so." I wanted to sooth the anxiety.

"Jane's mother has died." Jane was the receptionist at the surgery.

"Was she ill?" I asked.

"No, it was just so sudden." I felt a final sob escape her. "There will have to be a post-mortem." She wiped her eyes. "It's been too much today and now the ladder."

"Don't worry about the ladder now; we'll manage."

She turned away without comment.

It was time to go upstairs; we both knew it was inevitable. I had been up once during the evening without saying a word.

"You just go up naturally and I will be right behind you as you step to the side. Hold onto the post on the left," I softly encouraged.

In the morning we dressed and reversed the exercise. I stood on the ladder, two rungs from the top.

I held the remaining newel post.

"Hold the ladder with your right hand and put your right foot on the rung. You can feel my arm behind you; it's perfectly safe." I kept up the commentary. "I'm going down now; it's OK."

Rosalind descended quite easily, seemingly reassured.

It was a matter of juggling building priorities. Now that the new concrete flooring had been done, covering the kitchen area, utility, hallway and old bathroom, the stairs really had to be next. I had taken copious measurements and ordered stairs to fit the new space where the old bathroom had been. It had been a master plan of my brother-in-law to move the stairs, but we had not fully realised the disruption it would cause. Rosalind had reminded me that "upstairs is half the house" and she looked forward to proper stairs. She expressed this desire more forcibly as she didn't like turning to descend the ladder. The new stairs became my absolute priority.

The plan specified five steps down to a quarter landing and six from there down to the hall level. The carpenter making them advised that stairs should be hung from the top and any fraction of an inch made good at the bottom. This in mind, I hoped Colin and I would find there would only be a fraction of an inch in my measurements to cope with. Working from first principles, and what I hoped was practical sense, we decided on a dry run. Any reader skilled in building and carpentry, please skip the next paragraph.

The void from hallway to first floor was like a lift-shaft with no lift. We started with a number of concrete blocks and bits of timber to support the quarter landing in exactly the correct place against the back wall. The top half of the stairs was then offered up, supported by various timbers, and the finished floor level of the landing marked on the wall. Everything was dismantled so that we could work downward from that level to fix floor joists between the two side walls. The joists were covered with flooring grade chipboard and the upper flight secured to wall and newel posts.

All measurements proved accurate. We had a lunch break and fixed the lower flight. Remarkably, there was no drama to report to Rosalind. We had tested the structure as perfectly safe and invited her to do the same.

"You are the first lady to ascend our stairs," I said, although I had no bouquet to offer her. Nonetheless, I have never seen more gratitude in a face than then.

The ladder had gone from the dining room and Rosalind was stepping up and down on the bare stair boards with aplomb. It was another sign of progress.

Now that the stairs were operational, safety demanded the hole be covered where the old ones had been. I cut new short joists and flooring and nailed plasterboard underneath. The finished job had made the dining room nearly three feet longer and the previous landing above became a double bedroom. The upstairs would need a lot more time and effort spent on it, but priorities again demanded that Rosalind had her kitchen finished first.

The cost of a complete kitchen equated to the cost of a tractor, which in principle was too much. Old farmers, apart from the gentry, in my experience apportioned money to where it might increase the business rather than the house where it was considered a luxury. Farmers' wives might not agree but they do have a thorough understanding of business finance.

I had witnessed this concern with unnecessary luxury when visiting to advise a farmer on a diversification scheme to improve his business. His wife called me into the kitchen just after their breakfast.

"Come in," she called from the back door. "He is expecting you."

I obeyed and walked into a familiar scene. The large oak table, which had obviously known many generations, was central to the room. A Belfast sink, two dressers and some cupboards were arrayed around the walls, including a butcher's block. The farmer stood over the table, apparently reading the *Farmers Weekly*. I was struck by his height as his wife directed me to a chair. He came to me, hand extended and noticeably only my height. He saw me looking across at the magazine and two concrete blocks protruding from under the table.

"I've been reading the *Weekly*," he announced. "My eyes are not what they were."

Rather than pay for spectacles, 'growing' the table by four inches had the same effect.

We had been attracted by a private advert in the local paper offering a complete kitchen. I turned up at the address one morning with my large car trailer in case I could buy it on the spot. There was nobody in at half past eight as the owner had advised. At nine, two workmen arrived and informed me they were fitting a new kitchen. They were about to destroy the old one until I pointed out that I had come to collect it. A small cash incentive changed their minds and they agreed to unscrew most of it, rather than to smash it to pieces, and to place it by the gate. Such were the number of units that I had to make two trips, taking all morning.

The next few days were spent cutting, fitting and arranging all the floor cupboards. We had decided on a new double oven on the internal wall and an electric hob sunk into the worktop at the window looking onto the road. This would make maximum use of the workspace. The worktop was new and, as per the latest fashion, fitted around two and a half sides of the kitchen. Care was needed in cutting exact holes to take the electric hob and a 'sink and a half' by the other window. This was achieved with the help of postman Ron, mentioned previously. The new wall cupboards were exchanged later with the old ones that had been left hanging on the walls. Although Rosalind had seen the work taking place (amid tools, trailing electric leads, assorted offcuts, and builders' detritus), it had really been a mess in progress. I had installed spotlights in the ceiling to light strategic work points; ceiling and walls had all been painted.

I timed the completion for Rosalind's return. I waited until she was due to get home from work and walked across from the garage as she drove into the yard.

"Have you had a good day?" I asked, still walking to the back door.

"It was OK. Sick patients made well." Her usual commitment to patient privacy.

"I am afraid you had better check this." I was deliberately misleading, softening her to another reversal in fortunes. I opened the kitchen door and nearly pushed her forward. The lights were on, highlighting the scene. The cupboards, all doors shut, were in regimental order. The wall cupboards were strategically placed to maximise natural light and not inhibit space on the all-surround worktop. The lovely brick-coloured floor was illuminated to contrast the white units.

"It's marvellous!" She took another breath and scanned it all again. " *You* are marvellous."

We hugged and kissed. Still holding my arm, she led me on a conducted tour. I knew every nook and cranny from the top, sideways and even from underneath, but enjoyed her enthusiasm. Each time we came to an item, she listed it as if I needed an introduction. "The hob..." "The worktop, right up to the sink..." "Mixer taps..." "Cupboards, top and bottom..." "Double oven at waist level..." "Worktop to the door..." "Lights with dimmer..."

"OK, darling." I had to stop her.

She caught hold of both my hands and we hopped and skipped in a waltz around the kitchen.

There was a buzz in the kitchen, an air of utter delight. Rosalind had never welcomed even female help in the kitchen; it was her domain, the place where she fashioned dishes of delight. Now it was as promised, only larger. She treated it like a laboratory; careful measuring and following the 'researched formula' produced the perfect outcome. QED. No doubt she thought the rest of the house would take shape in due time, but her world had blossomed.

# 47

# Change of Gear

The house was completely habitable. Some skirting boards were needed and paintwork touched up but we could now live in it and even entertain our friends. The garden beckoned and plans had not been unwrapped for the garage complex, but it was time to change gear; a time to slow down, to live a little more, without being idle. The shift more accurately would be to 'cruise control', powering along without having to put my foot on the pedal.

Rosalind was counting the months until her retirement. She was enjoying the nursing home but was looking forward to the prospect of stepping out of paid work and becoming more involved with the village. She increased her attendance of the Woman's Institute, which afforded a relief from medical matters and added the opportunity to practise her 'chemistry' skills in cooking. It was no surprise when both were combined in a social experience for the village as she instigated the 'Coffee Spot'. This was a monthly Saturday morning coffee club, open to all, held in the village hall at rock bottom cost. A rota of hosting soon sprung up, with volunteers supplying the coffee and a wider number the cakes. The cost of coffee and cake was expected to be two pounds and refills were free of charge. The till was a soup bowl where payment and change was received or extracted. It was, in effect, a freewill offering that exceeded expectations and grew to make an annual surplus split between the hall and church. Such was the success that people from adjacent villages put the monthly date in their diary. A culture grew that 'gossip' could be better shared if, by a refill of cups, one alighted on another table with fresh news to receive or dispense. This circulation was a cord drawing the village together to everyone's advantage, as any illness or need was soon addressed in the most tasteful way.

Life, although full, became more relaxed and, away from active farming, we contemplated holidays. We talked about what place we would really like to visit and unanimously chose New Zealand or Canada. We readily put New Zealand first on account of its climate plus the fact that Canada would be too vast until more research could refine an itinerary.

## New Zealand

It was coming up to Christmas, and Rosalind always sent a card to a great-aunt in Australia whom she had never met, mentioning the possibility, we hoped, of one day going to New Zealand. An airmail letter flew back suggesting she visit her cousins in New Zealand and even call in on New South Wales. She made it sound as if a train on a circular route would find them as adjacent stations.

We joined Rosalind's parents for three days over Christmas and mentioned our 'wish list' and the great-aunt's letter.

"I thought Aunt Carmel was the only relative left," Rosalind's dad tried to recount.

"There was nobody in New Zealand, was there, Geoffrey?" Rosalind's mum, Vera, joined in.

After the Queen's Christmas message, Geoffrey disappeared, returning after twenty minutes with a box.

"I've found this," he announced. "Vera, they were sent from the workhouse, I think." He wanted confirmation of the story.

By teatime we had the jigsaw of an epic adventure pieced together. The great-aunt's forebearers had fallen on hard times and were in the workhouse in south London. Their future was grim; a mother with four children, and no hope of a meaningful job, destined to abject poverty. Apparently, the parish council could not afford to maintain them forever in the workhouse and took advantage of a government scheme to send them to Australia.

Geoffrey found a ticket for their passage in the box and passed it around for examination. We wondered what the ticket could tell if only it were able to speak. It was steerage class, which was so basic that one would never willingly step on a vessel again with such a ticket. Our later research revealed the conditions below deck consisted of bunk beds stacked together with a straw mattress and nothing else. The only privacy for males and females crammed together was the relative darkness of the hold. Sanitation was minimal and soon overwhelmed. This, together with no facility for cleaning up seasickness, made it unbearable. To endure to the end of the voyage must have made any future privation relatively pleasant. I have since wondered if this ticket was 'surplus' due to death or sickness or whether it was kept as an horrific memento.

Rosalind wrote to Aunt Carmel, finding out more about her New Zealand relatives and resulting in invitations to visit them. We had growing excitement for the trip of a lifetime; a new country, new relatives, new wonders; awesome! The flight was amazing; we never expected to fly over the Arctic... to get to Los Angeles! The abiding memory of the flight to New Zealand was its length; we couldn't wait to arrive. There was a short second stop at Auckland giving a welcomed chance to walk, which was more than novel. The quick hop to Christchurch gave us a bird's eye view of the landscape that we had craved.

We were collected from the airport by Aunt Carmel's sister, Pamela, who drove us to her bungalow in the suburbs. It was 'England' comfortably dropped into a subtropical climate but without any pretension of class. On three of the roads there were items of furniture standing on the grass verge. They were apparently surplus to requirements and free to anyone to re-own before the householder became duty-bound to burn or otherwise get rid of them. Pamela's property had a joint garden with her next-door friend, Roger. He was actually our chauffeur as Pamela's eyesight was failing. They were literally close friends and mercifully an aid to each other, both of them feeling the effects of age which practically is better shared. Having unloaded our cases, we were all ready for proper introductions around coffee and cakes. Rosalind explained her family link with great-aunt Carmel as best she could by the fragmented story spanning continents and time. Pamela, who herself had not had close contact with her sister for several years, could add little to the story of the original migration from London. She understood that the family had all survived the dreadful journey and climbed from a very low base to reasonable employment on the infant railway but that was in New Zealand rather than Australia.

Rosalind had anticipated family photos were vital in tying together loose ends and soon we were poring over prints, doing our best to remember names and relationships. These settled two current generations but revealed little of the history of others. However, this did not diminish the joint excitement of the newfound blood tie we were unravelling. We expressed our real gratitude for Pamela's invitation of accommodation but insisted it was only a bed and light breakfast that we needed. It had become obvious when face-to-face, rather than through letters and Christmas cards, that Pamela could not be expected to fully entertain us. We would be most grateful for a bed for two or three nights, but during the day we would be exploring and looking after ourselves.

We toured their adjoining gardens enjoying the tail-end of their southern summer. The sun and warmth had turned our sixty-watt UK experience up to a hundred watts; everywhere was brighter and more vibrant. The vegetation was more luxuriant; even the insects seemed healthier specimens. Christchurch was relatively busy, but spaced more generously than our towns at home. This generosity had spilled over to pretty well everything. The parks and public gardens were spacious, roads were wider and property comfortable with space all around. Life seemed lighter; nothing was too pressing, even time was not rushed. We had been transported within twenty-four hours from a life of a gallop to that of a trot. Immediately we felt we could live with this, an extra quality that had passed us by at home.

We hired a car and hit the open road; the same generosity lay before us in their roads: straighter for long miles and with absence of traffic furniture. During our two-day stay with Pamela, insisting at eighty-three that everybody called her

'Pam', we learned some subtleties that might render us less touristy and more native.

"Yer have to obey police on the road." Pam's drawl was softer than an Australian's.

Rosalind and I glanced at each other at this caution.

"If yer flagged down, stop straight away; don't get clever," she added.

"What's the speed limit?" I asked.

"Thirty 'k'." Pam was straight to the point. "If there is a '30' sign, then that's it."

We noted this with another knowing glance.

A few days later we were en route to the south; it was their major highway. I noticed a sign saying "Road Work Ahead" and then a three-foot-high wooden stick with "30" painted on it, presumably a gentle reminder. However, little had prepared me for the scene that was engulfing us. Three or four men, a big reduction on the UK number, were simultaneously building a hard shoulder and resurfacing the road. Without any demarcation of barrier or warning tape, a Hymac 370 was swinging around its long trunk, oblivious of the traffic. A few hundred yards further a road roller was finalising the surface, defying any car to challenge it. We were used to several warning notices and hundreds of cones narrowing cars to a single lane. At home there would have been plenty of notice in the media and on the roadside of impending restrictions. Plainly, in New Zealand they enjoyed a 'no fuss' approach which was understood by the natives. The "30", insignificant as it was, had to be observed.

Motoring south, it was not long before we encountered timber trucks, no doubt hauling from forest to sawmills. It was particularly daunting, as they travelled seemingly with their accelerator pedals fastened to the floor and right up to one's rear bumper. I assumed the drivers were paid on a piecework basis on tons delivered per day to the mills, including any rear bumpers they found attached. The speed limit was 100 km/h for cars and 90 km/h for lorries, leaving me to decide between damage to our hired car and a hefty speeding ticket from the police. Bearing in mind Pam's strict caution, I found I had to keep one eye on the speedometer and the other on the rear view mirror, relying on Rosalind's description of what the scenery was like.

On rural roads, traffic was much lighter and it was great to take in the things that were typical of New Zealand. Long straight roads with tall firs on the side acting as windbreaks, with occasional drives revealing neat homesteads. The paddocks stretched away between lines of firs sheltering at various angles to cope with differing winds. Fine cattle grazed the flat lands that were too good for sheep. It was a tidy picture of good farming, clean and productive. Even the roadside firs were cut back, much the same as England's hedges, with tractor-mounted hedge cutters. The cutting heads were reaching heights of twenty feet and concerning passing motorists about their stability. The countryside changed to small rises and then hills in the distance, the large fertile paddocks becoming smaller and more interesting; villages recognisable as shades of England but in a greater vista. Dwellings were less grand than in the modern towns and more in the spirit of pioneers. The emphasis seemed to be on what mattered most, the business or the dwelling. If the livelihood came from the land, the dwelling appeared a convenience on the corner of it. What would it be like when we arrived at Rosalind's cousin's property? We soon found out.

We followed the a couple of miles from a small village up another narrow lane, hoping to find the names of properties, before driving into another anonymous cul-de-sac and having to knock on a door to ask the residents if they knew "Lyn and Bernie".

"Look!" Rosalind pointed, no need to say any more.

I could read the large message myself; the bed sheet was tied to the hedge. "Welcome, Rosalind & Peter" – with a kiwi painted one end and the Union flag at the other.

"Wow, our names up in lights!" I stated the obvious.

The sound of the car drawing into the drive alerted the occupants; we were soon surrounded.

Bernie kissed and hugged her unknown relative whilst Lyn nearly shook my hand off. The collies scattered the few hens, vying for our attention.

"I can't believe it." Bernie was in tears and so was Rosalind.

"It's lovely, lovely," Rosalind kept repeating.

"What a welcome, and a fellow farmer." I embraced Lyn.

We had an immediate rapport as friends of the soil. Worldwide there is a bond that nature cultivates; the common battles and interdependence draw us together. Whatever the language there is an empathy born of common contest with the elements.

After a wonderful meal we shared photographs and tried to piece together families. The cousins continued, heads together, all evening, whilst I accompanied farmer Lyn on his rounds of the sheep, hens and dogs and got to know their feeding and close-of-day routine. The sun was setting on our quest of finding relations, and we were sure it would be rising the next day on the beginning of newfound relationships. Our happy sojourn lasted three days before we set off for more tourism and especially to find the other cousins in Wellington.

We met at Mount Victoria viewpoint, overlooking the harbour and surrounding city. The views were breathtaking, the more so by the stiff wind accompanying them.

Les, Rosalind's cousin, led the way to the top of the city and his wife Dianne. The introductions were similarly effusive and the hospitality splendid. We learned of more connections and more family history. A couple of days later we met their daughter and family and compared notes on domestic life and opportunities for families half a world away from the UK. Interesting as it was, the 'ups and downs' and 'strains and stresses' of life experiences were very familiar.

The glorious countryside and agreeable climate constantly impressed us, together with the spectacular natural wonders, from hot springs to waterfalls and the 'fjords' of the west. Indeed, it was both a holiday and adventure of a lifetime, as well as finding a blood connection that would be cherished whatever the distance involved. The eventual flight home carried with it great memories fleshing out further contacts in an ever-shrinking world.

# 48

# Beginning of the End

At home, life carried on where we had left it. Rosalind picked up her retirement, which all people in her position know means less time available than when in full-time employment. Her interest in people continued with the village activities, the Coffee Spot and the church, as well as the Women's Institute. She volunteered one day a week at the local tourist office and another pattern was emerging. I continued with the finishing of the house, really amounting to 'snagging', as well as continuing with the consultancy and responsibilities at the church. The rush of farming had subsided and the weight of responsibility lifted. Life was good.

A year later we were in and out, busying and in our routine, when suddenly there was a crash. Then there was silence! The crash was a moment of suspended animation, then the silence; the two together triggering adrenalin. It was the unexpected sound that signals itself as a defining moment. It said "stop everything and investigate". I jumped out of the office chair and ran onto the landing towards the bathroom. Whatever could have fallen down? My eye caught a glimpse through the open bedroom door, stopping me in my tracks. Rosalind was sitting on the floor.

"What's happened, dear?" There seemed nothing out of order. "What's happened, dear?" I had to repeat myself, but she only groaned.

I threw her broken glasses onto the side and squatted by her, my arm around her shoulder.

"My neck," she murmured, more a comment rather than an answer.

I quickly looked around for an answer to my original question; there was nothing out of place.

"Have you broken anything? Where does it hurt?" I knew it was a silly question but what had happened to hurt her neck? She had not been climbing or reaching anything. A full-length mirror on the wardrobe unit was intact; there was nothing else amiss except my poor wife sitting on the floor, holding the back of her neck.

"Are your teeth alright?" I ventured, knowing she must have hit her head badly.

"I love you, darling." She was half conscious, only moaning.

Although I could not define the problem, I rushed to a phone.

I punched in 9-9-9 as if I rang it every day.

"Fire, police or ambulance?"

"Ambulance; my wife has collapsed on the floor." I just blurted it out.

"Is she breathing?" came the calm question.

"Yes, but she's not talking." It must have been the tone of voice that communicated enough.

"What is your address and postcode?"

I quickly answered the operator, adding, "She's only just conscious on the bedroom floor." I nipped back to Rosalind.

"An ambulance is coming." There was no answer; she was flat against the wardrobe, still clutching her neck. I ran downstairs and opened the yard gates for the ambulance still some twenty miles away.

I rushed up the stairs, two at a time, but she had not moved and wouldn't or couldn't talk. I knew it was serious.

"Jesus! Jesus! Jesus!" I shouted His name. There was no other name to call on. I remembered a scene at a church conference where a demon-possessed man had rushed the stage, scattering the team of speakers and smashing the electrical equipment. Flailing everywhere, this very large man was unapproachable. A spontaneous chorus rose in the congregation calling, "Jesus!" It lasted a minute. The man fell to the floor covering his ears, totally exhausted, and was led away by two strong doormen. Far from violent, he needed support in the name of Jesus to cast out the demon.

I didn't think Rosalind had any supernatural problem but we certainly needed Jesus. I talked to her and sat on the floor with her. It was a one-sided conversation but I told her I loved her. It was all of twenty slow minutes. I could do nothing; only a low murmuring was audible. On hearing the ambulance I rushed downstairs again.

"She is upstairs." I turned and led the way as if the house were on fire.

I left all the talking to the First Responder.

"Can you feel my hand on your foot, darling? And this one?" He was in charge, building the untold story.

I stood back, letting the second medic in. They administered an injection.

"We are going to take you to hospital, darling."

"I am going to work," she suddenly asserted angrily.

"No, you can't go to work. We are going to help you; they won't mind at work," the first man replied and mentioned his name to reassure her.

But she was adamant: "I am going to work."

"Get the chair," he quietly instructed his colleague.

He placed the chair near the bed and together they lifted her into it. It took some firm persuasion to strap her in.

"I am going to work," she insisted again.

Whilst one held her firmly, another injection was quickly administered. It was with some difficulty that they negotiated the stairs and quarter landing. Once outside the house, she was secured in the ambulance and I was told to drive to the hospital with her overnight bag. It took some time for them to move; I had expected it to be an emergency. I drove to the hospital and enquired where she was. To my surprise they had not arrived.

"Have they gone to another hospital?" I asked.

"No, they are on their way." It all seemed too casual to me; I could have driven her quicker myself.

Another ten long minutes elapsed. I stood as they came past me; she was on a stretcher now and appeared unconscious. They disappeared through swing doors whilst I was asked to wait in reception. It was another ten minutes before a doctor called my name and directed me to a side room.

"Rosalind is sleeping now; she has had a brain aneurysm. You realise this is serious?" The doctor's expression mirrored his words.

"Yes," I nodded but was only vaguely translating it as 'possibly fatal'.

A nurse appeared, saying Rosalind would be taken into the intensive care unit (ICU) fairly soon and I could sit with her or visit whenever I wished. I handed the nurse her overnight bag and walked out into the fresh air.

Completely dazed, I phoned some dear friends, a delightful and helpful Christian couple, to give them the news. Lesley answered, saying her husband was attending a meeting of church ministers.

"I must just tell you, Rosalind has had an accident and is in hospital; I am there at the moment." I spoke like a recorded message.

"*Our* hospital?" she enquired.

"Yes, they just say it is serious." It was difficult to release the words. "She collapsed on the floor at home."

"Are you staying at the hospital this morning?"

"She is in intensive care," I said, which seemed to clinch the matter.

"I am coming over now." The phone went dead.

Again, the calling of fresh air, I walked around the back of the hospital. It would have been better if I could have walked around fields. I tried to assimilate the doctor's comment; surely Rosalind wouldn't die, not when she had been so fit and had only collapsed. I spent my walk praying that Jesus would take care of her. He had answered desperate prayers before in the most remarkable way. She was not old, only sixty-one; surely the Lord had more work for her here. I tried to reason through the nightmare that had suddenly descended. Returning to the A&E entrance, Lesley was just arriving. We hugged as usual; well, not *quite* as usual, there was more to today's meeting. There was no point in going to the ICU as they had said she was in an induced coma, so we sat in the café with a strong coffee and I related the events.

We went up to the ICU; the nurse allowed us to go to the bedside. Rosalind was just lying there, sleeping with an oxygen mask on.

"It's me, Peter," I whispered right into her ear.

There was no murmur.

"Can she hear me?" I asked the nurse.

"I think they can sometimes." She was non-committal but smiled in sympathy.

"I love you, darling." I kissed her temple.

Lesley was the other side of the bed, gently holding her hand in silence.

The nurse was monitoring a screen with pipes and leads going I don't know where. She told us we could use the chairs she had pulled up, but after a while Lesley said she would have to go home but would phone me in the evening. I moved my chair closer and held Rosalind's hand; what else could I do? The doctor came through the door and explained that they were going to wake her up at about one o'clock. The team would assess her progress and decide how to proceed, inviting me to be present.

I readily agreed.

I told the nurse I wanted to get a paper but would be sure to be back by 12.30 pm. I was glad to descend the stairs rather than use the lift, and bought a paper at the shop. I glanced at the headlines but was not interested in any news. Walking out of the main door, the cooler air hit me. I didn't know why I had bothered with a paper or where I wanted to walk; there was nothing to do and no place I wanted to go. I walked purposely, I always did, but it was a vacuous exercise. How had all this happened? What was the treatment for a brain aneurysm? Would there be brain damage? The questions passed through my head with no expectation of answers.

I was back in good time and felt better in the ICU with Rosalind. I talked to her again, telling her about the coming assessment and then felt rather silly. The team gradually assembled and I was surprised that there were seven, including me. There were three doctors, and I guessed by the obligatory stethoscopes jauntily hung around necks that the others were part of the team responsible in this case. They were not able to wake her; she did not stir. There was much discussion and determination of delaying for another four hours. I returned home and phoned as many relatives and friends as possible.

I returned at five with hopes she would regain consciousness. I was asked to wait in a side room, but the consultant appeared in a couple of minutes.

"I am sorry to say we have not brought Rosalind out of the coma. I trust you realise the seriousness of the situation?" He spoke kindly but it was bad news. "We have scanned her and there has been very significant bleeding and, I must say, brain damage," he continued. "I am afraid there is nothing more we can do."

He was obviously used to such situations and had not minced his words.

"Do you mean she won't fully recover?" I didn't know how else to frame the question.

"We can't know for sure, but I am afraid it will certainly be life-changing." He put a hand on my shoulder. "Go home now, we will keep you informed, and come back around midday tomorrow."

I drove home, picking up fish and chips on the way. I resolved to keep praying and carried on as near to normal as possible. The evening was spent informing more friends by relaying the precise words of the consultant. Going through the usual routine I managed to doze through the night. Friday dawned and I could not settle to any meaningful work. I decided to cut up cordwood for the fire, which at least meant concentrating on the chainsaw.

I met Rosalind's sister, Margaret, at the hospital and we went straight to the ICU. I moved a chair to the bedside for Margaret and sat myself as far away as possible. It was important for the two sisters to be together. I could see Rosalind was in the same 'sleeping' state and her sister was trying at least to impart that she was with her. I isolated myself in silent prayer.

"Lord Jesus, you can do all things. I need to have Rosalind back like she was. Please heal her and make it alright. I can't manage without her. You have done wonderful things for us both; please let her come home healed. I don't want to be selfish but I can't look after her if she needs a lot of care; she is the nurse. I know you can heal her as you did when you were on earth..."

I sensed people coming in, the consultant and two nurses. I crossed to the bottom of the bed and introduced Margaret.

"We have tried to bring Rosalind out of the coma and we are afraid she has not responded. I am afraid there is little more that can be done." He looked at us both with genuine pity.

"Can you try again tomorrow?" I asked; surely they couldn't give up now.

"I am afraid, Peter, the damage is very extensive." I looked at Margaret; she was simply gazing at the floor.

There was a moment where everything was still.

"I am afraid if she could regain consciousness she would have no life. She would be totally bed-bound," said another doctor.

"You mean, like a vegetable?" It sounded coarse but we needed the truth.

He nodded.

There was another pause.

"We can't do any more; we will have to turn the life support off," said the first doctor.

"Can you wait till the morning?" I repeated.

"She will gently pass away." The nurse put her hands on both Margaret's shoulder and mine.

"We do just need your agreement," the consultant insisted.

I looked at Margaret; this really would be final.

"I suppose we have to do it," I said to Margaret.

Tears were running down her cheeks. My eyes were much the same; I could hardly see to sign in the right place.

"It really will be peaceful. She may just breathe on her own for ten minutes or so, that's all." The nurse was doing her best to make it sound alright.

The nurse took over. I thanked them all for trying and pulled myself together. Margaret and I walked down the stairs in silence. We hugged each other in the car park.

"It was the only thing to do," Margaret whispered.

"I guess so. You have got to drive home to Graham now." It was simply an observation.

"Will you'll be all right? Have you got anyone to stay the night with you?" she asked me.

"I will be OK, thanks." I gave a confident reply.

At home I phoned both my daughters; they were miles away but at least had been prepared for the eventuality. I phoned the church minister and two neighbouring friends. I knew the best I could to do was to carry on as normal. Sleep wasn't easy; more accurately, I was only dozing on and off, waiting for perhaps 7.30 am, a decent hour to ascertain her passing. The call was directed to the ICU.

"Thank you again for nursing Rosalind. I am just asking if she passed away peacefully?"

"Yes, there was no change; it was all peaceful," the nursed assured me.

"What was the time?" I enquired.

"Six o'clock this morning," she replied

"I was told she would only last ten minutes!" I raised my voice.

"It does vary; some are a little stronger than others, but it was peaceful," she insisted.

I was angry inside. Half of me said, "There might have been hope;" the other said, "A vegetable existence is no life." I walked straight into the garden calling out to God, "Thy will be done" – and meaning it. I had learned that was the best prayer, to seek His will. He loves us and has His hand upon us. He has His plans for us. "'For I know the plans I have for you,' declares the LORD, 'plans to prosper you and not to harm you, plans to give you hope and a future.'" (Jeremiah 29:11)

It was a beautiful spring morning that in half an hour had somehow lifted me above some of the sadness. I walked into a silent dining room; there was not a sound. The grandfather clock had stopped. I opened the case; surely the winder would hang there. It was Rosalind who always wound the clock, her prized heirloom passed down through the family. Only she could take the responsibility of not overwinding the mechanism. I wound up the chimes and noticed the hands had stopped at five minutes to six, no doubt the actual time of Rosalind's passing. The clock has never worked since.

On Sunday I would normally have gone to church. I was up early as usual and a little anxious about an empty day ahead. I could not further any of the vital jobs that had landed at my feet, neither did I want to sit alone in self-pity. I resolved to attend church as usual but as low key as possible. I arrived five minutes late and crept into the empty back row. A few heads turned but the service had begun. It was the middle of the service, just before the sermon, that the notices were announced for the coming week. As the minister rose, I realised the awful situation: she was bound to mention Rosalind.

"I am sure most of you know" – I sunk as low as possible in the pew – "about the great shock of Rosalind's passing, and I see Peter is bravely with us."

Not only was I not invisible but the spotlight was now on me.

"I would like to extend to Peter our deepest sympathy and earnest prayers at this time and our willingness to help in any way possible."

I think I smiled weakly as all heads turned back to look at me.

"Before we pray, I think it is a good opportunity to mention the lovely memories we have of Rosalind. Just stand, as you feel led, and briefly mention what is in your heart." The minister paused.

Immediately people were vying to reminisce. I knew I should not have attended. I looked at my feet, not even wanting to hear. The plaudits rang out. I knew how good she had been; I didn't need others to tell me. It was my fault; I should have stayed at home. I couldn't stand and ask them to stop, nor could I walk out. I was trapped and could feel tears running, coursing down my face. I ignored them but I knew they would be noticed. I could only study the back of the head in front of me, neither looking at the speaker nor the minister. As soon as they bowed their heads in prayer, I crept out and drove straight home.

After the anxiety of the last two days there were suddenly jobs to do. I had to return to the hospital to collect the death certificate and then register it at the town hall. This was all new and my job alone. Undertakers had to be engaged. I phoned the undertakers that Rosalind had always dealt with through the nursing home.

"Ian, it's Peter... Rosalind's husband." I paused to gain some strength.

"Can you ask her if it will wait till Monday?" Ian spoke as if in the middle of a conversation. He must have been referring to a death at the nursing home.

"It's worse than that... It is Rosalind." I could hardly breathe.

"You mean she has had an accident?" Ian said slowly.

"Yes, she's died in hospital," I replied.

"My dear fellow, I'm so shocked." He was trying to retrieve his professional stance. "I am so sorry; I had no idea you could be talking of Rosalind."

I felt a little easier and related the whole scenario.

"I just wanted to fix a date with you, about a fortnight away, preferably a Saturday as some will have to travel a distance." I had worked that much out.

"Will it be at your church?" Ian asked.

"I don't think it will be large enough; I'll have to let you know."

That was a start. I had to get my daughters to help; they would want to do so anyway. They designed a card reporting the passing and giving details of the funeral and thanksgiving service on the same day. This could have been done online but they would be visiting me Monday or Tuesday, depending on their work schedules. By night-time I was suitably tired, having sorted out ministers and a church for the services.

# 49

# Funeral and Festival

Planning my wife's funeral I found surreal. We had talked, like most couples over the years, of what we would like in terms of the funeral service and favourite hymns, and whether wishing to be buried or cremated. Now I had to arrange such details, along with the closing of bank accounts and notification to official bodies and pension funds. I had to be sure the memory of the fast-approaching day would be without any omission or regret. I was determined that it would be dignified and a time of thanksgiving to the Lord for her life and love. The undertakers had a beautiful green burial orchard that Rosalind had chosen for her burial and the coffin was to be a Moses wicker basket. I arranged six bearers from our families, including myself as one of them. I wanted the privilege of taking an active part in the ceremony, fully in the knowledge that for a believing Christian it is an inheritance of eternal life with Jesus Christ (John 3:16).

I planned, with the help of our pastor, a small family funeral service, to include close friends, for 11 am on the Saturday morning; followed by an open thanksgiving service at 2 pm in the same large Baptist church, which would enable friends to travel without needing accommodation overnight. Although I had been to several funerals before, Rosalind's of course was especially personal. I had made sure it included all her specific wishes; I had added a prayer and poem that only a husband would know were appropriate. The day dawned bright and the weather forecast was dry; I had prayed not only for favourable weather for the orchard burial but also that the whole day would be a blessing to those attending. I had pondered what a funeral was for and concluded that it should be honouring God our maker and the deceased. Rosalind had already passed to the Lord's presence, and we would be acknowledging our grief and our loss but also our joy that she was with her Lord. In the thanksgiving service we would be expressing our thankfulness for her life and all she had meant to us.

I had a nervous energy, wanting to remember every moment yet somewhat apprehensive about my role as chief mourner. I did not expect to break down during the service, but can emotions be kept in check with a stiff upper lip? In conducting funerals I had tried to be meticulous about detail, as I am conscious a 'bad' funeral is remembered forever. My father's funeral had fallen into that category.

The previous evening I had allowed that memory to pass through my mind. My sister and I had both left home and so our dear mother had organised the funeral with the help of the minister, who hardly knew her as she had only attended a ladies group at her local church. He did not know Dad at all and had to resort to a question and answer session to put together the service.

Dad's funeral was to be a short service at the crematorium.

"What music would you like as guests come in?" the minister had asked Mum.

"I don't know." Mum hesitated; she had no interest in music herself.

"You don't have to have any except for the hymns." He was trying to be helpful. "What about the hymns; any favourites?"

He met the same hesitation.

"We are only allowed half an hour at the City of London Crematorium. I'll choose some nice hymns," the minister concluded.

Mum readily agreed and it was left as fixed. We assembled at Mum's, and the undertakers' car chauffeured us to the crematorium at Manor Park for 4 pm on the Friday. The early evening was dark and wet and the traffic dense. We were all glancing at the time, trying not to concern each other.

"Is the traffic always as bad as this?" I called through the glass partition to the driver.

"We started out early enough but it is bad this evening," he replied.

Ten minutes later I had to ask another question. "Is there a shortcut anywhere?"

"There is no other way. It's best to keep to the main road and, of course, to follow the coffin."

"This is hopeless." I was addressing the family but certainly in the hearing of the beleaguered driver and his assistant.

We were openly discussing the possibility of being late, even missing the thirty-minute slot completely. We arrived for a shortened service but the family was ushered out through the side door. It was a complete disaster. We met not a single guest. We had no idea, not living at home, that our very capable mother was suffering from early dementia. She certainly couldn't be responsible for heavy traffic, but 4 pm on Friday was not a good choice either.

I was determined Rosalind's funeral would be remembered as wonderful. It went off without a hitch until the six bearers (I was shouldering the rear corner of the wicker basket) negotiated the right-angled turn from the side aisle to the main door. We had to manoeuvre to and fro in order to exit. This caused a flexing of the structure, simulating a stretcher rather than a coffin. Suddenly it was personal; I felt as if I were carrying my wife to her grave. It was a moment of emotion that overwhelmed me; silent tears ran down my cheeks, tears of sorrow and embarrassment.

The thoughts passed. By the time we reached the Orchard of Remembrance, the spring sunshine spoke of new life and my soul was lifted. Later I would plant an apple tree at the head of the grave and only a flat stone of remembrance at the foot. No vertical gravestones were permitted, in order to convey an air of life not death.

The small party of five cars returned straight to the church, for there was little time before the 2 pm thanksgiving service. There was a buzz and we could see the building was full. The steward let some of our group find their way to the front, but took my arm as if to impart a great confidence.

"The aisles are filled with chairs; it's not seemly that you and your daughters should squeeze by. Go round to the side door and come in from the vestry," he advised.

Opening the door, we were confronted by a full house; every seat was taken and the gallery, never needed on a Sunday, was full. I smiled at the assembly as we made our public way to the few seats reserved in the front row. There was an air of festival; it was electric. Grace, as arranged, had been playing the piano from the time the first people had arrived. Now she had moved to the organ and was making the building vibrate. There was informal singing as people recognised the hymn or chorus; the celebration had started.

The minister, Duncan, conducted the service, along with his wife, Lesley, who had supported me at the very outset at the hospital. The funeral notice had specified bright ties rather than black ones; this was also embraced by the minister, who was dressed in a handsome sports jacket. The whole service was upbeat with no sadness – because of our confidence in Jesus' promise that he had gone on ahead preparing a place for believers (John 14:3). Lesley gave a wonderful eulogy and Duncan an inspired service, reflecting Rosalind's faith and love for the Lord. The church doors were open as if the singing and joy couldn't be contained.

The wonderful ladies of the Baptist church had insisted on providing tea, refusing any payment, as their contribution to Rosalind's life and friendship with them. They can hardly have anticipated such a large gathering but some miracle was enacted that not only was the crowd fed generously but there was still leftover food. It was a thanksgiving service few will forget, including the undertakers, who told me they could not remember about four hundred people at such an occasion previously. They had represented her life nursing in London and, locally, as a health visitor, practice nurse, nursing home matron and friend.

In the days that followed, I received letters and cards that were a great encouragement; not least from a lady I had never heard of and to this day have never been able to trace. She wrote to say Rosalind had called on her every week after her son's fatal motorbike accident... and continued to befriend her in her loneliness until her own passing. I had no knowledge of this nor have any of our friends; only the Lord knows.

In the week that followed, the warmth of that thanksgiving service lived with me, enhanced by comments from those who attended. It was a real blessing rising out of what might be seen as a tragic loss. Week by week life settled down to a solo routine; satisfactory but hollow. I managed better at home in the familiar and had the support of friends and the church. Their hospitality was so welcoming and affirming, but there were inevitably times of sad reflection. Memories were great but acted as a past vision, looking backward rather than to the present. The daily reality was like a party when the guests had departed. The reality showed up more outside the house when shopping. I could cope with the necessary groceries, although much reduced in quantity and especially in variety.

It was deciding to stop for a coffee that became a thorn. I had time to indulge in the brief luxury but it felt lonely. The coffee shops were full of couples. I looked around and saw two people at every table; even two women sitting together were a 'couple'. I found I had nothing to *do*. I could have read a book, but I could do that at home. All I had to do was to drink the coffee or eat the cake I always purchased. Other people were talking and not twiddling their thumbs. Anyway, I didn't want to look around at all the couples; it never took long to consume a cake and coffee, and that was it.

## Where Next from Here?

There was no time for self-pity or any need for it. Six months later I was invited by dear friends in the church to join them on holiday in south-west France. We drove down, taking two days, and joined another delightful couple making a party of five and taking a country house only a mile from the Spanish border. It was a new experience, in a foreign environment, sharing cooking and many joint excursions. My personal scars healed remarkably, as I am sure Rosalind would have wanted. True, there were moments when I was sorry she couldn't be with me, but that was part of the healing. I considered the scars of separation covering the pain are but a potent healing reminder of a great relationship.

There was a future ahead; just as God had guided our past, I was sure he would not give up on me now. The next couple of years were uneventful except for the fact that our church pastor was leaving after several years of faithful service. All change is challenging and mostly unwelcome. Suzanne had a gentle manner and was particularly good with people in times of crisis. She had been a wonderful support and conducted a most fitting funeral at Rosalind's passing. There was concern that our small congregation could hardly finance another minister, and anyway, there was no queue wanting to take her place. The church leaders were prayerfully seeking a replacement but we struggled on with visiting lay preachers.

Out of the blue, the deacons asked me to consider taking the pastor's place. There could be no immediate response nor did they expect one. Once again I had to cry out to God for guidance rather than dismiss the invitation outright. I had become a lay preacher many years ago, and I knew leading a church was costly. I had previous experience having been sent from a large church to lead a small chapel in need of help three miles away, but that was in different circumstances. I did not jump at committing myself again.

I naturally committed the request to the Lord and wrestled with my reluctance. I knew the commitment that was needed and wanted freedom; not to travel or embark on a 'bucket list' but just to be unfettered. Anyway, I didn't have theological qualifications or I might have thought of a career in the church earlier. My career had been in agriculture and I told the Lord so. I even had the audacity to remind Him how much He had answered my prayers and had guided me in that vocation. God in his wisdom let me wrestle with myself for over two weeks before the Holy Spirit spoke: "This church does not need a theologian; it needs a manager."

Within twenty-four hours it had sunk in that I was qualified after all; in fact, I had spent thirteen years doing a similar job at that small chapel. It came to me that God was calling me to be the pastor. I learned it was not what I wished but what He was directing me to accept. I had committed my future to Him. If He would enable me to farm without disgracing His name, now the same pertained when directed to managing a different flock. I dared to remind the Lord that I could not take it up without His enabling.

I replied to the deacons that I regarded it as a calling and, with their support, would lead the church. It was agreed I would be reimbursed for expenses but receive no stipend. I had my own house and a pension that I could live on. We saw God's hand in it all; there was no money to support a pastor so the Lord provided one.

# Epilogue

Just maybe you are wondering what I have made of my journey – the things that have stood out or perhaps mattered most; things that one can be grateful for, that have made a difference, favourable or unfavourable. My conclusion is all are valuable, even the stressful and regretful episodes. They are all part of life's journey, forming character and resilience, enabling one to cope, learn and carry on. This book was not aimed at giving advice; it is simply my journey.

The outstanding revelation for me has been finding that God is real. In my total helplessness and desperation, when there appeared no other help, He heard me and answered. He pulled me through a 'make or break' situation in a miraculous way that I have never heard replicated. I have learned to put my trust in Jesus Christ, and He has never deserted me. He has supplied my needs but not my wants.

Later in the book there are times when it appears He is not answering prayer or that disaster strikes, but the Bible never says life will be easy. On my journey, I have found if I really trust the Lord and commit everything to Him, even my life, He oversees it for my ultimate good. Furthermore, we are encouraged to trust further as it becomes clear He really is in charge.

Essentially, from a standing start, I found there is a God and He answers prayer; in other words, faith in Jesus Christ works. He has proved it to me. That is good news in anyone's language.

May He enrich your journey too.